IMMACULATE FRACTURE

A MEDICAL ODYSSEY

JEFF KREHBIEL

Mayhaven Publishing, Inc.
P O Box 557
Mahomet, IL 61853
USA

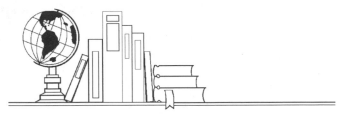

Cover Design: Doris Replogle Wenzel
Copyright © 2012 Jeff Krehbiel
First Edition—First Printing 2012
Library of Congress Control Number: 2012935036
ISBN 13: 978 193227880-4
ISBN 10: 193227880-X

DEDICATION

This book is respectfully dedicated to family, friends and medical professionals who helped me cope in the aftermath of the discovery of my illness. Without your strength, support and expertise I could never have achieved the level of recovery I enjoy today. I was privileged to have each of you on my side as I fought through the darkest of times. You have all helped pave the road to better days ahead.

CONTENTS

Author's Note	5
Prologue	7
The Beginning (Day 1 - 37)	23
Driving a Stick-Shift Ford! (Day 38 - 78)	45
A Solution? (Day 79 - 102)	65
Sudden Impact (Day 103 - 115)	82
Reverse Course (Day 116 - 289)	96
The New Guys (Day 290 - 300)	137
Renewed Hope (Day 301 - 367)	150
Trying to Do it All (Day 368 - 469)	175
Disasters (Day 470 - 600)	203
New Dr., New Meds and Racing (Day 601 - 712)	268
Back to the Emergency Room (Day 713 - 723)	321
A Time of Darkness (Day 724 - 775)	337
Fresh Water Sailing (Day 776 - 874)	365
Epilogue	413

Author's Note

It has been said that a person can be measured by how they respond in the face of adversity. I woke up one morning and found myself thrust into the depths of a devastating illness. Learning how to cope with a major medical condition left plenty of room for mistakes to be made and lessons to be learned. It was through the compassion of others, and their willingness to offer help and support, that I survived. It would have been a much different outcome if it where not for these contributions from countless people during my numerous times of need. My objective in writing *Immaculate Fracture* was twofold. First, I wanted to give back and provide others who are going through the process of dealing with a difficult health-related issue a close-up, inside view of how I handled my particular set of circumstances. The health system we find ourselves in today can be daunting—and difficult to maneuver through. A first-hand account might help some of you avoid the same mistakes I made, and as a form of therapy in helping overcome the many months of suppressing the reality's of my illness. Acknowledging the issues by writing about them has helped provide a more balanced and successful day-to-day management process. My deepest wish in providing my story is that the readers will find the information helpful when faced with their own battles in life.

—Jeff Krehbiel, 2012

St. Croix—A new Beginning

PROLOGUE

Although my father was an intelligent and caring man, over the years he became increasingly frustrated over matters of his health. His first heart attack occurred during "finals week" at graduate school. Refusing to seek medical assistance, he chose to push through the pain and finish his exams. Doctors later found the scar tissue on the heart muscle following his second attack. It would not be his last. I can only imagine being forced to face the reality of his illness day in and day out while working hard to successfully care for his family and advance his professional career.

Over the years, the heavy price he paid included triple bypass surgery, angioplasty, and mountains of medications, diets and rules to abide by. Some of the most renowned physicians in their fields dictated the path of my father's health care. Even with these skilled advocates on his side, tragically he did not live to see his fifty-fifth birthday. The end came from a massive coronary soon after delivering a speech on the campus where he had taught for over twenty years. When faced with my own medical demons, I came to realize, watching these events unfold, had a profound effect on shaping my life. I emerged harboring an understandable, but misguided, lack of trust in the medical profession.

During the early morning hours of November 19, 2006, I was awakened by a horrible pain. I sat on the edge of my bed, rocking back and forth, rubbing my right shoulder. What had happened? I felt little comfort as the cool, easterly trade winds whipped through my windows. The journey that followed would be the most trying years of my life.

In March 2002, I'd walked away from the stability of a management position at Cincinnati Bell Telephone. The decision did not come easy but I chose to follow my inner voice that was screaming for change. My job would have provided me with a lucrative retirement plan that included a pension, matching 401K, stock options and fully paid health insurance for life, but I was working twelve to sixteen-hour days, in charge of more than forty unionized customer service and sales representatives, and I was under constant pressure to get results. Life's only focus was work and little else. To say I was out of shape would be a huge understatement. I'd been at my heaviest weight, 260 pounds, for some time. I felt miserable most days and thoughts of a similar fate as my father's were never far from my mind.

In 1999, my friends Pat and Kathie Ellison had sold most of their possessions in an auction and moved to St. Croix, United States Virgin Islands. Pat and I'd met working together as managers of a Staples Direct call center in Northern Kentucky a few years earlier. Believing that managing a handful of lawyers and their assistants on a Caribbean Island would be more enjoyable than running the profit-driven sales teams, Pat accepted a job managing his brother-in-law's firm. I admired the Ellison's for taking a risk and believed they were making the best choice for their future.

My first visit to the island was an eye opener. I'd never been to the Caribbean and for the first time in my life I snorkeled, fished and played poker as a guest at Pat's regular Thursday night game. I was impressed with the physical activities available within walking distance of their home and the unbelievable natural beauty of the island. I visited a second time later the same year.

My life in the states left little time for activities outside the daily commute. I was making a good living but not doing much of anything else. After experiencing some health issues, including chest pains, decisions were made and details were finalized. I started sending boxes of my personal belongings to the island of St. Croix in February 2002. In April I drove my truck from Northern Kentucky to Port of Palm Beach, Florida, and had it loaded on a cargo ship. I flew out the next day from Miami. Twelve hundred miles southeast, and three hours later, I landed on St. Croix for good.

Pat and Kathie had helped line up an efficiency apartment in a house close to their home. The house, divided into three separate living quarters, sat on a hill to the south of East End Road. The front windows of my apartment faced north and the view looked out across the beach-front neighborhood of Cotton Valley Shores. Beyond the rooflines was the Caribbean ocean, surf breaking on the reef, with a full view of Buck Island. At low tide the silhouettes of St. Thomas, St. John and the British Virgin Islands, sixty-five miles to the north, were in full view. From my vantage point I watched boats sailing, kite boarders racing across the water, fishing and dive vessels in action on a daily basis.

Vowing to get healthy, I worked hard at becoming more active. My first job was painting Pat and Kathie's new home. Climbing up and down the ladder over bushes and banana trees for six weeks, in the bright sunshine, paid huge dividends. I dropped some unwanted weight and was off to a good start.

My next job was for Jonathan and Amanda Cohen. They owned JKC Communications, consisting of three radio stations: The Mongoose, Sunny 95.5 and Isle 95. I sold advertising slots, wrote copy and helped promote events. It turned out to be a great way to meet people and learn the lay of the land. I knocked on a lot of doors and spoke with a lot of business owners and had a whole lot of fun while generally taking life fairly easy.

I soon became a member of the Beeston Hill Gym, settling into a regimen that included swimming in the pool every morning before work. I ignored the usual aches and pains of exertion, and eventually I could glide through the water. As my fitness level increased I joined a group called the Fin Folks. Every weekend we would swim two to three miles in open ocean. The group usually consisted of ten to twelve swimmers, most of them being tri-athletes, who also ran and biked to train for their next competition.

It was during these swims that I came to appreciate and respect Mother Nature. The ocean is unbelievably powerful and during each swim came at least one moment of doubt. When you're a mile off shore in hundreds of feet of water you have no choice but to fight through those moments.

I also started golfing at an old goat pasture converted into a nine-hole course called The Reef. Located on the east end of St. Croix, as arid as a desert, the course has little to no grass and plays like a cement parking lot for the nine dry months each year. Soon my weight had dropped to 220 pounds.

The desire to learn how to sail was high on my list of things to do. During my earlier visits to the island, I'd caught the fever after a couple of trips to Buck Island with Captain Lewellyn Westerman. I began reading anything and everything related to sailing and fixing up old boats. As my thoughts on the subject grew, it became evident, just learning how to sail was not going to be enough.

After a few months of searching, I was able to find a sailboat that looked promising. I tracked down the phone number of the boat owner. As he lived in Colorado, and was not coming back to St. Croix in the near future. I felt it was a great opportunity. He definitely wanted to sell but was unwilling to come down in price. Not happy, I called him back. The second conversation was short as he hung up with me in mid-sentence. Still, I felt I could crack him. By the end of the third call he was softening. By the end of the fourth he relented.

Folly was sitting on a broken-down rusting trailer at The St. Croix Yacht Club in Teague Bay. I'd purchased her on looks alone. I knew almost nothing about boats at the time. Turns out she sails like a dream. Pat had grown up on the great lakes and had an impressive sailing resume. When I drove him to the Yacht Club and pointed out my new boat he knew I'd taken him up on his promise, made over many beers at a bar, to teach me how to sail.

Eight months into my move to St. Croix the job at JKC Communications was fun and enjoyable but it did not carry benefits. I was in relatively good shape and improving with each passing day. However, in the back of my mind there was always a nagging pressure to secure health insurance. It took two months working the radio advertising job, and part time late afternoons, evenings and weekends at Bohlke International Airways (BIA), before the owner made me an offer. I accepted the position of Marketing Manager. It was a modest salaried position but it came with paid health insurance. I started out creating brochures, placed advertisements in local papers and trade journals and spent a lot of time re-writing the employee manual. Although the job title was Marketing Manger some of my other duties included learning how to move planes around hangars, meet and greet customers who flew in on their private planes, and help manage a tank farm.

Besides running the Fixed Base Operation services on St. Croix with his wife, and flying charters around the Caribbean, Bill Bohlke also owned a second FBO operation at the Cyril E. King airport on St. Thomas. Bill's son had his own plane and it was common for us to fly between islands weekly.

The number of wealthy business owners attracted to the Virgin Islands for the benefits offered by the Economic Development Authority gave Bill a renewed interest in building up his charter business. He bought a used Cessna Citation from Net Jets. Although it was older, Citation Jet N267BB looked almost brand new after a complete overhaul. My first ride was southeast over the islands of Saba, St Eustatius, Nevis and Montserrat, turning west over open water then heading north for home.

Founded in 1984, the Economic Development Corporation (EDC) had been a tax haven for companies that set up offices in the Virgin Islands. The majority of the beneficiaries were hedge funds, investment professionals and financial services companies. In exchange for as much as a ninety percent tax break the beneficiaries had to employ at least ten local residents, offer above average salaries and provide paid benefits. To be considered a resident you had to have lived on the island for at least one year. The governing body's main goal was to find work for local citizens, preferably ones who were born and raised in the Virgin Islands. I put in my time working for Bohlke International Airways knowing at some point I would start to look for a job making better money at an EDC company.

11

Outside of work, sailing and swimming became my passions as I was becoming more and more confident in both. The pool at the Beeston Hill Gym is twenty-five meters in length requiring thirty-two laps to make a mile. Usually, after four or five laps I would start to question why I was doing this work out as it become a struggle of mind over body. Pushing these feelings aside, I would find my rhythm in the pool and always persevered through to the finish. Large clocks bracketed either end of the pool and timing my workouts became an obsession. I set a goal of a sub thirty minute mile. I was able to come within seconds of reaching this goal on my best day.

Ocean swimming was a different story. We cared less about how long the swims took and more about settling into a good rhythm throughout the distance. My longest swim started off the beach at Boiler Bay on the north face of Point Udall (furthest eastern point in the United States) and ended three and a half miles west on the beach at Coakley Bay. I'd inadvertently taken a wave to the face as I was breathing in air and drank what seemed like a gallon of salt water. My pace slowed for the remainder of the swim and by the time the swim was finished, two hours later, I was spent. I slept for six straight hours after collapsing on my bed at 11:30 a.m.

I sailed *Folly* for the first year without a motor. You really learn fast when you have to sail everywhere including on and off your mooring ball, into docks and crowded beach areas. Pat had taught me well and we had some great adventures plying the Caribbean waters off St. Croix. We once got stuck in a freak storm that blew up out of nowhere. About two miles north of Buck Island the seas grew quickly and the wind started to gust upwards of twenty-five miles per hour. Eight feet waves broke on *Folly's* stern as we raced down the face burying the bow two to three feet underwater. *Folly* shuddered and made unfamiliar noises before popping up from under the weight of the water and riding the face of the next wave pointing towards the sky. It felt great taking on the challenge of the ocean and knowing my boat and crew could handle it, though I purchased a Johnson Outboard motor soon afterwards for insurance.

12

I found myself settling into island life and moved to a guest house further back in the valley. It didn't have the ocean view of my tiny efficiency apartment, but it offered more living space. My new landlords were Tony Spillar and Donna Bakley. They lived in the main house on the same property. Tony was a retired engineer and Donna worked as a CPA. At the time I didn't have any way of knowing how lucky I was to have made the move.

After working for Bohlke International Airways for over a year, I stumbled on a position posted in the local Avis Newspaper. The job included managing a ten-person EDC office in Fredericksted, an old Caribbean trading post surrounded by the remains of sugar plantations located on the furthest western point of the island. Although St. Croix is only twenty-six miles long, it is close to an hour drive, one-way, east to west. I applied after several days of mulling it over. Unfortunately I was too late. They liked my resume, but had awarded the job to someone else. I didn't think about it again until a couple of months later when, again, the same job appeared in the newspaper. The previous manager had left to take the head of human resources position at another EDC company. The job was mine—if I wanted it.

Cambridge Management LLC was owned by three brothers who rarely visited the island. My interviews were over the phone, and I was flown up to Lakewood, Florida, for my first face-to-face meeting. The Musa brothers had owned and operated Lasik surgery centers and Eye Glass World retail stores across the U.S. and had recently sold controlling interest in their business. The main revenue for Cambridge Management LLC was generated by conducting post-surgery customer surveys with Lasik patients. Our other duties included keeping track of some of the real-estate dealings involving the Musa brothers' retail sites.

Our office was housed on the second floor of a vintage 1700s building overlooking the Fredericksted Pier used as the island's cruise-ship dock. The brothers had spent considerable money renovating the space. The staircase leading to the office was cut coral, the doors were heavy beveled glass and the floors was covered in marble. The courtyard at the bottom of the stairs was home to Pier 68, a bar and restaurant doubling as our employee lounge.

Not long after I took over the business, the focus shifted to new business opportunities the Musa brothers wanted to explore. They had interest in finding apartment complexes in south Florida they could buy and flip as condos. The brothers also had our group doing research into acquiring a Marriot or Hampton hotel franchise and high-end restaurant chains. Early on, it became obvious there was a lack of long-term focus. The one big hole in the business plan was that the controlling owner of Lasik and Eye Glass World could decide to cut costs and use cheaper out-sourced customer service representatives at any time. That would be the end of our revenue stream and the Musa brothers more than likely would be reluctant to pay our salaries out of pocket for research alone.

The New Year brought rumblings from the Economic Development Authority about some rule changes. State governments from the mainland, who were losing millions of dollars in tax revenues as EDC beneficiary companies declared residency in the Virgin Islands, lobbied the Federal Government to step in and stop the bleeding. The ensuing investigation revealed some EDC beneficiaries were guilty of tax evasion because they were not actually living on the island while receiving benefits. The rules committee was forced to strengthen the laws governing citizenship, business practices and reporting requirements. The new rules package was set to take place during the 2005 fiscal year. The new residency requirement stipulated proof that an EDC tax beneficiary had lived on island for no less than 186 days per year. The Musa brothers believed the islands did not hold enough entertainment, shopping or excitement for them or their spouses to permanently move. Their real homes were located in South Florida where they spent the majority of their time. They could not adhere to the new rules and chose to shut down the business at the start of the New Year.

I had finally reached a position at Cambridge Management Group where I made enough money to start saving again, had insurance and enjoyed the people I worked with. It was a big let down when the business closed. Finding work on a small Island is difficult and I didn't like the idea of being unemployed. The EDA passed out packages to all employees and we were encouraged to visit the unemployment office. On my initial visit, I spent two hours filling out paper work and waiting to see a counselor. I was called back for a consultation for fifteen minutes. And when the counselor got up to get my paper work from processing, it had already been lost. They asked me to fill it out again. I found the whole mess frustrating and not worth the effort for the small check. I ventured out on my own, leaving the government aide behind.

I was soon climbing the walls without work and was spending much of my time researching and applying for any position that looked like a match. I sent out several resumes and visited business owners I'd met in past jobs. What I hoped would take a few weeks dragged on for months and became my first real test in continuing to live "on island."

In my short time on St. Croix I knew several people who had come and gone, most of them lasted for six months or less. They thought the idea of living on a Caribbean island was going to be like a dream come true. The reality of heat, storms, a multitude of bugs, and the living expenses are major handicaps to a state-side lifestyle.

During hurricane season the shipping companies eliminate runs to the islands because the risk drives up the cost of insurance. The product variety shrinks and shelves are nearly empty for weeks. Work is scarce, and job opportunities, other than bars and restaurants, are few and far between.

I kept my free time busy solo sailing, swimming and playing poker every Thursday night at Colonel Bud Orpen's game in Rust Op Twist. It was quite the honor. Bud had been in-charge of a squadron of B-29 planes that flew bombing missions over Japan at the end of WWII. Their efforts had helped end the war. After the war Bud worked in the aviation industry, sailed, traveled and generally loved life.

Unlike Pat and myself, the rest of the regulars at Bud's poker game were self-made millionaires, lawyers and business owners. Mike Mulusky had a couple of partners that were in the early stages of building Broadband VI. Today Broadband VI is one of the few high-speed internet options in the islands. Mike offered me a consulting job paying a fee per installation. I was trained by Mike's partner Jerry, and spent the better part of a month riding around, climbing on roofs and drilling through walls. The installation process involved mounting a broadband radio on the roof of a home or a business and running the wire from the outside into a computer. Sounds simple, but it was different from anything I'd done in the past and I found it difficult. I was unwilling to purchase the tools out of pocket and generally had second thoughts when it came to drilling permanent holes in the walls or roof of people's homes or businesses. In addition, the summer heat was raging. Some days I would be on roof tops for several hours. It definitely helped keep my weight down, but it was a constant struggle to stay hydrated and from getting light headed. I kept my eyes open for other work.

Stuart Logan at Pinnacle Services, who I'd done a lot of work with at Bohlke International Airways, and Cambridge Management Group, offered me a part-time job as a trainer. Every contractor that passes through the gates at the Hovensa Refinery has to go through safety training. Right to Know training lasted the better part of an eight-hour day. I learned the material and eventually found myself fitting right in with the rest of the training department. At 500,000 gallons a day, Hovensa is the largest petroleum refinery in the western hemisphere. It is a partnership between Hugo Chavez and the Venezuelan run Petroleos de Venezuela and America's Hess Corporation. The oil refined on St. Croix is shipped daily in large tankers from Venezuela. The final product is then moved to the states. Needless to say I learned a lot. I got to the point of anticipating questions and being able to deliver reasonable answers. The whole point of the training was to cover basic safety material and make sure all workers who entered the refinery were up to speed on current regulations. The one problem with my arrangement at Pinnacle was similar to the arrangement I had with Broadband VI—the job carried no medical benefits. I was keeping my eyes open for a permanent position.

After ending my short-lived stint at Broadband VI, working part-time at Pinnacle and living through another summer and storm season on St.

Croix, I finally got a job offer. It turns out that TMG was an EDC benefi-ciary company that had been operating on island for over ten years. This fact alone gave them credibility.

When I joined TMG they had ten employees and had gone through several incarnations as a business. Their main purpose was to function as a Mergers and Acquisition Firm. Soon after joining the EDC program they had strayed from their core business and started bringing in as many in-vestment partners as possible. The focus had been shifted from selling client's businesses to servicing the partners and their business needs. When they hired me they were starting to ramp back up for one last run at be-coming a major player in the middle-market mergers and acquisitions field. They pared back the number of partners in the business—freeing up re-sources. George Gifford, one of the owners, lived on island. The other owner, Bob Scarlata, lived in Nashville, Tennessee. Over the course of the next four years The March Group would grow from a base of ten employees to over 160. I started out as the only Associate Managing Director. My job was to call business owners, gauge their interest in growing through acqui-sition and get them to sign a confidentiality agreement. Our marketing de-partment would then send them a detailed analysis of our clients business complete with financial statements.

The job required that I learn everything there was to know about our clients and their business practices. The detailed information gave me a better understanding of why I was calling a particular company as a poten-tial buyer. I was building this position from the ground up and there was a lot to learn. The plan was to eventually record the information in a database to be used in future marketing campaigns. Building the buyer database was my responsibility as the company grew and my role expanded. Things moved slowly at first, but George and Bob had big plans to re-tool. They worked hard and demanded that everyone in the company do the same. I was happy to be back in a structured, goal-oriented company.

I'd been hiking and biking and was generally feeling good physically. On top of swimming and sailing, these additional activities brought me to a new level of aerobic fitness. Soon I would be putting that fitness level to the test. My brother Rod and his family had taken a year off and gone to Peru. A doctor, Rod donated his time to help set up a medical facility in the fishing village of Mancora. Near the end of their time in Peru my brother had some of his friends from the states coming to visit to take a mountain-bike camping trip in the Andes Mountains. I was invited and jumped at the chance. I knew I needed to get into better shape and only had about five weeks to prepare. I extended my swimming routine and added a forty-five minute elliptical workout to my regimen at the gym. I still was carrying some fat on my frame but I'd lowered my weight to 210 pounds.

I met my brother in Lima where we wasted no time taking a crazy crammed bus ride across the city to a huge outdoor flea market. I was coming from St. Croix and rarely had been dressed in anything other than shorts and tee shirts for the past four years. I needed to buy some mountain clothes—including a coat. After shopping we left Lima and flew to Cusco. Cusco is at an elevation of 11,000 feet. We stayed there a couple of days to acclimate ourselves to the thin air. As the mountain bike tour started we road out into the Andean highland past Inca stone structures, through villages that have not changed much since the 1500s and finally up into the higher elevations. One night we camped out at Manu National Park in the cloud forest. The parks elevation is more than 14,000 feet above sea level. Our camp site sat on a cliff. At the base of the mountains below us sat the Amazon Jungle. At night you could make out the faint flicker of Indian village fires in the vast forest below. Clouds would race up the mountain face towards our campsite, pass right over our heads and travel up to the snow-capped peaks, standing more than 20,000 feet. We rode up and down the mountains, and spent a couple of days in the Amazon Jungle near the end of the trip. My extra cardio preparation seemed to have paid off as I held up quite well to the thin air and the rugged mountain biking. Peru had been a trip of a lifetime and I was thankful to have returned without a scratch or any physical ailments.

TMG was growing and was soon interested in filling a financial analyst position. Bud had recently been inviting Kiril Logvinoff and his fiancée Sara to play at the Thursday night poker game. Kiril, it turned out, was a financial analyst and was looking for a job. I put two and two together and several weeks later TMG hired him. It was not long after the addition of Kiril the company decided to move to a new office space.

We relocated to the second story of a building above a courtyard that housed Dee Anna's Restaurant and Bar on Company Street in Christiansted. Christiansted is a considerably shorter drive from the east end where the majority of us lived, and our new office was in the heart of downtown where we had more lunch and after work socializing options.

Dee Ann was a good cook and employed her daughter Dawn as a bar tender. They were downstairs every day before lunch until long after we would leave at night. Kiril, Melissa Miller (TMG's Marketing Manager), Linda Camacho (who worked with me at Cambridge Management Group and now at TMG), a few others and myself would frequently hang out downstairs. It turned out to be a great group of people to work with.

I'd recently bought a two-man kayak and had it on the rack at the Yacht Club. I used it to get out to *Folly* when she was on her mooring in Teague Bay. Sometimes I would take it out for a good arm workout through the channel past the reef into open water. I'd been telling Kiril about some of my adventures and he told me he knew a spot on the south shore where we could use a kayak to hunt for lobster. We talked about going several times but something always came up. With our backs against the famous Caribbean Christmas winds and the choppy waters that accompany them, we finally locked in on a date.

Kiril and I met on the morning of Saturday, November 18, 2006. Earlier in the week, Dawn had become sick and was in the hospital. Dee Ann told us what room she was staying in. It was sketchy about what was wrong with her, but we wanted to go see her and try and cheer her up before heading out on our lobster hunt. Thankfully I'd never had reason to visit Governor Juan F. Luis Hospital before. The building seemed like a relic from the late 1950s. I already had a dislike for medical facilities, and as we walked through the front doors I felt uneasy. We were informed it was over thirty minutes before visiting hours started. We went outside and climbed a staircase to a second floor entrance. It was unlocked and we walked down a long hallway, lucky to not be spotted by hospital personnel, before finding Dawn's room. She was surprised and impressed with our story of having to break in to see her. She assured us she would be back at work pouring drinks for us the following week. We left the hospital around 11:30 a.m. Little did I know, I was less than twenty-four hours away from a return visit.

Turning down a dirt road at the twin pink pillars marking the entrance off of the south shore road to Hey Penny Beach, we headed towards the water. The quarter-mile dirt road winds through cattle pastures, past burn piles, a couple of shanties and finally to an opening in the Tan Tan and Kasha bushes. Kiril and I lowered the kayak from the roof of his Toyota and drank a beer. There were a half a dozen locals hand fishing and splashing in the water as I surveyed the site. I could see the reef line a quarter to a half-mile off the beach. We paddled to the first coral heads on the eastern edge of the bay. We were free diving in ten to twelve feet of water. In the past I'd had swimmers ear and salt water seemed to set it off. When I did ocean swims I always wore ear plugs. Because I would be holding my breath and diving, I wasn't wearing them on this day. That turned out to be a mistake. Once I would get down to ten feet or below, my ears felt like they might explode. Kiril, on the other hand, had no problems as he would take his home-made lobster snare and dive down, hold his breath and become entangled in the coral below. It seemed like he could stay down for several minutes at a time. I had the lobster bag tied off to my waist. Kiril would pass the lobster to me and I would fight with one hand to hold the crustacean and open the bag with the other. I dove a few times and snared a couple small ones that I later released. The pressure in my ears grew and grew each time I went down. We finally clamored back aboard the kayak and went out to some coral heads that were in fifteen to eighteen-feet of water. I tried going down that far but my ears throbbed. Kiril continued to dive and would surface with larger and larger lobsters. Each time they were changed out and the smallest in the bag were set free.

We spent between three and four hours out on the water leaving both of us tired and ready for some dinner. After loading up the kayak and examining our catch, Kiril wanted me to take all the lobster home. I was beat and didn't want the responsibility of cleaning them. He later told me he had grilled two of them and given the rest to his neighbors. I was pleased to have had the experience and even more pleased to be headed home for some much needed sleep.

I stopped at a mom-and-pop store overlooking Salt Pond in Union and Mt. Washington. I bought two Coors Light beers—cold out of the ice chest. One was for the road and one for dinner. When I got home I showered and made some sort of melted cheese over pita bread concoction, drank my beer and promptly fell asleep. I woke up about 9:30 p.m. I watched some TV, and read a few stories in the sailing magazine *Cruising World*. I'm not sure the exact time I dosed off for good on the night of November 18.

Folly Moored

Folly's Teak Cockpit

The Beginning (Day 1 – 37)

November 19, 3:30 a.m.—I woke with a piercing pain deep within my right shoulder. As I shot into an upright position the intensity took my breath away. In total darkness, confused and not sure what was happening, I swung my feet to the floor and stood up. I quickly realized I had to hold my right arm bent at the elbow and tucked in close to my waist because the weight of it, pulling downward, elevated the amount of pain that shot through my upper body. My breathing was labored, as if I'd swum a fast mile in the pool. I felt as though I was going to pass out. I carefully paced my small, 550 square-foot guest house rubbing my shoulder. Nothing helped as the pain grew with each passing minute. I decided to take a hot shower in hopes of relaxing muscles, now clamped down as tight as I'd ever felt. The slightest movement caused tremors of pain to shoot through my shoulder into my head. The hot water lowered the intensity—but only for a few brief moments.

Without even toweling off, I sat on the edge of my bed. I tried to lie down and found the motion way too painful. I stayed in the upright sitting position, rocking back and forth, rubbing vigorously as time seemed to stand still. At 4:30 a.m. I'd already resigned myself to calling for help, but I didn't want to wake anyone that early in the morning so I set a goal to hold off until at least 8:00 a.m. Allowing my water heater to fill back up, I repeated the warm shower routine every half hour. The pain was not going away, and I'd reached my personal threshold by 6:45 a.m. My upper body was shaking as I pressed the numbers.

Startled to hear from me that early on a Sunday morning, Kathie jumped into action. I don't remember my exact words to her, but she understood the urgency behind the message. Pat was at my doorstep in less than ten minutes. Soon I was loaded into his truck and we were on our way to the hospital emergency room.

My house was down an uneven, one-lane dirt path—about a quarter-mile of rocky trail before reaching the pothole-rich asphalt of the main road. There are few smooth paved surfaces on St. Croix, and the hospital was a thirty-minute drive away. Pat took it as easy as possible, but the pain was excruciating. It intensified with each bump, crack and hole we passed over.

I had broken a number of bones in the past, including wrists, forearms, my jaw, nose and ribs. They all have a story behind them and are fairly easily explained. This pain was more intense than anything I'd ever experienced in the past. Even more mystifying was the fact that I was sleeping in my bed and had not fallen, tripped or slammed into anything to cause this problem. Having no explanation was troubling, but for the time being I was too preoccupied with stopping the pain to figure out why this happened.

Over the years I'd heard some particularly scary tales of the service provided within the government-run hospital system on St. Croix. What I knew for fact from newspaper articles and local television news stories was that Governor Juan F. Luis Hospital had not been upgraded or benefited from advancements in modern management technologies and the efficiencies that come with them. While I'd lived on island, corruption charges were leveled against members of the hospital board of trustees, and the medical sanctioning board for the U.S. had not given favorable reviews, but there were no other options on island and I was glad, at this point, to go to a hospital of any standing.

The double doors leading to the waiting room are located just off of the parking lot. Pat must have read my mind because I was unsure if I could make it on my own. He got out, propped my weight over his shoulder and walked me in before going back to park his truck. I sat down in the front of a dimly lit room with background fuzz blaring from a small TV in the corner. There were five or six rows of hard plastic chairs and some posters in Spanish on the walls. Several people were either sleeping or playing cards, and kids were chasing each other around on the old linoleum covered flooring.

Pat came back from parking to find me hunched over and just about ready to fall off the edge of my chair. Each move increased the pain as I staggered to my feet and approached the admissions window. I took a deep breath. I'd made it to safety and that thought gave me some comfort. The admitting nurse was situated inside a small, enclosed office. She took one look at me and shook her head as if she did not approve of me being there. The heavy Crucian accent made it difficult to understand all the questions, but it turned out we did not have the proper admitting papers. They were located in an office down the hallway. Pat got busy filling out the paper work and ran between the two offices on my behalf.

I had long since lapsed into a pain-driven shock and was useless to the cause. Over an hour passed before I was placed in a wheelchair and pushed back to the examining area. By the expression on her face I could tell the emergency room physician was less than pleased to deal with me. Dr. Carmen Cintron's early communications were short and curt at best. After ordering an x-ray she said she would get back to me. I sat by myself, rubbing my shoulder in vain.

The nurse's station was directly in front of the open holding area where I was seated. I continued to try and make eye contact with someone, anyone, that could provide me some relief. For one of the few times in my life I was agreeable to taking some strong, pain medication. No one came to my rescue. I was exhausted and my stomach felt nauseous. The thoughts of golfing later that morning had long since faded from my mind. I'd been looking forward to it but there was going to be no way I could play with this level of pain.

Over two hours later, Dr. Cintron finally returned. She held the x-ray up into the light, walked over and poked me on top of my right shoulder— prompting an immediate moan. "You have a case of tendinitis."

She scribbled a prescription for anti-inflammatory pills and dismissively said, "If you are still in pain in four or five days feel free to visit another doctor." I tried to explain that the amount of pain seemed to indicate something more. Although I'd never experienced tendinitis, I was sure she was wrong, but I was in no shape to argue and was definitely not thinking clearly. As it turns out her misdiagnosis cost me valuable time—time that turned out to be vital and key to my recovery.

The pain had dulled out a little and numbness prevailed. My arm did not move without reawakening the sharp throbbing sensation in the shoulder. My only recourse was to hold it as still as possible. The ride home was filled with the same obstacles we had crossed when driving to the hospital over four hours earlier. I felt every crack, coconut husk, palm frond, rock and pothole lining the roads.

The events that followed the remainder of Sunday the 19th and the early morning of Monday the 20th are still blurry at best. I know Pat took me home. I must have been able to lie down because I remember waking up still grasping my arm tight to my waist. I also remember Kathie checking on me. Somehow, by Monday morning there was a plan in place to see Dr. Bishop.

The doctor's office is located in Sunny Isle Shopping Center's Medical Building. It is a further drive west than the hospital was the day before. In Kathie's mind, and many others on island, Dr. Bishop is one of the most competent physicians on St. Croix. He is known for his tremendous bedside manner and taking the time to explain the issues. Because of his favorable reputation he is difficult to see. I'm sure the only reason I was able to on such short notice was because of Kathie's persistence. I don't remember having an MRI that morning but my records show one was performed at Advance Radiology LLC—just down the hall from Dr. Bishop's office.

It was a short conversation. The news was hard to comprehend. My shoulder was broken just below the "head." It would take major surgery to fix. Dr. Bishop could come up with no plausible reason for the break without several more tests. He emphasized the importance of fixing it as soon as possible. In the back of my mind I resented Dr. Cintron for her lack of caring and her disregard for a patient who obviously did not have tendinitis.

In my mind, I was fixated on a six to eight week recovery time like most of my broken bones in the past. I would be swimming, sailing and golfing again within that time frame. I was not factoring in the concern on the faces of the people immediately surrounding me—including Dr. Bishop.

Dr. Bishop had quickly checked, and the only orthopedic physician who was capable of performing the surgery on St. Croix was Dr. Peterson—and he was off island on vacation. Dr. Bishop said I would have to live with the pain and fly to St. Thomas and see Dr. Jeffery Chase. There would be no pain pills until a cause was determined. My memory of the events that took place after leaving Dr. Bishop's office are sketchy. I was in extreme pain and grateful for any lull from the constant throbbing. Kathie basically took over—making all the arrangements.

Traveling in my condition would prove to be the most awful experience I'd lived through to that point in my life. I'd flown the sixty miles north to St. Thomas no less than forty times in the past. On an average day it's a twenty-five minute flight. Before it was over, this flight would feel like days of torturous traveling.

The only time slot Dr. Chase had available to see me was 8:30 a.m. on Tuesday morning. The one flight to St. Thomas that left early enough, and had two available seats, was with Cape Air. Flying meant yet another long drive across the island to the airport, standing in lines and going through customs. I found the realization that I could not handle this alone very upsetting, but was extremely thankful that Kathie volunteered to accompany me.

I remember being clammy, with sweat running down my neck and the back of my shirt. I moved as if I'd aged twenty-five or thirty years in less than seventy-two hours. My arm was frozen to my waist and all movements were labored. My shoulder throbbed, and we had not gotten down the stairs in front of my house to Kathie's car yet.

On a good day it is a thirty minute drive to the Henry E. Rohlsen Airport located in the southwestern part of the island. The one saving grace is that the South Shore Road had been repaved when the Casino opened a few years earlier. The road is one of the few on island not filled with cracks, potholes and missing sections of pavement. Kathie did her best to drive in a manner that caused me the least amount of pain. I was fixated on keeping my upper body as still as possible, but was unsuccessful in the endeavor. By the time we arrived I'd sunk deeper into pain-induced shock. My mind had nearly blanked out, and I was unaware of my surroundings.

In some ways it was a blessing. I do not remember much about the ticket or customs line, the waiting area or walking to the plane. Cape Air flies Cessna 402c aircraft. They are small, nine-seat un-pressurized planes without the comfort of full standing headroom. At six foot two inches, I had to duck, leaning forward with the shoulders to enter the cabin. That was the closest I came to completely passing out. The pain was waging war and it was winning, though I was doing my best to stay calm and quiet. As flight 851 taxied out of the tarmac parking area and headed west, I continued to concentrate on not moving my upper body. I kept telling myself all this was going to be fixed soon.

Every bump, swerve of the wheels and decompression of the 402c's shocks sent powerful reverberations with the force of a sledgehammer throughout my right shoulder. The sweat continuously poured out of my body. I was trying to stop my sudden urge to scream, and surely moaned out loud a few times. We finally turned to the east and the pilot revved the engines. Suddenly, I was thrown back against my seat. My mind went blank as we went hurtling down the run way and lifted off. I was grinding my teeth as the pain shot through my right shoulder and around to my back. It was the usual flight pattern I'd taken so many times in the past. We headed east to mid-island and turned north over Christiansted climbing to 2,500 feet. The weather was calm, and I hoped for a short ride. I knew the landing would be rough, but I tried to concentrate on deep breathing. I took solace in the fact I was headed towards help.

Minutes into the flight the pilot turned and gave us a peculiar look. There was no co-pilot next to him. He had the stick in one hand and the radio in his other as he spoke to the tower. A few moments passed and the pilot turned to us and said the plane had an indicator light that was registering a potential problem. Cape Air's only maintenance hangar is on St. Croix. We had to turn around and head back.

Flight 851 turned west away from St. Thomas. The pilot made a textbook approach over Fredericksted and down towards the runway where we had just taken off a few minutes before. A scream crept out between my clenched teeth as the jolt of the plane hitting the hard surface made the pain unbearable in my shoulder. As we disembarked on the tarmac I remember Kathie, half hoarse—collaring the pilot. She was forceful with her demands to know when the next plane would be ready. It is good to have a strong advocate on your side. She explained that this was a medical emergency. I thought to myself, "That is what I have become—a medical emergency? Wow!" Kathie and I shared an awkward laugh. What else could go wrong? We had no choice but to suck it up and try it again.

It was a half hour of standing around until the next Cape Air 402c was ready to attempt the flight to St. Thomas. I took several deep breaths before climbing the short staircase leading to the small cabin door. It was just as painful the second time around. We rolled down the taxi way, revved up and took off. My body and mind had worked in congress to block out this second beating. I really do not remember much of the flight.

Twenty-five minutes later we touched down at Cyril E. King Airport on the west end of Charlotte Amalie Harbor in St. Thomas. Dr. Jeffery Chase's office is located on the ground floor of the Paragon building behind Schneider Regional Hospital on the east side of the harbor. Traffic on St. Thomas is every bit as bad as downtown Manhattan, Boston, Dallas or Chicago. It just comes in a smaller space. Our cab was an open-air safari bus—basically a pickup truck with bench seating in the back. It was another five mile, thirty-plus minute ride swerving through heavy traffic punctuated by several stop lights. Somehow we managed to not fall out. Being tossed around in the back of a truck put me at the point of passing out by the time we reached our destination.

My first memory of Dr. Chase was him interviewing me alone in an examination room. His straight forward approach left an impression on me even in my shock-induced state. He was positive he could fix the break. He went on to explain the make up of the bones in the upper arm and shoulder. He used large diagrams that hung on the wall to show me where the break had occurred. He was sure of his capabilities, and had an air of egotism about himself. There was one big problem. Dr. Chase only had space in the hospital for surgeries on Monday's. I would have to wait for an entire week before getting fixed. That worried him. He explained that the longer period of time could cause the bones in my shoulder to suffer from the lack of proper blood supply. He explained the muscles that surround the shoulder had clamped down to protect the broken bone. The bone could literally die.

Now that the diagnosis was in, he told me I had to be straight with him. He believed I was a drunk or a heavy cocaine addict. These are the only likely conclusions he could come up with after hearing my story. By this time I'm sure my appearance was questionable, too. I did not take his conclusions personally. I knew nobody wakes up in bed with a broken shoulder without falling down in their sleep or having some sort of trauma take place. He again explained his belief was that I either drank way too much liquor or used copious amounts of cocaine on a regular basis. Both of these habits could lead to a person not remembering the trauma that caused a broken bone. I assured him I am no saint, but a drunk or cocaine addict I was not. I was always more of a beer and occasional shot of tequila kind of guy. All I could think of was to explain my two beer rule when sailing or driving. Dr. Chase soon left the room for fifteen or twenty minutes. When he returned he again asked me to come clean. For whatever reason, I trusted him for his convictions however wrong they were. My shoulder was definitely broken. Other than that, I had no answers for him.

I found out, later, when Dr. Chase had left the examination room he had consulted with Kathie. She had chosen to help me out and now she was getting interrogated. Dr. Chase was sure I was a drunk or a heavy cocaine user. Kathie stood her ground and reported the exact opposite. When he returned

30

to the room Dr. Chase assured me that none of my recreational habits in the quantities I explained to him had anything to do with my broken shoulder. However he was still cautious with the pain killer prescription. I actually admire the way he handled the situation. He was honest, and confident that he had the talent to fix my shoulder. Very reassuring. Yes he had an ego, but as I would come to find out, most surgeons who try and piece broken bodies back together do.

Jamie Calvo, a friend of mine who I'd sailed with on his C&C 27 and occasionally played a round of golf with, ran a medical supply business. He sold products to doctors and hospitals throughout the Virgin Islands. In a strange coincidence, Jamie had supplied the metal product that Dr. Chase used to shore up my shoulder. Jamie later told me he was interrogated by Dr. Chase about my alcohol and drug use. Again I'd passed the test.

I was given an arm sling with five-inch thick padding on the back side which helped lock my upper body in place, and there was a pharmacy in the same building that filled my pain pill prescription. We were finally making headway and getting to see the doctor who, once and for all, would fix my problem. I knew the diagnosis, the immediate cure and had faith that Dr. Chase would do the best job possible. After another long cab ride to the airport, take off and landing and thirty minute drive to Cotton Valley, Kathie had delivered me home. My surgery was set for Monday, November, 28, 2006.

My house was soon full of activity. I received several calls and visitors. Baskets of fruit were brought in, offers of assistance with rides and plans to bring in groceries were put into motion, but I was pretty out of it and lacked any clear knowledge of the preparation that went into my care. Mom, family members, extended family members (Pat & Kathie), Donna and Tony (my landlords), friends and co-workers all came to my aide. I lived on an island 1,200 miles from the states, far away from my family but I was surrounded by great people who chose to help me during my time of need. When someone is faced with this type of situation, family and the generosity of friends makes all the difference in the world.

Over the years, I'd grown to appreciate Pat's wife Kathie. I always enjoyed her conversations, and the first time I tasted her apple pie I knew she would be a great friend. In fact, every Thanksgiving on St. Croix was spent at the Ellison's. Their finest china and silverware are used on that day, enhanced by candles and lovely table settings. Kathie worked in the kitchen for hours, as Mom did when I was younger, to create a masterpiece of turkey, mashed potatoes, pie and all the trimmings. 2006 would be different. Kathie stepped up to go with me to St. Thomas, stay in a hotel and bring me back from my surgery. She was putting her Thanksgiving on hold for me.

Mother had insisted on flying down, but I was worried about her safety and security as she was unfamiliar with the islands. I finally talked her out of it. I didn't want her wandering around St. Thomas alone. My surgery was on Monday and I would be in the hospital for four days. I insisted on booking Kathie a room at the Frenchman's Reef Hotel. She still talks about how nice it was. I spent one night there after my surgery and can not remember anything except they had a good looking buffet in the dining room. Unfortunately I was too sick to my stomach to give it a go.

As my brother Rod is a physician, he spoke directly with Dr. Chase before the surgery. He was making sure everything was on the up and up. My brother Tim spoke to me at length, making me laugh and lifting my spirits. I understood, to some degree, the severity of the situation, but as far as I was concerned I would have surgery and be back to normal within eight weeks. Where that number came from I'm not sure. Before the surgery, Dr. Chase had explained the need for rehab following the procedure. Kathie, Mom and my brother understood, but my mind was cloudy during this whole time. All I cared about was getting fixed. In the past, a broken bone meant being in an itchy cast for six weeks and then taking it easy for a few days. I was naive at best. I had no idea how unrealistically optimistic my hopes were. I had nothing to compare this experience with.

When you break a humerus bone in the shoulder the surrounding muscles, tendons and ligaments reverse their main functions and contract to protect the area and keep it from moving. By the time I'd had a consultation

32

with Dr. Chase my shoulder was like a hard chunk of cement. I was unable to move the arm even an inch without severe pain. I literally passed every minute of every day concentrating on not moving my arm. Although this was the right thing to do at the time, it would cost me down the road with extended rehabilitation and limited mobility. I was oblivious to what this fracture meant to me and my immediate future. More importantly I did not have time to consider why this had happened.

The week of waiting was finally drawing to a close. The days had been hard and sleeping nearly impossible. I would get one to two hours at best before I would wake in pain. Just getting into a horizontal position was a task. The pain medication prescribed by Dr. Chase took the edge off, but it did not stop the pain from being present every minute of every day.

As Monday approached I was able to speak to family and friends one last time before the surgery. The conversations, from my perspective, revolved around getting to the finish line. I was not used to having people fawn over me and I didn't want to have conversations about pain and broken bones anymore.

On Monday morning Kathie picked me up and we headed to the airport. The medication helped the long drive seem less traumatic. This time we took an American Eagle flight instead of Cape Air. The plane was a much larger turbo prop and I didn't have to bend over to get in. The process was still daunting, but I was in a better mood knowing the healing process was beginning. I just had to make it through surgery. Everything else would take care of itself.

I remember feeling almost upbeat as the cab from the airport reached the back door of Snyder Regional Hospital on St. Thomas. The hospital is much larger than the hospital on St. Croix and there are medical buildings located around the main complex. Although the Admissions office was crammed with people I was greeted with a smile and few inefficiencies. I was finished checking in within thirty minutes, seated in a wheelchair and rolled to the pre-ops ward.

Dr. Chase's operating rooms occupied an entire floor of the hospital.

The surroundings were clean and orderly. Everyone was professional and upbeat. At some point I was undressed and put in a hospital gown that did not flatter my large figure. With only one useful arm, it was impossible to keep from flashing my ass to several people in the surgical ward. Dr. Chase performed a pre-surgery check, vitals were monitored, a needle was stuck in my arm, drugs were administered and I was wheeled off.

The muscles, tendons and ligaments that were currently locked down on my shoulder would be peeled back. There would be a five-inch metal plate inserted. The plate looks as if it has a hand with spread fingers on the top. This apparatus would be screwed into my remaining healthy bone structure to hold my shoulder together. The procedure included a piece of cadaver bone to surround some of the metal. I was told later that the cadaver bone would likely dissolve over time. The muscles, ligaments and tendons would be cut and re-positioned over the metal and sutured back together. The surgery took just over three and half hours, the exact amount of time Dr. Chase predicted in our pre-surgery conversation.

I was rolled into the Intensive Care Unit for monitoring purposes before being moved to my personal room. As the drugs from the surgery started to wear off, I could sense a complete new level of pain I'd never felt. I'd broken toes, fingers, wrists, arms, my nose, jaw and ribs in the past. None of these experiences felt good but I'd never experienced anything like the pain growing through the fog immediately after surgery. I was later told that I was fighting to defend myself with my one good arm, throwing left-handed haymakers and jabs, generally giving the post-surgery nurses a real hard time. I definitely was not in control. Knowing I was violent, without having any memory of it, leaves a pretty chilling thought in the back of my mind.

To counteract the pain, I was hooked up to an IV and given a morphine drip—later a morphine pump. This device allowed me to press the pump, but it would only distribute one measured dosage every twenty minutes no matter how many times I pounded on the damn button. In the middle of the second day, I'd literally burned out the pump. The hospital had a limited supply of these pumps and I had to go back to hanging bags and an IV drip.

Regardless, the morphine was not eliminating the pain. There is no way to describe it, but bone surgeries using inserted screws have to be some of the most excruciating to experience. The overwhelming pain was unrelenting. I prayed it would end soon, to no avail.

Other memories of this time are vague. Kathie came to visit. Nurses checked on me on a regular basis. And I was immobile in a bed hooked up to a drug drip and feeling the worst pain of my life.

The third day after surgery was coming to an end. I was given news of my eventual release from the hospital. Enthusiasm for a quick return to the good life started to fill my pessimistic, cloudy head. A quick reality check would have dampened my new upbeat mood, but I marched on, happy to be leaving. My right arm was immobile—stapled together and swollen over twice its normal size. I had to rely on Kathie just to move. The drive from the hospital to the hotel, before flying out the next morning, was epic in nature. I was feeling sick to my stomach from all the narcotics in my system, and I didn't want anything to eat, which added to my run-down state. At the airport the next day, I asked a TSA officer to use his metal detector wand on my shoulder. It didn't set off the alarm. Somehow that was a little disappointing for me, but I was happy to be heading home.

Caught in the fog of anesthesia, morphine and anti inflammatory drugs I was a mess. I had no thoughts or instinct for what the process going forward should include. I refused to stay anywhere but at my house. The only certainty was that my body was hurting and I felt 150 and getting older by the minute. Movement was slow and deliberate, my energy had hit rock bottom, my skin was yellow, clammy and I was sweating non-stop.

Arrangements had been made to undergo physical rehabilitation at the Beeston Hill Gym where I swam. I would need to return home, rest for less than a week and start rehab. It was essential to get the arm moving and the blood flowing to the bone. I was unable to drive, so my landlord, Donna Bakley, offered to take me to the rehab center on her morning drive to work. From there I would take a cab to the office. Melissa Miller would drive me home. Through the haze of the prescribed Oxycodone the details often escaped me, but the others involved knew what needed to be done.

Basically right handed, trying to manage without the use of my dominant arm was challenging. Getting dressed was problematic. I took some old Bohlke International Airlines golf shirts with my name on them and cut out the right-side sleeves so I could pull them on without moving my arm. I had to buy a pair of slip-on shoes, too, because I could not bend over to tie laces. Five days after returning from St. Thomas I was delivered to the rehab center by Donna Bakley at 7:15 a.m. I carried my work clothes in my left hand, my pain pills in my pocket and headed through the door unsure of what to expect. I must have looked like the walking dead with my bandaged shoulder hanging out of the altered shirt, seeping blood through the stitches and staples that held together the five-inch cut in my upper arm.

The first day turned out to be nothing more than a checkup. The one thing I heard that excited me was that if I made good progress in a couple of weeks I would be in the pool for aqua therapy. I was assigned a physical therapist and told I would eventually work with most of the staff. At the end of the meeting I was asked to relax my shoulder muscles so measurements of internal rotation, external rotation and abduction could be taken.

As the therapist straightened my arm out and tried rotating my shoulder inwards about two inches, my knees buckled as pain exploded in my upper body. I jerked away with all my strength. I was the only one startled by my reaction, and was told I would need to work on fighting the urge to resist during manipulations. They came at me again, and I sufficiently resisted the survival instinct. With the series of movements and measurements over, it took me thirty minutes to fumble through changing my clothes in the locker room as sweat continued to pour out of my body.

I called a cab from the front desk, popped an oxycodone and waited in silence. The cab driver took one look at me and said, "God helps those in need." I took solace in the statement as he helped me get into the van. The first steps toward healing had been taken but deep down I'd been hoping for instant progress.

Christiansted was built in the 1700s and all sidewalks are uneven, made from cobblestone and loaded with stairs. It is difficult to walk under any conditions. I struggled out of the cab and under the arch way, walking past the covered storefronts and continued the trek up hill. I had to stop and rest, unable to make it the entire two blocks. After catching my breath and wiping the sweat from my forehead I continued on.

There are twenty-two stairs leading up to the old great house where TMG has its office space. I took a breath, clung to the handrail and started the climb. My head was spinning as I walked through the door and down the set of stairs to the receptionist area. As I rested before heading down the backstairs to my office, several people got up from cubicles located in what used to be the great house living room and came over to say Hello. I felt a little embarrassed at my appearance. I was wearing the cut-up polo shirt with Bohlke Airlines emblem and my name stitched into the chest. Blood had seeped through the heavy bandage on my arm, resulting in a visible dark black stain with red and yellow highlights. I was oozing sweat and feeling nauseous. I have never been the best dressed in this or any company, but my appearance had deteriorated to a whole new level. I thanked everyone for their concern and staggered to my office. Within five minutes, Kiril and Melissa were standing at my door. Several jokes were made about how bad I looked. I laughed and then tried to hide the fact it hurt like hell. Melissa was pretty sure I needed to go home. I wanted to stay. I fired up my computer and checked my phone messages. I recorded a note with my left hand, and the resulting scribble was barely legible.

I was currently in charge of two Associate Managing Directors who worked out of our Coral Springs office. I contacted both of them, thanked them for their concern, caught up on where we were with our monthly numbers and looked at recent e-mails. Usually, all of that would have taken less than an hour, but it was now past noon and I was fading fast. I called Melissa and asked for a ride home. The first day back had been a success.

I was scheduled to attend rehab every day for the rest of the week. My therapy consisted of removing my arm from its sling, squeezing a ball, walking on a treadmill, and involuntary movements performed by the physical therapist. It ended with electrical stimulation, ice and a ten-minute massage. The sessions lasted anywhere from an hour to an hour and a half, followed by the half an hour of dressing. I was constantly aware of time and how much I was missing from work. It became an obsession that would concern me for months to come.

My mind was also obsessed with protecting my arm. I was locking it to my side, and performing as little movement as possible. When it came time to relax and allow the therapist to manipulate it, I continued to resist. It was painful and I often pulled away several times. The conversations that followed centered on the limited amount of time we had to break up the scar tissue. If it solidified I would never regain my range of motion. The massage therapists were crucial in helping avoid this from happening. After each workout, they would manipulate the muscles around the wound. They could feel how much scar tissue had built up on the front of the shoulder and all the way around the back and under the arm pit. There's no way to prepare for the pain caused by the tearing process. Letting go and allowing another human to manipulate your broken body is a difficult hurdle to cross. But I was up against the clock so, pushing my apprehension and natural instincts aside, I tried to do everything asked of me and more.

The entire staff was frank, and by the end of the first week the general consensus was I would not regain all of my previous mobility. How much of a drop off depended on my attitude and willingness to work. It was going to take a huge effort, not only at the gym, but at home. These words stuck with me and I used them as motivation to prove everyone wrong.

Although I was eager to get to work, surrendering my arm for manipulation continued to be a challenge. I knew it was mind over matter and worked on deep breathing and relaxing. Remaining tense caused the nerves and muscles to clamp down to protect the area in pain. To help out at the end of each session, I was given fifteen minutes of electro therapy. Pushing currents of electricity through the shoulder causes the muscles to contract and relax.

It became apparent early on that I'd misjudged the severity of this injury and the scope of the recovery process. I knew, at this point, I was in for a long battle. I pledged to work harder than any previous patient in the history of this medical procedure, and to overcome the obstacles before me.

Pushing the pain aside, avoiding the emotional connection to my injury and having as few conversations about my health problems as possible became my modus operandi. I was able to keep my mind constantly moving forward, focusing only on the physical work that lay ahead.

No strategies or coping methods could lower the intense feelings of dislike for the absolute need to rely on others for day-to-day transportation, food and support. Even knowing the situation was temporary this reliance weighed the heaviest on my mind. The feelings of helplessness and dependency raced through my head each and every time I asked a favor from one of my friends. I did not like being the center of attention and communication became awkward, at best. No matter who it was, nearly every conversation started with, "How are you feeling?" I wanted to talk about something other than me. On the other hand, rehabilitation therapy offered me an avenue to do something about my situation. I could envision a future without pain and normal arm function. No matter what the doctors or therapists told me, I felt I could realize this outcome through hard work. I embraced the challenge.

Dr. Chase wanted to see me once a week for the first two months post surgery. Later it would be once every two weeks, and finally once a month until it was determined everything was working well. The one viable option to see Dr. Chase in St. Thomas, without missing an entire day of work, meant using the sea plane located at the west end of the boardwalk in Christiansted. Seaborne Airlines uses twin turbo prop 19-seat sea planes that land on water and taxi to docks in harbors rather than an airport. I could walk to their office from work and because they only fly within the territory there was no need to clear customs. This saved valuable time, and the cab ride from the docks on Charlotte Amalie Harbor to the Paragon Medical Building is much shorter than from the airport. I would take the first morning flight to St. Thomas, a cab to the Paragon and be the first patient to see Dr. Chase or his assistant at 8:30 a.m. I would finish my consultation, have a cab waiting to take me back to the docks, catch the next flight, land on the water in Christiansted Harbor and walk the five blocks back to work. If everything went smoothly I was back at my desk no later than 11:00 a.m. Keeping up this schedule would be no easy task.

The first post-op visit with Dr. Chase was on the Tuesday following the first week of physical therapy. I was ushered into an x-ray room by the doctor's assistant. A plate was pushed under my right arm pit as I stood against a wall. The pain intensified and sweat dripped off my forehead. As the assistant snapped x-rays, I was asked to contort the arm in different positions so the surgically repaired area could be seen from different angles. Ten minutes later Dr. Chase came into my holding room and showed me the x-rays on his hand-held PDA. His comments ranged from how well he'd performed the surgery to how it was too early to tell if the bone would live or die, as he still had concerns over the lack of pre-surgery blood supply. If the bone died I would need to have it replaced with metal. I'd believed I was in the clear, but after listening to Dr. Chase, the bone dyingquickly became my number one concern. After several nervous questions it became clear the concern would have to be shoved to the back of the line. There was nothing to do but wait and see. He added, "The only way we will be able to check if the bone lives or dies is monitoring the situation by x-ray, and at this time everything looks good."

Dr. Chase finished the visit by performing several of the same measurements that had been taken at rehab including internal and external rotation and abduction. Again, I had to surrender my arm to him and each movement produced untold amounts of pain. Somehow, throughout the process I became encouraged as to how far it could be moved. The therapists and Dr. Chase were able to move the arm three to four inches. I could only move it one or two on my own.

I was still taking Oxycodone. The number of these powerful pills was dwindling. Post-surgery, I had only been provided a two-week prescription. Dr. Chase explained I would be switched to Percocet, a lesser dosage mixed with Tylenol. I wouldn't say I was dependent on the Oxycodone, but I liked the drug. It has a pleasant high, though it clouds your head and makes dealing with pain tolerable. I did not want to make the switch and asked Dr. Chase if it was necessary.

"Absolutely!"

I ran the risk of becoming dependent on the drug.

At the end of our consultation Dr. Chase made several comments into a digital recorder for transcription, and I was on my way out the door to catch my cab. As we approached Christiansted Harbor I felt a sense of relief. So far, I'd made all of my appointments. I had five blocks of walking ahead of me. I took that time to calm down and push the thought of potential bone death out of my head. I had stacks of work waiting and could not afford to be distracted.

The stamina for an entire day at work did not quickly return. Every day Melissa would drop what she was doing at work and drive me home when I'd had enough. The first week I left work by noon every day. As soon as I reached home I would lie down to sleep, but sleeping in a sling is difficult. I would line up pillows along my sides to avoid any movement, or the pain shooting through my shoulder would keep me awake. I found it increasingly difficult to get more than two or three hours of sleep a day.

After the first week of rehabilitation, the number of visits was decreased to three per week. On the two off days Melissa would pick me up at home and I would ride into work with her in the morning. I felt like I was headed in the right direction. I knew I needed to clear my head. My short-term memory was poor and I frequently forgot words when I spoke and had to stop and think what it was I was trying to say. Communication had never been this difficult. The pain in my shoulder and back at this point was so common place I felt I was strong enough to just deal with it without the drugs. I filled the Percocet prescription given to me by Dr. Chase and set the bottle on my counter and never opened it. I needed to concentrate on my rehab and work. The only way I was going to accomplish those goals was with a clear head.

TMG had grown to over one hundred clients. My title had changed to

Manager of Buyer Services. My group worked in congress with the marketing department and the work on each client included internet postings, mailings and calling campaigns. I also was busy establishing relationships with private equity groups around the U.S., Canada and Europe. Slow moving half-days were just not going to cut it. I needed to pick up the pace.

My physical therapist gave me daily exercise routines for home and work as my arm needed exercise three times a day. One movement was an outward rotation. If you bend your arm at the elbow to ninety degrees and tuck that elbow in close to your rib cage, make a fist and rotate your arm straight out to the left or right, you will have a complete range of motion to about the two o'clock position for the right arm and about ten o'clock for the left. I had zero outward rotation capabilities for the right arm when this process started. I was given a stretchy, plastic band to take home, which I tied to a leg on a chair. Placing the chair to the right of me, I wrapped the loose end of the band around my right wrist and applied pressure. The band would cause resistance, pulling my arm in an outwardly motion. I could also pull back against the band working on internal rotation and strength. I started doing sets of three in a row. It hurt like hell and I was only able to stand about ten seconds at a time. With each session I was pulling at that scar tissue and would have to ice the arm down at the end.

In mid-December my brother Rod, sister in-law Theresa, niece Rory and nephew Jasper were scheduled to return from their year abroad in Peru. At the end of their stay they had traveled throughout Ecuador and Bolivia and were headed back to Hood River, Oregon via Mexico City. They decided to take a 2,250 mile detour in the wrong direction and check up on me in St. Croix. My mother decided to fly down from Illinois and join them.

They made arrangements to stay at the Divi Carina Bay Resort and Casino, familiar to all of them because at Christmas 2004 my entire family came to visit and had stayed there. We had hiked, sailed and snorkeled. It was one of best times I can remember. This visit would be much different and I felt uneasy. I was excited to have close family coming into town, but I could not shake the feeling that they would be let down. I was just starting to get back on my own two feet and I did not have the capabilities or the energy to entertain anyone.

By then, I was working on extending my days at the office past noon and getting my arm to move away from my waist. I still wore the brace all day and would have to for some time to come. I was making progress, but the longest I could hold up in a group setting was two to three hours before exhaustion won out. By the time I had rehab in the morning, and worked until two or three in the afternoon, my energy level was very low. In the evening, I would rest quietly before doing a round of arm exercises and then try to get some sleep.

When my family arrived, I wanted to take the days off from work but that was not possible because of the time I'd already missed. Instead my brother Rod rented a car and drove me to therapy and work every day. He would pick me up in the afternoon and we would go back to the hotel. It made me feel good to give all my friends a break from running me around. At the same time I was aware this was by no means an ordinary vacation for my family.

We managed to play cards, ate good food and generally laid low. I felt tired most days and would have to ask for a ride home early in the evening. I was so thankful they had come to visit, and their time on island flew by. Before I knew it, they were gone and it was back to relying on friends to take me to rehab and work.

For the past three or four Christmas holidays I'd attended an early morning brunch at the Newman's house with Pat and Kathie. It had become tradition. We always followed that up with a sail out to Buck Island. This year, I didn't feel up to the brunch, and there was no way I could sail. I needed time to rest and declined the invitation. Everyone understood.

Christmas morning I'd finished my arm exercises and heard dogs barking like crazy in the yard. Kiril, Sara and their dog Ruby showed up on my door step. They were headed to Cane Bay Beach on the north shore. They wanted me to join them and would not take no for an answer. I reluctantly agreed.

There were over one hundred Christmas Day partiers on the beach by the time we arrived. Several people brought their dogs and the Sprat Net Beach Bar was open for business. Pale tourist girls in bikinis ran around talking about how great it was being out of the snow. There was a group of five or six young Rastafarians that rode ponies bare back in the calm break water next to the beach. As the day progressed, my hesitation flip flopped and I grew into the spirit of the holiday. Sara and Kiril had brought an additional fold-out chair and we found a spot close to a group of mangrove and grape leaf trees. It was early afternoon and the smell of barbecuing hog wafted down the beach. The water was unusually calm for that time of year and Kiril and Sara jumped right in. I thought about it for a while and carefully removed my sling and clung to my right arm, holding it tight to my waist before cautiously wading into the blue Caribbean. When the cool water reached my mid section I sat down, removing the weight off my legs. The natural movement of the water began gently pushing me from side to side, rhythmically, and I was able to relax all my muscles. It was wonderful getting back in the ocean.

The staples had been removed from my arm a couple of weeks earlier and the scar was still raised and healing. The salt water and bright sun seemed to help dry out the tissue around the wound. I didn't want it to become sunburned and decided it was time to get out of the water. I also knew, from past experience, it was easy to have a wave cause you to loose your balance and fall. After a few anxious moments, I was able to use my body weight to my advantage, and step out of the ocean on to the dry sand— without a problem. Kiril and I walked down the beach to Sprat Net Bar. As we watched the tourists splashing in the water I forgot, for a brief moment, that I had a broken shoulder and could not use my right arm. It was the first time since all this had started, over a month before, that my mind took a break. As the sun was setting over Ham's Bluff we drove through the north shore cliffs east of Cane Bay on our way home. Looking back over my shoulder I could see the dramatic colors of the sky. It was a beautiful Merry Christmas!

DRIVING A STICK-SHIFT FORD (DAY 38 – 78)

My weekly routine continued to include physical therapy sessions, working until late afternoon and seaplane flights to Dr. Chase's office. Dr. Doug Menzie, a chiropractor who runs the Beeston Hill Rehabilitation Center, suggested a wrist bone density scan to help determine the health of my bone structure. After putting it off a couple of times I finally agreed to take one on January 7. The scan took several minutes as the report printed out. The results were shocking. My left wrist bone density was negative 2.8. indicating severe osteoporosis—meaning my bones were thin and brittle. After some brief research I discovered the lack of bone density is most commonly found in elderly women. It was extremely rare for a relatively healthy thirty-nine-year-old man to have this level of osteoporosis. I ran a high risk of breaking more bones if this was not corrected. The reason for this anomaly was not easily explained. After having the results faxed to Dr. Chase, his response was to prescribe three months' supply of Fosamax and suggested seeing a specialist.

"Fosamax (alendronate) is in the group of medicines called bisphosphonates. It alters the cycle of bone formation and breakdown in the body. Fosamax slows bone loss while increasing bone mass, which may prevent bone fractures."
Read more: http://www.drugs.com/fosamax.html#ixzz0vAI4FbEg

Fosamax is taken by ingesting one pill per week. Soon after taking the first couple of pills, the drug made me dizzy and I, again, began having short-term memory lapses. I explained my side effects to Dr. Chase. Not

45

needing further complications, I stopped using Fosamax at the end of the three-month run in March. Dr. Chase agreed that we could re-visit this type of medication at another time.

As the days passed, my energy level started to rebound. With all my attention focused on work and rehab came the added benefit of gaining efficiencies in my daily routine. I was more productive and my group was performing at its highest level. TMG powers that be treated me well and without their understanding this could have been a really bad situation. They never pressed me on when I was going to return to work after my surgery, and later gave me carte blanch on time for rehab and doctors visits. In return I felt it was my duty to not only keep up with my work load but surpass expectations. As the pain level decreased I started to type and write with my right hand. I had to sit close to the keyboard because my shoulder could not extend out from my body, but it was good therapy to move my fingers and keep the injured arm as active as possible. Slowly my head was becoming unclouded as the drugs and shock faded.

In mid-January I started aqua therapy. I loved the pool. My biggest strides in mobility came from these exhausting workouts. They consisted of eight-to-twelve exercises I would perform in an hour. I was starting to see good results on the internal rotation. However, I was not getting any results on the external rotation. I struggled with abduction: moving the shoulder and arm toward the central axis of the body. Three times a day I religiously performed arm exercise routines at home and work hoping to some day regain full mobility.

I owned a stick-shift Ford Ranger truck, and on a weekend late in January I got in and started it up for the first time since my injury. As the engine warmed up, I studied the steering wheel, gear shifter and the distances away from the seat. I figured out a way to drive by letting go of the wheel, reaching across my body, and shifting with my left hand. I was soon rolling down the driveway on my way to Lorie's Deli at The Reef Golf Course. I bought a paper and drove home. It was liberating. It was a little awkward but I found I could hold on to the bottom of the wheel with my right. From that day forward I had my independence back and my friends were free from their daily burden. We all take our independence for granted. When it's snatched away, a cruel reality has to be faced. I felt like a huge wrong had been corrected.

My activity level increased with my new-found independence. I started working out at the gym at the pool on my days off. After getting comfortable with that I began thinking of new ways to challenge myself. On the weekends I hiked Goat Hill performing my arm exercises when I reached the top. The strenuous hike begins at sea level and climbs vertically for over 600 feet, covering just under two miles start to finish. The trail is littered with rocks and kasha bushes. The first quarter mile is on the north face of the hill and has little breeze. Extreme sweating purged my system and the hike tested my resolve. I would certainly face concern from doctors and family members if I mentioned these hikes so I didn't tell anyone. It gave me an opportunity to rely solely on myself. Although there were still some unanswered questions, my confidence level was growing.

On my birthday, January 28, I went to South Grape Tree Beach with Pat and Kathie, removed my arm brace, and got in the ocean for the second time since my surgery. Bobbing up and down with the waves helped me reach a wonderfully relaxed state. It was a much less cautious approach than Christmas day had been. My condition was improving and the right arm did not hurt as much as it had. I was able to roll on my back and kick around the bay. It was great to be in the sun and get a good workout. Not long after this test, I started to remove the arm brace for short periods of time throughout the work day. I could not let it hang at my side for long before the pain returned, but I could hold it with my left hand and be comfortable.

Visible progress was being made on a weekly basis in physical therapy. During one exercise the buoyancy created by holding Styrofoam floats in each hand raised my right arm directly out in front of my body at shoulder height. This was big progress, but I still struggled moving the injured arm to the side or behind my back. The progress paid off and one morning I was able to reach the stick shift knob in my truck with my right hand for the first time. It hurt like hell as I struggled and stretched, my fingertips barely touching the knob, but from that moment on I started trying to shift every gear using the right hand. Each attempt brought with it pain that I promptly pushed aside choosing, instead, to marvel at the latest accomplishment.

February is a big month on St. Croix. The Agra Fair takes place and the St. Croix Yacht Club hosts the annual Cort Series Regatta. I was really trying to increase my endurance and strength so I could enjoy these two events. I knew I wouldn't be racing, but I wanted to attend the opening party and, for a few hours every day, socialize. The Agra Fair is similar to a county fair in the states complete with local food, plants, music, and product demonstrations. I planned on attending a few hours opening day.

I continued increasing my output at work and felt things were moving in the right direction. I was nowhere near swinging a golf club, sailing *Folly* or swimming, but I could wear button-down shirts and tie my own shoes.

I expanded my cardio routines in the gym and rotated hikes on off days to Jacks & Isaacs Bay, Goat Hill and the beach between Cheney Bay and Green Cay Marina—all in hopes of increasing blood flow to the injured bone. I never missed a scheduled physical therapy appointment and I gave it maximum effort every time out. If my arm did not come back to being fully functional, it wasn't going to be because I did not do everything in my power to get it there.

I received a lot of help from everyone, and it seemed everyone was giving me information about how to better my situation. Diet, exercise and therapy methods were all hot topics. Not knowing why my shoulder bone broke in my sleep kept me from studying the yet unknown cause. I was, however, able to have conversations with other physical therapy patients, all the professionals I was in contact with and friends and family that had dealt with serious bone injuries. It was around this time Dr. Chase started referring to the injury as the Immaculate Fracture. When I would be in the waiting room with other patients, he would walk in and say, "How's it going Immaculate? Come on back." Although it was funny I also knew it was meant to question why this had happened, but the most pressing issue was concentrating on keeping the bone alive.

Pat's childhood friend Andy Hooker, a Great Lakes sailing champion out of Youngstown, New York, started to come down to St. Croix to get his winter boating fix at our annual regatta. When Andy was in town, I would lend Pat my boat so the two of them could get some sails in before the racing started. The previous year I'd missed the regatta kick-off party because I'd been on a business trip to Florida. Pat and Andy had taken *Folly* out for a sail on Friday morning. The fact that people were having fun on my boat while I was stuck in an office 1,200 miles away was seared into my memory. I vowed this year was going to be different.

Looking forward to the annual regatta started each year about the time the bruises from racing in the previous year's event had healed. I'd already begun my annual ritual of increasing my workouts to get physically prepared when my shoulder broke in my sleep on November 19th.

Being suddenly relegated to the sidelines left me a little more than down, but I was still looking forward to the kick-off party and watching some of the action from shore. Racing is different from the day sailing I was accustomed to. A typical day included a stop at Buck Island where you can snorkel the east end, or anchor on the west end and hike the trail and walk the beach. Depending on the wind direction, some days we sail downtown, tie up at the boardwalk, have lunch at the Brew Pub, sail over to Isle on the Cay, swim in for a beer or two at the bar and head home. As long as nobody gets hurt, and everyone has fun, the day is a success.

Racing, on the other hand, is all about being competitive, going as fast as possible in the prevailing winds and applying proper tactics to beat the other boats in your class. Posting the lowest time across the finish line is the number one goal. The courses are generally laid out in a six-mile triangle marked by large orange buoys. There is usually one twelve-mile race during the regatta that includes rounding a marker in Gallows Bay, downtown Christiansted, and racing back across the start line. Most days you get at least three or four races in. A race committee boat keeps track of all the different classes and posts finishing times.

At one point in time the St. Croix Regatta drew between eighty and one hundred race boats each year, but a number of hurricanes roared through the Caribbean from the 1980s through the early 2000s destroying property—including dozens of racing sailboats. This diminished participation levels in regattas across the islands. The year before forty-nine boats participated. Most of them came from St. Croix, St. Thomas, St. John, Tortola, Norman Island, St. Martin, Antigua and Puerto Rico.

After racing in the St. Croix Regatta the boat owners can choose to attend the remaining regattas in the CORT Series held on different islands. Most years the CORT Series culminates with the Heineken Regatta on St. Thomas. It was disappointing to be sidelined. I would miss out on all the action. I kept telling myself that there were a lot of people in the world worse off than I was. "All you have is a broken shoulder and that will eventually heal. Get over the negative thoughts and enjoy the party."

By the time I arrived at 6:00 p.m., the parking lot and the boatyards were full of vehicles. There were 300-to-400 people milling about. I'd made a conscious decision not to wear the arm brace, taking it off at the last minute before climbing into the truck. When Andy got into town a few days before, he started saying I was operating with only one good flipper. After sailing all day on *Folly,* and consuming several free rum drinks, he was the first to see me walk down the front lawn of the Yacht Club. "Flipper, Flipper" half slurred is all I heard. We started to mingle into the crowd. I was a little nervous not wearing the brace and tucked my right arm in tight to the side, guarding it with the left hand when I was walking through the masses crammed into the clubhouse bar area. I ran into some sailors from our club who were racing the next day and we talked about weather, winds, sails and what boats were coming from Puerto Rico, British Virgin Islands and St. Thomas.

I was at the bar drinking a beer when I caught a glimpse of Pat heading out the front door through the crowd. I wanted to see how the sail had gone earlier that day. Andy had given up little coherent information other than it was a good time. I'd just caught up to Pat when a pretty woman approached us. I remember Pat saying, "This is the one who came down by herself." It turns out Pam had sailed earlier that day along with Ella, Pat and Andy on *Folly*. Pat and Andy had met Pam the year before at Chicken Charlie's the night before the regatta kickoff party. She was visiting the island and was leaving the next day. We must have passed each other in the sky as she left island and I returned home just in time to race. Pam had made arrangements to come back to St. Croix the following year from Cleveland with her friend to attend the regatta. The friend canceled out, and Pam decided to come by herself. When Pat had gone to the airport to pick Andy up for his sailing vacation, they ran into Pam at the luggage carousel.

Our first conversation took place on the tiki torch lit sidewalk leading to the entrance of the St. Croix Yacht Club. She seemed to know more about my injury than I did, asking me several questions I was reluctant to answer. I was guessing that her information came from Pat. I was pretty embarrassed. My goal for the night was to try to have a good time and not dominate the night's conversation with talk about my injury. My first impressions of Pam were that she is pretty, smart and just a little bit crazy for coming to the island alone on vacation. After a few more minutes of me avoiding her questions she left to get a drink. I had no idea how much this chance encounter would affect my life.

As I watched Pam walk off into the crowd, I was pulled into several more conversations and eventually found my way under the tent where the band was playing. I saw Pam dancing with Ella. I was sure I would run into her again over the course of her vacation, and I was getting tired and called it a night. As soon as I got home I put my arm brace back on. I was not used to having it out of the sling for this extended period of time.

The next morning I woke up early and headed down to the Yacht Club for breakfast. The first morning before racing is quite the scene. Crews, piles of equipment and high energy filled the open-air bar next to the beach leading to the T-dock. I knew half the boat crews and got caught up in several conversations. More than one crew asked if I was sure I could not race.

51

There was no chance in hell of that happening, but it sounded good and lifted my spirits.

Around 11:00 a.m., I drove out to a sharp turn high on a ridge overlooking the race course below. Inside the reef, the IC 24 and Rhoades 19 one-design boats were waging war with the course conditions and each other. I was friends with most of these contestants and watched the action intently for over an hour. The wind was blowing at least twenty-five knots and the action was fast and furious. Boats were bumping and banging and the sail changes were interesting. Because of the strong winds, maintaining the full shape of the spinnaker sail on the downwind legs looked like hard work. The difference between winning and losing in the one-design class boats was going to be based on who got clear wind on their sails and had the least equipment failure. It was fun to watch.

In the open channel, bracketed by the reef that runs to the north of St. Croix's shore line and Buck Island, the class boats raced around the leeward and windward marks. The six-mile course was filled with masts, sails, chase skiffs and the Committee Boat. When you have been a part of the racing in the past, you realize the effort taking place on each deck, in each racing class and by the officials running the show. The Committee Boat is the central nervous system of any regatta. They send out radio messages and blow horns to give advanced warning for different racing classes as to their pending start time. Flags are hoisted on the Committee Boat's halyards to advise count-down sequences. All boats in that class start to jockey for position and then the shotgun (horn) goes off and everyone tacks across the start line. This is where most races are won and lost.

Two years earlier, I'd been racing on a J-145 named *Sequoia*. The owner had bought the boat in Europe and had it shipped to the Caribbean for the racing season. We were his first pick-up crew. This was by far the most modern and sophisticated racing machine I'd ever sailed on. It had equipment I was not familiar with including an asymmetrical spinnaker sail. In our practice the day before the regatta we all marveled at how well this boat pointed to weather. You literally felt the wind directly in your face.

That defies all logic and common sense. What a boat. Man, we were ramped up to start the racing.

We knew we would be faster than everyone on the course. It was just a matter of tactics, team work and how much time we surrendered to the other boats because of the handy capping system that would determine the race's outcome. The owner/driver was still working the kinks out of his new toy. He drove a couple of poor races at the start of the day. Trying to make up for the poor performance he drove the forty-eight foot J-145 right up the middle of the starting field after the shotgun start for Spinnaker Class Two. We started yelling from the front of the boat, "Drop down. Drop down!" There were boats in front of us and also to either side. We were traveling a knot faster than anyone in the field, when we overtook a brand new Farr 30 race boat from Puerto Rico. It was his unfortunate luck to be positioned directly in front of *Sequoia*. The noise created as the bow of *Sequoia* penetrated the stern of the Farr race boat was tremendous. We smashed through the boat at least three feet into the cockpit, splitting the Farr's driver and tactician, placing them on either side of the J-Boats bow. It took several seconds to realize the extent of the damage. The Farr did not sink, but had to retire to the docks for immediate repair. The regatta and CORT series were over for them. We had to tack back behind the start line for our penalty, a complete 360-degree turn before being allowed to resume racing. The owner of our boat paid the repair cost out of his own pocket—in cash. It came to over $20,000.

In 2007, I was happy to be watching the action from my lookout over the race course. It was not the same as being in the middle of it on a boat but I still was having a great time.

The racing continued well past the 3:00 p.m. scheduled end time. The exhausted crew members did not get back into Teague Bay and the safety of their moorings, anchorages or slips until 5:00 p.m. I stayed home Saturday night knowing most of the racers would be exhausted and the party would be over before it got started. The next day there would still be a lot of racing ahead, so they would shut it down relatively early.

I received a call from Pat later that evening. He and Andy had been racing on *Atlantic Raider*. The owner had sailed his boat from Houston, Texas, to St. Thomas in 2006. The boat was a J-27. Cruising one from the states to the Caribbean is a risky venture. The owner had learned to sail on the way. What a story. Pat explained that he knew nothing about racing and it was a miserable time out on the course with him. He was trying to learn how to race while Pat and Andy were trying to win the regatta. It was a bad combination for both parties.

Sundays are an abbreviated day of racing so all participants can start to pack up and head for home as soon as the awards ceremony is over. Around 4:00 p.m. I headed down to the club. Soon the mooring field was filling up with masts and the dock was jammed with tired and haggard looking crew members. I went to the bar for a beer and ran into Pam. We started talking and soon were laughing and having a good time. The conversation was much more relaxed than the first time we met.

Ella had joined us before long and we waited for Pat and Andy to get in off the water. When they finally approached I could see the disappointment on their faces. Pat said the boat was uncomfortable and he always seemed to have a cleat or piece of equipment up his ass all day. The owner/driver was afraid to trim the sails for optimum speed. The whole thing was a waste of time.

Pam and I continued our conversation under the food tent during the awards ceremony. After the last award was handed out we didn't say good night, instead opting to head into town with Ella in search of some Sunday night entertainment. My energy level was the best it had been in weeks. Our first stop was the St. Croix Marina. The Golden Rail Restaurant and Bar is located in the parking lot. Every Sunday night, they hosted a blues jam on a small stage in front of the docks. Pam was standing up, moving around and kept asking me to dance with her.

"I don't dance." Still seated, I relented, spinning her around with my left hand seemed to satisfy her need for me to embarrass myself in front of the crowd. She kept complementing me on my dancing skills. Wine and rum really help cloud a person's perspective.

This was already the longest night out since my surgery when Ella suggested we all go to another bar named Rebound, just up the street, and shoot a game of pool. I'd stopped drinking beer and was only consuming water. It was because of this fact that I, for all intents and purposes, a one-armed pool player, won all the games that night. After a couple of hours we all decided it was time to go. Ella went home and I escorted Pam to her condo. Before leaving her at the door I mustered up the courage to ask her to dinner with me on Wednesday night—Valentines Day. On Tuesday we would be meeting at Chicken Charlie's for Tuesday Night Trivia where we would finalize our plans for dinner the following evening.

The next day at work was rough going. I felt wiped out all day. I knew it had nothing to do with my recovery from surgery so I plowed through the day and made no excuses. By the time I got home I was ready for bed. I was fast asleep by 9:00 p.m.

Tuesday at work came and went in a blur of activity. I hardly had time to stop and think but was looking forward to Tuesday Night Trivial Pursuit. I'd heard about the game, but had never played.

As our small team of players filed into the tent-covered bar, I suggested we take the name Conquistador's after a boat I admired. Our group consisted of Pat, Andy, Ella, Pam and me. Our competition was made up of about ten to twelve other teams. The bar and food service was going on around us as the MC blurted out questions. One person at your table wrote down the answers and between rounds they were collected and the tally of correct answers announced. The team seated at the bar was known as The Bar Flys. According to Pat they never lost. They were made up of lawyers, engineers and insurance salesmen. They had enjoyed a long winning streak and it was our intent to take them down.

We did not come close to upsetting the quick-witted Bar Flys. We did, however, hold our own with a solid third-place finish. As the game and the night were breaking up, and everyone was going their separate directions, I pulled Pam aside and reconfirmed our dinner date for the next evening, but a moment of panic came over me because I knew I'd not planned anything out. The next morning I called the owner of my favorite restaurant, Sunset Grill. I had sold radio advertising for Bret when I first moved to the island and could not think of a better place for Valentine's Day dinner.

Bret was booked solid but told me not to worry. He would take care of it. At lunch I ran to Schooner Bay Marketplace and bought Pam a bottle of her favorite wine as a gift. The timing had to work out for me to be able to leave work at five, pick Pam up from her condo and drive to Fredericksted in time to catch the sun going down at 6:00 p.m. Traffic was bad and I was getting anxious. After hearing a few outbursts of foul language at other drivers, Pam explained how she would get angry with drivers in Cleveland and the things she would yell at them. We shared a laugh and that put me at ease. We made it just in time. The sun was ducking below the low cloud cover and barely sitting on top of the waves as we arrived. The best view was coming down the hill as we entered town. We drove north along the beach to the restaurant in silence as the sun was suspended just over the water minutes away from disappearing into the depths of the ocean. It was perfect!

We ate barefoot in the sand as the waves lapped up on the shore ten feet from the table legs. The pastel colors of sunset gave way to a brilliant star display as dinner neared its end. After dinner we moved down the beach to the lounging chairs, laid back and watched for shooting stars. We shared our first kiss on that beach. It was quite a romantic Valentines Day.

Before the evening had ended, Pam promised to go to Bud Orpen's poker game with me and Pat the following night. Although I was tired and my arm hurt at times I had more energy than I'd been able to muster since before I woke up with a broken shoulder. Three nights out in a row was going to be pushing it but what a fun way to test my endurance level.

TMG had been struggling with trying to integrate new sales operating systems and a company-wide phone platform. We had started out with Sales Logics, moved to Sales Net and back to Sales Logics. The problem was: the same system had to operate for the front end of the business, which included our client development group, and for the back end, which included the marketing team and my group. The systems needed to provide a level of functionality that allowed all groups to input data and be able to retrieve it. Sounds simple enough but there are literally thousands of hurdles to clear when you're starting from scratch. Just getting an affordable phone system was difficult. The cost of marketing to Europe, China and South American based businesses over copper wire was extremely costly. Months earlier we had switched to voice over internet. The quality was constantly an issue because these systems were using the World Wide Web as an operational platform. We started out using Packet 8 and switched to Polycom, losing our original phone numbers in the process. After several months of trying to make it work, we ended up switching back to a new and improved Packet 8 system. Many hundreds of man hours were wasted.

Because the company increased the number of our clients on a weekly basis, the time to hire a third Associate Managing Director had long since passed. With only two managers working, my group was calling on behalf of twelve clients per month. Our client base had grown to over 100 with another 200 projected for the next year. We were working as efficiently as possible and still falling behind. I was constantly making my case with my new boss Sara Sheldon to get approval for a third team member. As soon as I received approval I would make arrangements to go to our Coral Springs office, interview, hire and train the new person.

On the other side of my job I was busy forging new relationships with private equity groups. George Gifford and some of the new Directors of the company wanted to explore the marketing avenues available to us. I'd been building a working relationship with Capital Roundtable in Manhattan. Capital Roundtable held monthly workshops with panels of experts on various private equity and venture capital topics. The people they brought in for their roundtable discussions were the top business men and women in the private equity field. I was making plans to fly to New York and attend one of their master classes. With all these issues on the table, Thursday's work day came and went in a familiar fast-paced blur.

Bud Orpen's poker game on the North Shore was canceled at the last minute because three of the regular players had to bow out. I explained to Pam that this was only the second time in all the years I'd been playing that the game had been canceled. To my surprise she wanted to see the North Shore anyway. We spent Thursday night together and had plans to see each other on Saturday for the fourth annual Marti Croix. Aside from being tired, I was having a great time. Pam was a blast to hang out with and easy to talk to. By the end of the night I knew I was pushing my limits of endurance by going out as much as I had been, but wanted to spend as much time with her as possible.

Work on Friday hadn't didn't slow down, and I hosted my weekly private equity roundtable call. TMG used these calls to build relationships and give our front end Business Development Group information on what types of companies the investment world was looking to purchase. I invited a partner or associate of one private equity group to join us every Friday morning. All March Group employees were invited to join in to a conference call. Usual attendance was forty to fifty employees. I would introduce our guest and have them talk about what types of businesses their company had an interest in purchasing for add-on growth purposes, what sectors they had interest in as platform investments and their business philosophy moving forward. The roundtable lasted from 10:30 a.m. to 11:00 a.m. I had three marketing meetings that day and a one-hour meeting with the new systems engineer who was in charge of designing the functionality my group would need in the new operating system. I was thankful when the day finally came to an end. I needed a good sleep to recharge my batteries.

Cane Bay is situated on St. Croix's north shore—one of the most picturesque spots on the island. Horseshoe Bay is over a half-mile long and is framed by tropical rain forest covered cliffs rising to the west and large rock breakwalls to the east. The Wall, a few hundred yards off of Cane Bay Beach, is a famous dive spot with depths of over 2,000 feet. There are a handful of beach bars and restaurants, small hotels, a dive shop and a kayak business all within walking distance of each other. Visible in the hills surrounding the area are sugar mill ruins from the late 1700s along with the remains of destroyed hurricane-ravaged properties, including a hotel, condo buildings and several homes.

Our trip to the north shore became a party of three as Andy was itching to go to the Mardi Croix party. I reluctantly picked him up at Pat's house and we headed to Pam's rented condominium at Sugar Beach. Along the way, the three of us stopped and took pictures at the sugar mill base below Bud's house in Rust Op Twist. Sugar mills are the remains of Danish wind mills used to power the large stone wheels that crushed the sugar cane on the Danish plantations. To reach this area you turn off the main road at Salt River and pass by the spot where Columbus landed in 1492. By the time we reached the north shore there were cars lining the road and parked in the ditches for almost a mile.

Hundreds and hundreds of people packed the beach and lined the road side. Even more people were crammed into every watering hole and beach restaurant in Cane Bay. Bands played continually at three or four bars, and the sounds mixed in the middle of the street. There were large barbecue pits cooking hogs, fish and beef. The smoke was pushed along by the constant winter trade winds flowing east to west. The parade was scheduled to start at 12:00 noon—sharp. As most start times on St. Croix go—it came and went without anything happening. I think the first sign of the parade starting up was around 2:30 p.m. By this time there were several hundred drunk revelers mingling in the middle of the north shore road. Everyone had a drink in their hand and the noise level was growing to a feverish pitch.

The parade, consisting of four floats, three old cars—one towing a boat with crepe paper on the side followed by several people who had dressed up their dogs—finally got underway heading west from Off the Wall Bar. Other people wore masks and walked alongside the parade goers. They tossed beads and handed out shots of rum and other liquors. Andy had disappeared into the crowd over an hour before and Pam and I were seated in the Sprat Net Beach Shack on bar stools watching the last of the parade go by while catching strings of beads and candy. Looking back through Cane Bay we could see an old Chevy Chavelle had broken down and several people were pushing it along to keep it part of the parade procession. As they made their way past we could see Andy had joined the group providing propulsion for the broken down muscle car. They got a lot of applause for their efforts. Soon after passing the last bar I think they lost their steam and joined the street party behind them. The parade never came back through Cane Bay as planned.

Unfortunately, as the festivities came to an end, I had to be responsible and take Andy back to Pat and Kathie's house. Pam was scheduled to leave the next morning on a flight back to Cleveland and needed to pack. As we were saying our goodbys, Pam and I promised to see each other again—soon. In the short time we had known each other I really felt a comfort level with her and had way too much fun to put into words.

By the end of Monday I'd solidified my travel plans to New York City. I would be attending a Capital Roundtable seminar on investing in the financial services market on April 25th and 26th. With our client base growing weekly, we were getting more and more business from owners who serviced the financial sector either as consultants, insurance companies, wholesale insurance brokers or software designers. I was excited for the opportunity. There were several well-known financial sector experts scheduled to speak including some of the top banking professionals in the business.

On Wednesday morning I had to fly to St. Thomas and see Dr. Chase. After receiving the customary x-rays, I was led to a waiting room down the hall. I was nervously reading a *Time Magazine* when Dr. Chase knocked on the door. "How are you doing, Immaculate." The break was healing fine and it appeared the bone had not died from lack of blood flow. What a huge relief. As usual Dr. Chase admired his work, especially the scar and how the bone and metal were fusing together nicely. After taking some measurements he commented on the continuous work needed if I was going to regain my full range of motion.

For the first time, both of us were comfortable enough with my recovery to have a brief conversation about possible causes for the shoulder fracture. To help determine a potential cause Dr. Chase thought it would be a good idea to have some blood work done. Although he was primarily a surgeon, he had taken some time out of his busy schedule and thought about my case. If I could get the blood drawn and back to the laboratory within a couple of days we could cover the results at our next meeting. The laboratory in the Paragon building was unable to fit me in on time before the next sea plane left for home. I agreed to have the blood work done on St. Croix as soon as possible.

While I was waiting for a cab, I called Mom and told her the good news about the bone surviving. She mentioned to me that someone she knew had a friend battling osteoporosis due to a thyroid problem. She went on to explain that it was not the main thyroid. It was called a parathyroid. She believed it had something to do with my broken shoulder and that I should look into it. I admit that it all went in one ear and out the other. I'd never heard the word parathyroid and had no clue what it meant. I thanked Mom for the thought she put into it and assured her Dr. Chase would handle it. Now I had to hurry up, catch a cab to the seaplane dock, fly back to St. Croix and get to work.

In mid-December I'd switched my general practitioner from Dr. Frank Bishop to Dr. Charles Braslow. Dr. Bishop is a very good doctor, so much so that he has too many patients. Scheduled appointments had to be made six weeks in advance to see him. Every morning Dr. Bishop would open his office for walk-in visits between 7:00 a.m. and 8:30 a.m. The line was forty to fifty people deep each and every morning. There was no guarantee you would get a chance to see the Doctor after waiting in line. On the opposite side of the spectrum, Dr. Braslow had fewer patients and offered Saturday hours. The problem I was running into was missing a number of hours at work each week with the travels to St. Thomas and being delayed because of physical therapy. I was constantly working to make up lost time. I knew I would need to see a general practitioner on a regular basis, so I asked that all records from Dr. Chase be shared with Dr. Braslow going forward.

Everything I did from finding a new doctor to staying later in the evening was meant to extend my work hours. I needed every additional minute. Recently Carl Doerksen, TMG's Research Manager and I'd started holding Buyer Strategy Meetings with our new clients. Prior to a call we would study the rough draft of the Confidential Business Review, prepared by the Managing Director and a financial analyst, and form our questions to ask the client. We needed to get more specific information we felt necessary to better understand the business, how it operated, what products or services it offered and who its customers were. We would use the information gathered during the Buyer Strategy Meeting to create the best-suited marketing campaign for this particular client. Carl's job was to create the marketing lists best suited to gain the most interest from prospective buyers. My group's job was to lure those prospective leads into wanting to buy our client's business. It turned out to be a useful tool and we continued making ourselves available for these meetings despite the fact that both of us had full workloads pertaining to other responsibilities.

It felt great to be back in the swing of things at work. I really enjoyed my job and position within the company and it kept me with little time to think about my arm. Like any other job, there were frustrations, and decisions made that did not always sit well with me. But all-in-all this was a fun job where I was basically getting paid to learn about companies and emerging markets, systems, financial information and people.

I faxed the prescription for the blood draw from Dr. Chase to Dr. Braslow who faxed it to the Clinical Laboratory, Inc. located at Sunny Isle shopping center. The prescription included a T-3 Resin Uptake, part of a thyroid function evaluation. The thyroid gland is located in the neck and produces hormones that help regulate several bodily functions including growth, energy balance, body temperature and heart rate. Along with the T-3 test was a T-4 two-part test (T-4 Thyroxine and T-4 Free). A T4 test measures the blood level of the hormone T4, also known as thyrozine, produced by the thyroid gland that helps control metabolism and growth. The blood work Dr. Chase ordered also included parathyroid hormone and calcium level tests. PTH (parathyroid hormone) level, Intact Calcium and Intact PTH blood tests are designed to help distinguish between parathyroid related and non-parathyroid related causes for any abnormal calcium numbers in the blood stream. Dr. Chase and I'd briefly discussed the reason behind the different blood tests but we did not go in-depth into each one. I'd left that meeting only knowing he was checking if the thyroid was malfunctioning and if it was related to my weak bone structure and subsequent broken shoulder.

I have no problem seeing blood, but the idea of a sliver of metal entering my vein has always bothered me, and the recent IVs did little to assuage my feelings. On February 2, 2007, I was pacing the small waiting room in the Sunny Isle Shopping Center Clinical Laboratory. I knew the blood work was necessary, but the anxiety level over the thought of the needle was growing with each passing minute. I prayed my number would be called soon so I could get the hell out of the place. After being seated in an old school desk in a tiny back room the moment had finally arrived. My shoulder muscles rose around my ears as I gritted my teeth and turned my head. The nurse told me to relax as she was just tying off my arm to raise the veins. She asked if I could clench my fist and after a couple of seconds commented that I had nice veins. Nice veins, what does that mean? Staring at the opposite wall, the moment came and went without me realizing it. The next thing I heard was, "All done." Thank God that was over! I was free to go back to work.

In the days ahead Mother continued to press upon me the need to get my parathyroid hormone level checked, mentioning it again and again. Not one conversation went by without her bringing this up. She had done some research and directed my attention to a website www.parathyroid.com. I did not immediately look at the site, but remembered to ask Dr. Chase during a phone call later in the week about what would be involved in getting my parathyroid checked if for no other reason than to appease my mother. He mentioned he had put some preliminary parathyroid tests in the first blood work and thought it was a good idea, based on any elevated numbers we got back, to include more conclusive tests on the next draw. I was disappointed to hear there was going to be a next draw.

The laboratory on St. Croix was unable to process the calcium tests onsite. My sample was sent to Quest Diagnostics in Miami, Florida, 1,200 miles to the northeast. That delayed the results for over a week. I was anxious to receive the information and called Dr. Chase and Dr. Braslow. Neither Doctor had received anything. I called Clinical Laboratory and found they were still waiting for the test results from Quest. It would not be until March 13th that the faxes were received. The number elevated way out of normal range was my parathyroid hormone. It was 127 milliliters (ml). Parathyroid hormone levels should be between 10 and 65 ml, representing units per volume of blood.

Mother was sure the parathyroid had something to do with my situation. Now the doctors agreed. More blood tests were needed to figure out the exact issue, but everyone believed we were on the right track. Man I love my mother!

Pam and Jeff

A Solution? (Day 79 – 102)

~~~

Dr. Chase ordered another round of blood tests before I left for New York. This time he added an Ionized Calcium test designed to help diagnose and monitor a range of conditions relating to bones, heart, nerves, kidneys, and teeth. Blood calcium levels do not directly tell how much calcium is in the bones, but how much calcium is circulating in the blood. At the time, I had no true understanding of what these tests really meant. I read about them on-line but did not really grasp the magnitude of what the parathyroid function had on the human body. All I knew was blood tests were the first step in figuring out why all of this happened. The blood was taken, again with anxiety on my part, on April 23rd. I anxiously awaited the results, finally faxed to Dr. Chase and Dr. Braslow on May 14th.

My relationship with Pam had been growing, even though we were thousands of miles apart, and I found myself discussing my medical issues with her over the phone. She had insight into navigating the health-care system and the conversations seemed natural and effortless. I was frustrated with the inefficiencies I'd experienced and wanted quicker results. Pam seemed to accept my views and put some order to the whole process.

March 17—St. Pat's Day weekend, Pam was on a plane from Cleveland headed for St. Croix. She stayed for the weekend and left on Monday morning. Her plane had been delayed coming in on Friday evening. She arrived on the first flight out of San Juan early Saturday morning. We did not attend the big parade taking place downtown Christiansted that afternoon. I didn't mind. Because her time was cut short, Pam wanted to visit again and would soon buy another ticket.

Pam arrived April 6th for the Easter holiday weekend. Along with the progress in my personal life the rehabilitation of my right arm was advancing at a steady, slow pace. I possessed more mobility and was no longer wearing my sling. However, the arm was still too weak and sore. There was no chance of me sailing by myself, so with Pat's considerable help, Pam, Kathie and I were able to take *Folly* out during her visit. This was the first time I was able to get out on the water since the injury happened in November. We sailed off the mooring, down the shoot, through the cut in the reef and across the channel to Buck Island where we anchored and had a picnic on the beach. The water had never been more vibrant and the wind more steady. For me it was perfect. I was able to steer my boat with my left hand as Pat did all the work. It felt awesome!

I mentioned to Pam that I was traveling to New York City for work. Neither one of us had spent any time in the Big Apple. By the end of the conversation, Pam had agreed to join me for the weekend after my Roundtable Conference ended. She left St. Croix on Tuesday April 10th.

The aqua workouts at therapy continued with new exercises added on a regular basis. The payoff was evident. I'd regained my energy level and was feeling positive about the future. I still could not move my arm behind my back, or raise it above my head, but the water workouts provided natural resistance which had started to strengthen the muscles. I would use paddles, styrofoam weights, a wood stick and a kickboard during the workouts. Over time, they grew easier. The therapists encouraged me to swim. I tried to perform the free style stroke, but it hurt like hell. My arm did not rotate around the shoulder and I did not have the strength to pull it out of the water. I was still encouraged that the therapist thought I should try.

The days of therapy and gym workouts dragged on. I experienced minor triumphs, but I was not completely mended. In my mind, anything less would be a failure. I was told by the physical therapists I would be adding a light-weight lifting routine. The outward rotation in my shoulder was limited, and though I was gaining strength in my arm, I found it was still too weak to be used for bearing weight. I was able to bend my arm at the elbow and raise it above my waist. The mental aspect of showing up everyday to tackle the workouts and the pain of freeing up scar tissue was challenging. There were several days where I did not want to go to the therapy session but I knew I would have to explain my absence to the therapists and was assured they would pass that info on to Dr. Chase. I didn't want to give anyone a reason to imply my lack of mobility was because I did not do my part. Every day I had to look inward and push myself. A real sense of duty to not let all of these people on my team down prevailed. These individuals were doing their job and being paid for it, but I felt a true desire from them to see me succeed. I knew I had the right team behind me to overcome this issue.

As the gap between the date we launched a marketing campaign for a client and the date we started the calling campaign widened, I finally got the approval from my boss to hire the next Associate Managing Director (AMD). I was already set to go to New York at the end of April, so the plan then became to fly from New York down to Coral Springs and spend a week at our office, hire my third AMD and train that person to get started on the phones. My long weekend in New York City had just became a week and a half travel marathon.

My flight landed at JFK and the executive-van ride made fourteen stops at various destinations throughout the city before I was finally deposited at The New Yorker Hotel late on the evening of April 24th. Registration for the roundtable started the next morning at 7:30 a.m. at the University Club in Manhattan. The private club dates back to 1863 and its member list reads like a book of who's who of financial pioneers. I noticed the quality of the old world granite and stonework was like nothing I'd seen. Floor-to-ceiling stained glass windows framed either side of the great room. Members in jackets were seated at antique wood tables, quietly skimming through financial journals under the early morning light. I couldn't help think it was a scene straight out of the early days of Wall Street. The banquet hall was located down a short corridor lined with hand-painted portraits of past members. A butler instructed us to speak softly as to not disturb the members.

Hosting the Capital Round Table discussion was Burt Alimansky, Managing Partner of Alimansky & Bethell Group. The keynote speaker for the first roundtable was Mitchell Hollin from Mitchell Hollin, LLR Partners and James McCormick from First Manhattan Consulting Group. The next panel included perspectives from five prominent middle-market private equity investors. The knowledge base these professionals were speaking from was very impressive. Whether they were financing buyouts, or offering lines of operational credit, their average deal size was over $100,000,000. It was educational to hear their point of view on the current state of the market and what was happening with the economic downturn. My mission, when I returned to St. Croix, was to give George Gifford a detailed report of what I'd learned and to this end I feverishly took notes throughout the day. My right arm was burning by the end of the last panel at 5:30 p.m. Learning opportunities like this were why I loved my job.

Outside, a storm was brewing and weather related flight delays at JFK pushed Pam's arrival back from 6:30 p.m. until after midnight. Needless to say there was not a lot of energy left in either one of us by the time she arrived. Exploring the Big Apple would have to wait until morning.

Neither Pam nor I had experienced the city, so we decided to go for a walk and see the sights. By mid-morning we had covered most of Manhattan including Times Square and the areas around Broadway. I was struck by just how crowded the city streets were. Traffic moved at an unbearably slow pace and there seemed to be thousands of people packing every sidewalk. The city was filled with sights and sounds I was not accustomed to. As we rode the subway for the first time, missing our exit for the Museum of Natural History, I was thankful I did not have to live in this congestion. After a half-hour wait on an underground rail station platform, we were back on a train going the opposite direction. We toured the museum, rode to Central Park and walked some more. Later that night we ate pizza and went to a comedy club, stopping to have drinks in a few bars along the way.

Saturday we hit the ground, walking again, and before noon we ended up at The Hells Kitchen Flea Market under an abandoned section of elevated road. We left empty handed and later had lunch in a bar and spent the rest of the afternoon outdoors walking around the city. Before we knew it, Sunday morning was upon us and we shared a cab ride to JFK. It was time to say goodby.

I landed at the Fort Lauderdale airport on the afternoon of April 29th, retrieved my rental car and drove to the Marriot Comfort Suites in Coral Springs. I'd interviewed two possible new hires on my previous visit to our Florida office. One of my counterparts on the buy side of our business, Terry Dibert, knew a lady he felt had a background suited for the AMD position and would prove to be an excellent employee with good work ethic. I was operating on a limited schedule but took Terry at his word and agreed to add her to my short list of candidates.

I arrived at the office at 7:00 a.m. Monday the 30th of April and set up in the conference room. The first of the three interviews was scheduled to start at 8:30 a.m. By 11:30 a.m. I was half way into the interview with Susan Kressivich and could tell she was head and shoulders above the other two ladies. I offered her the position on the spot.

Everything fell into place and we started training after a short lunch break. I had to maintain my scheduled meetings and also find time to answer e-mails and return phone calls while cramming five days of new-hire training into three and a half. Susan was very talented and picked up on the nuances of the job quickly. She was definitely the right choice. The rest of the week flew by without any time to spare. By 7:30 p.m. on Thursday May 3rd, Susan was prepared to start calling on her first client.

It is always more difficult to maintain a workout schedule while traveling, but even with this hectic pace I continued to do my arm workouts three times a day and get a walk in every evening. My goal on this trip was to maintain activity level and test my new-found energy. I felt I'd held up well. The right shoulder was not one hundred percent, but it was improving.

The situation was pointing in the right direction.

I touched down at Henry E. Rohlsen Airport late in the afternoon of Friday, May 4, 2007. Over the weekend I pulled up the web site my mother had requested I look at, www.parathyroid.com. Why I'd chosen to ignore her suggestion is beyond me at this point. My mother holds a Ph.D, is well read and one of the smartest ladies I know. If any one had my best interest at heart it was her. I skimmed over the web site and learned the sole purpose of the parathyroid glands is to control levels of calcium and potassium within the blood:

> In doing so, parathyroids also control how much calcium is in the bones, and therefore, how strong and dense the bones are.
>
> Calcium is the element that allows the normal conduction of electrical currents along nerves—it's how our nervous system works and how one nerve 'talks' to the next. Our entire brain works by fluxes of calcium into and out of the nerve cells. Calcium is also the primary element causing muscles to contract.

It was as if a light switch had been turned on. My parathyroid glands were not functioning properly and in my sleep muscles contracted hard enough to break a brittle bone. I was eager to receive the latest round of blood test results and see if they supported this theory. When I checked with Dr. Braslow and Dr. Chase they had not yet received the blood work. I was frustrated with the delay. I contacted the laboratory on St. Croix. They had received the results and said they had faxed them to my doctors. I asked them to please fax them again. This back and forth went on until faxes were finally received by both doctors on May 10th.

My ionized calcium was 4.8 ml, at the low end of normal. The straight calcium level was 10.7 ml.—a bit high. My parathyroid hormone level was 125 ml—extremely high. The numbers indicated something was wrong but I was unsure of exactly what they meant.

Friday, May 11—I flew to St. Thomas for a scheduled meeting with Dr. Chase. We discussed the parathyroid issue. He was not an expert on the subject, but believed we had found the cause of my problems. His advice was to look for a doctor specializing in endocrinology to explain the situation in more detail.

The website run by The Norman Endocrine Clinic in Tampa provides a wealth of information on the parathyroid, its function in the body and how to fix hyperparathyroidism. Below are a few quotes from the website www.parathyroid.com:

> James Norman, MD, FACS, FACE, is recognized as one of world's foremost experts on parathyroid disease and is unquestionably the most experienced parathyroid surgeon in the world. Dr Norman is a board certified surgeon and a Fellow of the American College of Surgeons (FACS). He is also a Fellow of the American College of Endocrinology (FACE). He is recognized as the inventor of minimally invasive radio guided parathyroid surgery in the mid-1990s, and is credited with dramatically changing the way parathyroid surgery is performed. In the spring of 2009, Dr Norman would perform his 10,000 outpatient, mini-parathyroid operation.
>
> Douglas Politz, MD, FACS. is an accomplished surgeon who works side-by-side with Dr Norman. Dr Politz trained in mini-parathyroid surgery under Dr Norman in the late 1990s, and practiced in Texas from 2000, until 2006 when he re-joined the Norman Parathyroid Center. Dr Politz has performed more parathyroid operations than anybody in the world, other than Dr Norman, and operates with Dr Norman on every operation.
>
> The Norman Parathyroid Center is dedicated only to parathyroid disease. Dr Norman and Politz are the only surgeons in the world that limit their practice to this one uncommon disease.
>
> Parathyroid surgery is all we do! We don't do breast biopsies, gallbladders and obesity surgery—just parathyroids. Because of our expertise, people from all over the U.S. and many other countries travel to Tampa to be cured of their parathyroid disease. This experience gives Dr Norman and his team unparalleled results. Currently 99.86% of all patients are cured at their very first operation—almost all via an operation that takes between 14 and 21 minutes, going home in about 1.5 hours.
>
> Our expertise has made parathyroid surgery a very straightforward, routine outpatient procedure that usually takes about 17 minutes! 'Build a better mousetrap and the world will beat a path to your door.' This is clearly what has happened to our practice. Nobody can do what we do.

71

Note: Don't let the fact that we treat so many patients with hyper-parathyroidism and perform so many parathyroid operations make you think that we don't treat our patients well. We do! In fact, every patient is given Dr Norman's and Dr Politz's home telephone numbers and cell phone numbers so they have access to them whenever they want/need. We don't use an answering service—our patients can call us at any time.

With encouragement from Mother, I contacted the Norman Endocrine Clinic and spoke to a nurse who directed me to the website. I explained that I'd read the information about the parathyroid gland and the surgery on the website and would like to arrange a consultation with Dr. Norman. I discussed my situation and the fact that I would be a visiting patient from the United States Virgin Islands. The nurse encouraged me to read the entire website and fill out the two on-line patient sheets and e-mail them to the office. To determine if I was a viable parathyroid surgery candidate the Norman Endocrine Clinic needed the results of my previous blood tests. I knew to expedite the process it would be necessary to go to the laboratory on St. Croix and ask for copies of my tests and fax them to the clinic in Tampa. According to the nurse at the Norman Endocrine Clinic, it would take two weeks for them to get back to me after they had received all the information.

I was thrilled to get this process started. I believed I was heading in the right direction and soon all of this would be over and done with. From the information I'd gathered on the website I would be feeling like a new person as soon as I was finished with the surgery. It sounded like a short, minimally invasive procedure followed by a quick recovery. I remember speaking to my brother Rod, looking for some reassurance this was the right avenue to pursue. Though he is a doctor, he didn't know that much about the subject but would look into it for me. All signs seemed pointed to malfunctioning of the parathyroid as the cause of my broken shoulder. I filled out the patient information and sent it off immediately.

Monday, May 7—Before going to work in the morning I drove to Sunny Isle Medical Center and stood in line from 6:30 a.m. until the doors opened at 7:00 a.m. The laboratory is first-come, first-serve. I was still making up for lost time and wanted to get to work as soon as possible. The earlier this side trip could end the better. The mounting frustration over lost time at work would only grow from this point on. I cursed at every driver who had the audacity to slow down my steam roll to and from the laboratory. I ran past slower moving patients on the sidewalk to get a few spots deeper in the line. When I arrived, I counted twenty-three people ahead of me waiting to get into the building. Speed and efficiency had become so important to me, and yet I felt I couldn't delegate this simple task to anyone else. I could only envision successful delivery of the blood test to Dr. Norman's if I sent them with my own two hands.

Proof that my recovery was going in the right direction soon came at physical therapy where they reduced my number of days from three per week to one. I'd started the light-weight lifting routine and was working out on my own three days a week in the gym. My arm was weak but the range of motion was back to sixty percent of its original functionality. The exterior rotation was still a fraction of what a healthy shoulder provides. I continued my attempts at swimming. I also started swinging a pitching wedge, lightly at first, and could only bring it back about three-fifths of a full swing. I was able to put my right hand on top of my head and reach behind and touch the bottom part of my lower back. Visible progress is wonderful to achieve, but it also came with a second consequence I'd not anticipated. At the end of May, the physical therapy center explained they had taken me as far as they could. They developed a comprehensive workout plan for the future and the rest was going to be up to me.

Uneasy about ending the therapy sessions I asked several questions. One of the main reasons for the abrupt end emerged. For each injury there are a set number of physical therapy sessions that are pre-determined by the insurance company. I found the insurance company's control of my rehabilitation based solely on their business practices pretty scary. I was genuinely concerned that without guidance I might re-injure my shoulder and undo the progress I fought so hard for. I pleaded for a couple extra visits to focus on improving my form on the new light weight routines.

Over the previous three months the physical therapists had become my crutch. I relied upon them to make sure I did not push too hard or walk away with an injury or a setback due to poor technique. Their presence allowed me to be in attack mode during each and every session. Working out on my own would mean I would have to be sharp, keeping one eye on progress and one eye on checks and balances. Each move, each lift, each stretch needed to be performed with precision. I'd proved I was capable of pushing through pain, but I could end up with serious problems by overworking the injured area.

The physical therapists went into overdrive the last couple of sessions making sure I was prepared to venture out on my own. Together we built a schedule that offset different muscle groups on alternating days. The workouts rotated between the swimming pool and the weight room. There was a lot of emphasis on proper warm-up routines and rest periods. The one thing they warned me about, repeatedly, was keeping myself in check. They did not believe a full recovery was likely, and I was destined to maintain my current status if no setbacks occurred. I believed the opposite— the harder I worked out the sooner I would bounce back. The more we talked the more I vowed to prove them wrong.

The entire rehabilitation process had been a test period to see how far I could push the envelope. At the beginning, my shoulder hurt all the time so it was hard to tell if we had pushed too far or to fast. As the pain subsided, over time, I was trained to gauge the pain and determine if I was creating new issues through any particular exercise. The physical therapists would ask me questions concerning pain and discomfort levels. I was always somewhat reluctant to answer truthfully out of fear of being shut down. Was it pain from tearing scar tissue, or stretching the muscles too far or was it something worse? Did adding more reps or a new exercise cause bone pain, or was it muscle pain? To be successful at rehabilitation the patient has to fully participate and become an expert on their situation. Ultimately success is determined more by the patient's determination than by the number of visits to the therapy center. You have to fight and be dis-ciplined, show up and continue your workouts and exercise routines at home by yourself. There were no days off. I worked as hard at home as I did in the pool or at the gym. In the end, I attended thirty-seven therapy sessions at the Beeston Hill Rehabilitation Center and now faced moving forward on my own.

The weekend of May 19th, I went to the golf course with Pat. As I tried to loosen up, the practice strokes caused my shoulder to throb with pain. I knew there was no chance I could drive a golf ball or hit long irons, but I wanted to play. The only shots on the course I could take were from a dis-tance of one-hundred yards onto the green. Pat drove off the tee on each hole, and we both played the second shot. I was golfing, but it came with a pretty severe level of pain. I was able to make a few good shots with my abbreviated swing. Before I had surgery on my shoulder I would hit a pitch-ing wedge for any shot up to 120 yards out. During this round I had to use a seven iron to achieve eighty-yards of distance. It was a constant reminder of how far I'd fallen.

Sunday, we went out on *Folly* for a short sail, close to three hours, and looked for turtles and dolphins. The waters were churned up a little but I was comfortable and loving the sailing action. As the day came to an end, I needed to ice my shoulder before I went to sleep. It was a great weekend. I was tired but I'd survived.

Tuesday night after returning from work, I received a phone call from Dr. Norman. He was pretty sure he could help me but he needed another round of blood tests to be sure. He questioned the accuracy of the level of PTH hormone reported in the previous test. He'd rarely witnessed such high numbers and wanted to be sure what he was dealing with. I assured him I'd have them sent as soon as they were available. He had his nurse call in the blood test prescriptions the next morning.

The test results came back on May 29th. My ionized calcium was 4.8 ml—acceptable but in the lower range. My straight calcium was 10.2 ml—at the high end of the normal range. My parathyroid hormone was 123 ml.

I was busy at work so I had the lab forward the test results to Dr. Norman, but when I called the Norman Endocrine Clinic later that morning they had not received the faxes. At lunch, I drove to the laboratory, picked up a copy of the results and faxed them from work.

Dr. Norman called me after receiving the blood work and said his procedure would definitely help. He went on to tell me that one of my four parathyroid glands was most likely a rogue that had taken over all the production of the parathyroid hormone leaving the remaining three parathyroids dormant and nonfunctioning. He would not know for sure until he performed the pre-surgery tests that determine the size of each parathyroid. The rogue parathyroid, removed in the surgery, would be much larger than the other three. He put me in touch with his scheduling nurse. The first opening they had was on Thursday, June 21, 2007.

I called Mom to tell her I was scheduled for surgery in Tampa, Florida. She insisted on joining me. Finally, some answers and a solution were on the horizon.

I contacted Dr. Chase the next day and he asked that I get a full body bone scan before going to Tampa. I had this done at the Imaging Center in the Sunny Isle shopping complex down the hall from the laboratory where I'd had my blood drawn. The scan was performed on Thursday, May 24th —during my lunch break.

Bone density scanning, also called dual-energy x-ray absorptiometry (DXA) or bone densitometry, is an enhanced form of x-ray technology used to measure bone loss. DXA is today's established standard for measuring bone mineral density (BMD).

DXA is most often used to diagnose osteoporosis, a condition often affecting women after menopause but may also be found in men. Osteoporosis involves a gradual loss of calcium, as well as structural changes, causing the bones to become thinner, more fragile and more likely to break.

http://www.radiologyinfo.org/en/info.cfm?pg=dexa&bhcp=1

The technician who reads the scan was on vacation for the upcoming Memorial Day holiday, causing a two-week delay before Dr. Chase would get the results. Dr. Norman also wanted to see the results before surgery, and thought we were cutting it close and it might delay the operation. I wanted all this extra testing to be over with. I desperately needed to be working every day. The extra medical testing and doctors' visits were doing nothing but elevating my stress level. I was determined to stick to the scheduled date.

Pam was flying in for the Memorial Day weekend. We were attending Kiril and Sara's wedding on Saturday May 26th. Sunday evening, we had tickets to sail on *Roseway* with Pat and Kathie. The wedding had gone off without a hitch and we stayed at the reception well into the night. Sunday afternoon, we worked out before heading to the dock in Gallows Bay. I should have been exhausted by all the activity, but instead found increased stamina. I was excited to be going sailing on the 137-foot, gaffed-rigged, double-masted schooner. The crew turned the helm over and allowed me to steer shortly after entering open water. She felt powerful under touch like a hundred racing horses tugging at the bit. As we prepared to jibe to the south and head back in to the dock a cannon was fired off the bow. The sun dipped below the waterline as we made our way through the cut in the reef past the fort into Gallows Bay.

The start of June was crazy. The preparation for my parathyroid surgery was in full swing. There were several calls and attempted faxes, failed faxes and finally fax confirmations. I felt like I was working a second job. I'd gathered all the information on the Norman Clinic, made all the arrangements to fly to Tampa and to stay at the Hilton close to the hospital, and I'd made sure all the test results and other medical information needed by Dr. Norman were received on time. It takes a lot of advanced preparation to be able to walk into a hospital and have surgery without lengthy delays for research and further tests. I talked to Mom a lot, and was calling Pam on a daily basis, expressing my growing frustration. Both reminded me of why it was all going to be worth it.

If everything happened the way it is written on the Norman Endocrine Clinic website, Mom and I would get to spend Friday, Saturday and part of Sunday together after surgery. I was looking forward to having the surgery over, and spending some quality time with Mom. Besides being one of the smartest ladies I've ever known, she has a tremendous sense of humor, and she's always game for new information or fun adventures.

Whenever I take time off work I have to prepare my team and cover all of my job functions. I'd booked private equity guests through the middle of July. Kiril would MC the Friday Roundtable call on the 22nd. If any of my team members ran into trouble, they could ask Melissa for help. I would check my voice mails while I was gone. I didn't want to bring a laptop with me, but thought it best to check e-mails while out of the office. I was set to fly out Wednesday, June 20.

Pam was leaving for a vacation to visit an old friend of hers in California at the same time I was headed to Tampa for surgery. I promised to call her on her cell phone and let her know how things were going.

Although it had been frustrating reaching this point, physically and mentally I was feeling much better than the previous few months. I had all my ducks in a row and this was going to be the end of this strange chapter in my life. I was ready for some healthy living and prosperous times. I continued to work on the mobility in my right arm up until the point when the wheels left the runway and I was headed for Tampa.

I met Mother at the Hilton Hotel the evening of June 20th. Over dinner, we discussed the game plan for surgery, but it was an early night for both of us knowing what lay ahead the next day.

The hotel was less than a half-mile from the hospital so we got in our morning walk and reported to the admitting station in Tampa General at 5:30 a.m. I thought, the earlier the better, and the sooner I can get the hell out of this hospital and on my way. I was placed in a single bed on a circular floor surrounded by ten to twelve other patients. We all had cloth room dividers providing privacy. My mother was allowed to sit with me and help pass the time prior to a brief test to determine the size of my parathyroids. We tried our best to avoid eavesdropping, but we could hear the conversations of the patients on either side of us. The dominating volume of Dr.

Norman's voice was easily discernable among the relatively quiet chatter as he made his way from patient to patient giving test results and briefings on upcoming surgeries. He was sure of his skills, procedures and proud of the success rate he provided his lucky patients. When he reached the bed of the lady on my immediate left, he told her, after reviewing the test results she was not a candidate for the operation. He explained that the surgeon who removed her parathyroid in the past had botched the job and he could not fix it. I was a little unnerved by this. I'm assuming his next comment was meant to console this elderly lady who by now had burst into audible sobbing that rolled through my holding area like a lingering shock wave.

He continued, "I have a 40-year-old guy lying next to you that has far worse bone structure than you." He went on to tell her that she would need to cope with her issues the best she could and see an endocrinologist moving forward. Seconds later my cloth wall parted.

As he sat down and went over the morning test results Dr. Norman was extremely confident that I would come out of this feeling better than ever. He could not answer how long the rogue parathyroid had been operating on its own, but he did mention that I was a severe case and it most likely had been a condition in my body for years. He reiterated that he would fix me as good as new. He had every confidence that after the surgery my remaining three parathyroids would start to regulate the flow of parathyroid hormone to the blood, my bone structure would return and life would improve fairly quickly. There was no mistaking Dr. Norman's bravado although I did not get the same comfort level when hearing it as I had in the past from Dr. Chase. He went on to repeat what he had said earlier, "Even though you are a severe case I will make sure everything goes smoothly and you are going to feel better than ever tomorrow." There was a bit of car salesman in Dr. Norman and for whatever reason that left me with an uneasy feeling.

Mom kept it fairly light and upbeat, and after the doctor left we even shared a laugh or two while playing a game of 65. There was no real reason for concern and there would be good reason to celebrate if everything went as planned. Voluntarily agreeing to an elective surgery was not at all in my nature, but I'd bought into the plan and was eager to get the problem fixed.

Mom leaned close to me. "I love you. See you when you get out."

A nurse stuck the IV needle into the vein of my left arm, and Dr. Politz, who would be assisting during the surgery, was introduced to me in the hallway outside the operating room. In contrast to Dr. Norman, I found his quiet, southern drawl comforting. He projected confidence and insured me of the team's success. I felt more at ease, and a little less concerned after the minutes with him. From there I was wheeled into the surgical ward and administered anesthesia. My last memory was glancing at a clock on the wall—12:58 p.m.

An incision was made just below my Adams apple. The doctors located the rogue parathyroid gland on the side of my neck using specialized tools. The procedure took longer than expected as a nodule from my thyroid gland was also removed. They then performed a biopsy on my remaining three parathyroids. There are four parathyroid glands in the human body and the removal of one should not hinder parathyroid hormone production or regulation. The body can actually function with as little as a half a parathyroid.

As I started to come around my throat felt raw and I soon noticed there was a drain in my neck oozing blood into a plastic container. A string of nurses checked on my condition regularly. Eventually Mother was allowed to sit with me as the day passed into evening. One-by-one other Endocrine Clinic Patients undergoing surgeries that day were released. Soon the entire post-op ward was empty—except for me. I was not feeling well and the blood continued to flow. Frequent monitoring by nurses continued until, eventually, the blood slowed to a few drops and stopped. I was the last person to be released at 9:00 p.m.

Upon arrival at the hotel we found the restaurant was closed. As we hadn't eaten all day, Mom spoke to someone at the bar and convinced them to open up the kitchen. I tried to eat some salad but my throat was too sore. Besides, I felt sick from the anesthesia and needed sleep. A long, long day had finally come to an end. I hoped for better results the next morning.

Friday morning I woke feeling much better. I was able to eat breakfast and everything seemed to be going well. Later that day we went shopping. I had plenty of energy. We returned to the hotel, played some cards, decided to go to dinner and even checked out a comedy club. I went to bed that night confident I was on my way to a healthy future. What a relief it had been to be able to figure out the problem and get it fixed by the most successful parathyroid specialists in the world.

Saturday, June 23—6:30 a.m. The upbeat mood of the previous day had vanished. I found myself awake and unable to get comfortable in any position. I had tingling sensations in my head, arms and legs. I woke Mother and explained what was happening. I was looking forward to the day we'd planned together and hoped this strange feeling would not ruin my time with her. I became irritable and started pacing the floor. When the symptoms continued to increase in intensity, I called Dr. Norman at 8:00 a.m. He answered his phone on the weekend as promised. Dr. Norman believed I was experiencing symptoms of low calcium levels in my blood and was not to worry. He reassured me that it was normal in some patients, and asked if I'd taken my three calcium pills the previous day. I said I had, and he again assured me everything would be fine. His instructions, tempered with an authoritative demeanor, included taking an additional ten calcium pills over the course of the next four hours and calling him at noon.

Mom tried to calm me down as best she could and was met with an increasingly frustrated disposition. The tingling sensation had intensified to the point where it felt as if there were constant needle pricks from my head to my toes. My leg muscles were cramping, and I felt horribly uncomfortable in my own skin. When I was not pacing or stretching, I could only sit on the edge of the bed and rock back and forth. Time seemed to be standing still. By 11:00 a.m. things had turned from bad to worse with stabbing sensations throughout the back of my head, severe muscle cramps in my legs and heightened anxiety. Never experiencing anything similar to this left me at a distinct disadvantage. In any other scenario, I would have long since taken control and made a decision on a new course of action. Unsure what to do, Mother and I waited on instructions from Dr. Norman.

81

SUDDEN IMPACT (DAY 103 – 115)

After taking ten extra calcium pills and waiting four excruciating hours, I stood up from the bed at exactly noon, but as I called Dr. Norman's cell phone number, I faded to black. Mom was unable to do anything but watch me fall. As I bounced off the hard stone floor, the right side of my head was split open and the impact caused me to bite almost completely through my tongue. Blood from my wounds sprayed across nearby furniture and onto the wall. Mom later told me that she believed she had just witnessed my death as my eyes had rolled back in my head a split second before the quick decent to the hard surface. To some degree it was comforting for her to hear the constant screaming in pain as I came to.

She pressed 911 and the emergency team arrived in short order. There was a beehive of activity in the hotel room. I was bleeding profusely as they cut my shirt off and loaded me on a stretcher. Weeks later a foggy memory surfaced of grabbing one of the responding technicians and trying to push him away with my right arm. What ever he was doing at the time caused severe pain in my left shoulder. He leaned over me and yelled, "You have to calm down." They rushed me back to Tampa General Emergency.

Because of my head injuries the doctors could not administer pain medication. It took seven stitches in the right side of my scalp and four in my tongue before they were able to stop the bleeding. A series of tests including an MRI revealed the head of my left shoulder had broken off the end of the humerus bone. This was a more severe break than my right shoulder had been subjected to seven months prior.

It's amazing how the brain functions, especially during times of severe stress. To this day I have absolutely no memories of what transpired. According to records I was moved to the intensive care unit where my overall serum calcium level had fallen to 7.4 ml—dangerously low and definitely the cause of the tingling and stabbing sensation, and uncomfortable feelings and anxiety earlier in the morning. Without the proper calcium levels in the blood, my nervous system had ceased functioning properly causing me to pass out. Surgery on my left shoulder was delayed as they waited for the calcium level to normalize. To accomplish this, liquid calcium was administered through an IV in my jugular vein. Doctors continued testing for internal head wounds, necessary before I could be given anesthesia during the extended shoulder surgery. I was not completely cleared or given any pain medication until the hours leading up to the actual operation—nearly two days away. Mom sat in the ICU with me and watched as I screamed and wailed in pain for the next several hours. Needless to say she was in shock and feeling overwhelmed.

Late Saturday night I was moved into my own room—C715. My admitting team included Doctors Gullapalli, Kennedy, and Nesbaum. As the full extent of my injuries and the daunting task it would take to piece me back together was revealed, I was moved to Room C711 because it had better accommodations for an extended stay. A neurologist met with me and talked about past seizures. The MRI taken the day before showed no seizure-type lesions on the brain but as a precaution he prescribed Keppra twice a day. The medication has one major side effect—irritability. It was chosen because of my unique situation and the fact that it does not require monitoring liver enzymes and testing blood counts. I was given a set of rules to follow for the next six months. They included no driving, and only taking showers for fear of drowning in a bath, no swimming alone and no climbing.

I have one faint memory of what transpired over the next two days— that was of meeting Dr. Mark Mighell. Much like Dr. Chase, he is an orthopedic surgeon and was put in charge of rebuilding my shoulder. Through all the confusion and pain-induced shock, he had a calming effect. He was confident in his abilities as he covered the x-rays with me and Mom. He had a good understanding of my past history and wanted to have a CT scan taken before surgery so Dr. Chase could see the difference in the two shoulder breaks and administer therapy treatments accordingly during the rehabilitation phase. The official explanation was that I'd suffered an anatomic four-part (neck of the shoulder head) fracture, compromising the blood supply. Because it was a four-part fracture the shoulder head was completely dislocated from the shoulder joint. Before he left, he attempted to manipulate the shoulder head back into place. There are no words to describe the eruption of pain as Dr. Mighell took my arm and shoulder into his hands. Before leaving, he reiterated that surgery would have to wait until the calcium levels were stabilized. He would consult with Dr. Norman, and the second he got the okay we needed to be prepared to head into surgery.

The hospital staff suggested Mom return to the hotel and get some much-needed rest. Half-jokingly, she later told me that it was nice of the hotel to pick up the hazmat cleaning fee. By the time she returned to the room they had removed the blood from the floors, furniture and walls.

I don't remember making the call or how it was placed, but I must have employed help from a sympathetic nurse. How I recalled the correct numbers of Pam's seldom-used cell phone I will never know. Amazingly I got through to her at 3:30 a.m. California time. My only memory of the conversation was Pam telling me for the first time that she loved me. She had been in Palm Springs, California, for less than a day. Her week-long vacation plans were quickly changed. She later told me that I did not make a whole lot of sense when I called, but she was able to get enough information out of me to understand I was in bad shape. Pam scrambled to pack and woke her friend to drive her to the airport.

When Mother arrived later that morning, I casually mentioned that a girl would be showing up and to let her into the room when she arrived. Mom thought I was talking crazy. I had only briefly mentioned Pam the night before and they had never met.

The day was filled with doctors and nurses checking and rechecking temperature, blood pressure, heart rate etc. An MRI was performed early in the evening. Blood tests showed the serum calcium level was holding steady at 8.3 ml, just below the normal range. Hours passed without the consent to perform surgery from Dr. Norman.

For Mother, this was quickly becoming a long ordeal. She was stuck trying to figure out how to handle the present situation and formulate plans for the immediate future. Around 6:00 p.m. on Sunday, June 24th, the cavalry arrived in the form of Pamela Case Berry. I wish I could say I remember that first meeting between Mom and Pam, but I have no recollection of it, but the severity of the situation forced these two strangers to quickly become team members united in the same cause.

Both Mother and Pam are highly educated, extremely intelligent and detail oriented. I knew they would get along. Pam's work involves evaluating processes and relies heavily on organizational skills. It carries over to her personal life and she naturally asks lots of questions. Soon she would start keeping a journal of who came to do what and why. She was given permission to stay in my hospital room, well equipped with a full bathroom, Lazy Boy chair and a couch. Mom got a much needed break and was able to return to the hotel. As Kathie Ellison had done for me in St. Thomas, Mom and Pam would be my eyes and ears, digesting, interpreting information and overseeing the process of trying to piece my body back together.

Monday, June 25—I was administered my first doses of morphine for pain at 3:30 a.m. and 4:00 a.m. I had a calcium blood draw. 5:15 a.m. a nurse took my temperature (99.4) and blood pressure (162/92). My mother came back into the room at 7:30 a.m. Not long after we said our goodbys, I was wheeled into the surgery ward. Dr. Mighell took just over three hours to piece my left shoulder back together. In a strange coincidence he installed the exact same hardware in my left shoulder as Dr. Chase had in my right shoulder. The muscles and tendons that surrounded the shoulder had to be pealed off the bone, the metal plate screwed in and the muscles and tendons sewn back in place. A piece of cadaver bone was used to cover the metal plate before the upper arm was stapled back together. At five-and-half inches long, the resulting scar is identical to the one on my right shoulder. I was returned to my room at 1:30 p.m.

Post procedure report written by Dr. Mark Mighell:

Preoperative Diagnosis: Four-part fracture dislocation of left proximal humerus.

Postoperative Diagnosis: Four-part fracture dislocation, left proximal humerus.

Procedure performed:

1. Open treatment of the left shoulder facture, 23615.
2. Open treatment of dislocated articular segment

Indications: The patient is a very pleasant gentleman with a history of a parathyroid condition with previous history of pathologic fracture of the right shoulder. The patient underwent surgery for his parathyroid condition several days ago. Postoperatively, the patient sustained a fracture dislocation of the left shoulder confirmed by plain film radiographs and CT scan. It explained the patient had a severe fracture with a high risk avascular necrosis, malunion, limited motion that he would require open reduction internal fixation of fracture. He may require future arthroplasty as well as the inherent risks of the anesthesia with the surgery. Given an under elevated level of calcium, the surgery was delayed until the patient could receive adequate replenishment of his calcium stores. After he had been cleared by Dr. Norman, his treating surgeon, he was taken to surgery. Risks, benefits and alternatives were discussed in the physician-patient family session.

Description of Procedure: The patient was taken to the operating room, prepped and draped in usual sterile fashion for surgery of the left upper extremity. After adequate anesthesia, the procedure was begun. Deltopectoral approach was made. Incision was carried through the skin and subcutaneous tissues. Planes were developed. The subacromial and subdeltoid spaces were developed. Due to the posterior dislocation, the humeral head was dislocated and unlocked behind the glenoid. At this point, the biceps tendon was identified and followed proximally and it was released and tenodesed subpectoral, having done this, traction sutures were placed in the subscapularis tendon. Similar traction sutures were placed in the infraspinatus tendon. The head segment was then reduced into the joint and after reduction of the head segment into the joint, it was pinned into position. At this point, the reconstruction of the shoulder was undertaken. An allograft

86

fibular strut was placed in the humeral canal.

The nurse's log includes temperature and blood pressure checks at 3:00 p.m. (98.7 and 131/68). At 5:00 p.m. I was able to sit up in a chair for a few moments. They removed my urine catheter and promised to leave it out if I could urinate on my own. 5:25 p.m. temperature 100.3/blood pressure 170/81. 5:30 p.m. Dilaudid was added to my IV for severe pain. 7:20 p.m. temperature 101.2/ blood pressure 157/96. The nurse commented to Mom and Pam that I was in a high level of pain. She could tell because my diastolic blood pressure level read 96. More dilaudid was added to my IV. 11:45 p.m. my temperature was taken 98.1/ blood pressure 157/96. I was given more dilaudid. I was unable to urinate on my own so the nurse put the catheter back in. My evening serum calcium level was 8.2 ml.

In future consultations with Dr. Chase, he would comment on the high quality of Dr. Mighell's work. Because the head of the shoulder had broken entirely off the bone, the risk of post-surgery failure was much higher. Dr. Mighell's skills had given me a fighting chance, though the final outcome would not be determined for months.

I have no recollection of any thoughts or fears. There was a lot of worrying going on my behalf as Mom and Pam kept constant vigil by my side. They said I was lucid, funny and even played cards with them. In their renditions I supposedly lost every game. I still find that hard to believe.

Besides being worried sick over my condition, Mother was in complete shock and concerned how all of this would play out. What was she going to do when I was discharged from the hospital? Should she take me back to Illinois? It was supposed to just be a quick half-day outpatient operation. That's what she signed up to be a part of. She got so much more than that and now the tough question was what to do in the immediate future.

On the other side of the equation, Pam was nervous to be meeting Mother for the first time, but soon came to realize she is very likable. The two of them got along well and were united in the cause to see me recover as soon as possible. Pam and I attended a holiday dinner at Mother's home later in the year. We were circling the dinner table, each person explaining what they were most thankful for in the past twelve months. Mother's turn was last, and she explained it was the day Pam walked through the door at Tampa General Hospital.

As the third person in the triangle, I was unable to add much insight. To control the massive amounts of pain after bone surgery I received a steady dose of narcotic analgesics. I was hooked up to a series of intravenous infusions in my arm and neck administering calcium and drugs. As the combination of morphine and dilaudid coursed through my blood I was aware of the heightened levels of unrelenting pain but didn't care. My mind was once again cloudy. Excerpt from Pam's notes:

Tuesday, June 26—4:45 a.m. Temperature 99.8/ heart rate 86/ blood pressure 133/75, given pain medicine, urinated on his own. 6:50 a.m. took 1 Citracal calcium pill, 7:15 a.m. temperature 99/ heart rate 102/ blood pressure 147/95. 7:20 a.m. sat up in chair. 8:35 a.m. extremely cold, needed lots of blankets. Dilaudid was administered for severe pain through the IV line in his arm. 9:10 a.m., Jackie (OT) washed Jeff down with aloe vera warm wipes. 9:30 a.m. sitting up in chair. 9:50 a.m., temperature 97.2/ blood pressure 146/90; took one Percocet for mild pain; ate peanut butter and graham crackers. 10:45 a.m. EEG performed. 12:00 p.m., Deanna (nurse practitioner OR) redressed arm bandage and administered Dilaudid for severe pain. 4:00 p.m., took 2 Citracal; nurse named Jackie said per doctor Norman's orders, Jeff to take 6 Citracal calcium pills daily instead of 4, temperature 99.1/ blood pressure 154/93; increased ampules of IV + calcium drip; Erica (OT) did arm exercises with Jeff; hand down, squeeze and release hand 10 times, hand down, move wrist back and forth ten times; arm bent at elbow, raise and lower in front of chest ten times....

Some time during the day, Pam, Mom and I had a discussion on what was going to happen when I was discharged. Mom wanted to take me to Illinois. Supposedly I said I wouldn't go and wanted to return home to St. Croix as I needed to get back to work. Pam volunteered to take me home and stay with me for a couple of weeks. She had worked for the same school system for over twenty years and could take the time off. Despite retaining no memory of it, I am sure the conversation continued throughout the day. This was not an easy decision for any of the parties involved.

Mid-day Thursday—Dr. Norman stopped by the room where he quickly found himself engaged in a pointed discussion with my two advocates. Pam was upset that the events did not bring out more concern from him. Pam and Mom were less than pleased at the way my case was handled. They believed that the volume of surgeries performed by Dr. Norman usurped his ability to connect with each individual case and prevent outcomes like the one that had befallen me. He maintained his confident, superior demeanor. The conversation got heated and Pam locked herself in the bathroom. Mother was upset and Dr. Norman retreated. Before leaving the room he asked me to tell Pam that he does know what he's doing—my case is extremely rare and the outcome could not have been prevented.

Friday, June 29—After several long discussions and much thought process my mother agreed to allow Pam to escort me back to St. Croix. She felt relief in the sense that I would be taken care of but was still concerned how all of this would turn out. Having been a caregiver to my father for their entire thirty year marriage she understood the challenges that lay ahead. The bond between the two women had been forged immediately and she had sensed in Pam a strong woman who is capable of handling me and my immediate recovery. Later that day she reluctantly said her good-byes and took a cab to the airport and headed home.

Dr. Norman stopped in and discussed the pain I'd been complaining about in my jaw. He declared nothing to be wrong with the jaw bone. At 1:00 p.m. I was discharged from the hospital.

I read the daily logs of my hospital stay for the first time while writing this book. I am struck by how much professional care and attention I received around the clock from countless nurses, technicians and doctors. I was one patient among many and my caregiver's level of attention to detail and desire for perfection was second to none. The hospital staff at Tampa General went out of their way to accommodate Mother, Pam and me. I'm grateful for all of their professional help and compassion.

Pam and I left Tampa General and headed to the Hilton where Mom and I had started this journey. I have a few memories of Pam and me eating in the hotel restaurant. We stopped at the bar to get Pam a much needed glass of wine. According to her, I was alert and semi pain free. I called American Airlines and booked us on a first class trip back to St. Croix for the following day. Pam kept me current on my calcium and pain pill schedule. She also took my temperature and administered other medications.

Saturday, June 30—After waking at 7:00 a.m., Pam made sure I took 1 Nexium, 2 Percocet, 2 Oscal, 2 Citracal, 1 Senokot and 1 multi-vitamin. At the time I had no idea my life on a regimented pill schedule had just begun. Movements were slow and always taken with the utmost care not to induce more pain. We worked our way to the lobby of the hotel, checked out, and slowly and carefully climbed into a cab. My arm was in a padded sling and my wound was covered with fresh bandages. Pam had bought me a sleeveless shirt from the hospital gift shop to fit over the harness. We made it to the airport where long lines stretched out before us in all directions. Because I'd bought first-class tickets, we were able to avoid most of it and quickly pass through customs down to our gate area. I have no memory of booking the tickets and neither one of us had flown in first-class before but according to Pam it sounded as if I'd done it several times.

My body was busy expelling all the heavy narcotics I had ingested over the past week. Pam used multiple hot towels provided during the flight to wipe the morning sweat from my face. The captain's voice came over the radio, "ladies and gentlemen out the port side window you can see Cape Canaveral where NASA is located." We changed planes in Miami and Pam said my pain level was manageable most of the flight. She loves to tell me how she kicked my ass at cards all the way home.

Now a party of two, the job of keeping me on track fell on Pam's capable shoulders. She quickly mapped out the days on a pad of paper and kept detailed notes as to what pill was taken and when. My new pill schedule included 20 calcium, one Nexium, one multivitamin and two Senokot

90

pills, daily, along with Oxycodone for pain. Making sure I rested, took my pills and tried to stay cool was a daunting task as the mild winter weather, complete with its cool trade winds, had given way to the stale, calm recesses of the start of storm season. My house, like many on the island, did not have air-conditioning and the whirl of the large floor fan Pam had purchased from the local hardware store drowned out all other noise.

Tuesday, July 3—After religiously following my calcium pill schedule for the previous three days I started experiencing tingling in my nose, head, cheeks and calves just before 1:30 p.m. Pam asked me to take some extra calcium after consulting by phone with Dr. Politz in Tampa. The tingling continued to intensify as my anxiety and irritability grew. The decision was made to go to the emergency room.

By the time we got to the hospital I didn't care that this was the same facility where I'd been misdiagnosed in the past. I needed help. I was cramping from head to toe, and my face was locking up and feeling like someone was stabbing me with an ice pick.

I was admitted to Juan F. Luis Hospital at 3:00 p.m. by Dr. Burton the head of the hospital emergency room staff. Worried over the outcome of what could happen on the inside if Dr. Citron was on duty, I was more than relieved to be assigned Dr. Angel Lake as my attending physician. He understood my condition warranted immediate action and soon had performed an EKG on my heart and drew numerous vials of blood for testing. The emergency room has its own in-house laboratory—the only one on island that can process the serum calcium on site. The test results were back within the hour and my level was 6.9 ml. The extremely low calcium levels had caused my nervous system to crash again.

Dr. Lake continued to show a thorough understanding of the situation and ordered a calcium chloride IV (3 amps) drip. Liquid calcium is an irritant to blood veins and can cause Phlebitis (inflammation of a vein). Having the calcium administered through the main vein in my neck at Tampa General Hospital had allowed for quicker flow and less irritation. Although this action was warranted because of the need to elevate my blood calcium level in preparation for an emergency surgery, it also came with inherent danger. As in Tampa, I was expecting the needle to go into my neck, but instead it was placed in the small vein on the back of my right hand. This slowed down the process and eventually caused great irritation. It did not take long before my right hand swelled to half the size of a baseball and turned bright red.

Dr. Politz continued to monitor the situation, through information provided by Pam and Dr. Lake. He increased the number of calcium pills to twenty-four per day and added two Rocaltrol (high-end vitamin D). Rocaltrol is designed to help the intestines absorb calcium more efficiently. Dr. Lake advised that I keep an eye on my phosphorus levels because they can be negatively affected by the Rocaltrol use. Every pill has a side effect and soon it would be proven time and time again that my system does not handle most medications. Dr. Politz believed my calcium-starved bones were stealing it at the expense of the levels in the blood stream. This caused me to experience symptoms of hypoparathyroidism instead of hyperparathyroidism. He believed these symptoms would diminish over time as the remaining three parathyroid glands came back on line post-surgery. He agreed to call Dr. Braslow on Thursday, July 5 and bring him up to speed.

"In medicine (endocrinology), hypoparathyroidism is decreased function of the parathyroid glands, leading to decreased levels of parathyroid hormone (PTH). The consequence, hypocalcemia, is a serious medical condition.

Signs and symptoms
- Tingling lips, fingers, and toes
- Muscle cramps
- Pain in the face, legs, and feet
- Abdominal pain
- Dry hair
- Brittle nails
- Dry, scaly skin
- Cataracts
- Weakened tooth enamel (in children)
- Muscle spasms called tetany (can lead to spasms of the larynx, causing

breathing difficulties)
- Convulsions (seizures)
- Tetanic contractions
  http://en.wikipedia.org/wiki/Hypoparathyroidism#Signs_and_symptoms

The emergency room at Governor Juan F. Luis hospital seemed much more outdated after my time spent in Tampa General. There is little or no privacy for the patients. Cloth partitions separate holding stalls and the air is kept very cold. Blankets and pillows are in short supply. Pam worked out a deal to be allowed to stay with me in my curtained-off space. However dated the surroundings were, I was still extremely thankful for the doctors who attended to me. They not only took my condition seriously but provided the best possible care.

As the hours past, I continued experiencing spasms and cramping and my head tingled, my facial muscles locked up—distorting my mouth and cheek bones—impairing my speaking ability. I was scared, believing I was experiencing a stroke. The slow influx of liquid calcium into my blood stream eventually eased the symptoms and I was able to get some much-needed sleep.

I awoke on the morning of July 4th with Pam sleeping on a plastic chair next to my single-sheet covered metal gurney. After a long head to toe stretch and simultaneous yawn, she forced a smile before commenting on the freezing air. She scanned her surroundings while rubbing her shoulders and said something to the effect that it was nice to see me get so much sleep. Pam deserved to wake up in peace, so I refrained from blurting out the negative comments forming in my head. Spending the better part of a complete day hooked to an IV on a metal gurney only added to the robust pain that was flowing through my left shoulder. I was in no mood to accept even a small hint of positive thinking. Feeling more like a caged animal than human being, I was praying to be released soon.

After pulling the one thin sheet she was able to coax out of the staff the night before over my shoulders Pam made sure I started my daily pill regimen on time. Combating my negativity was like a chess match and Pam was an expert at delivering her brand of positive thinking whether I wanted to accept it or not. By late morning I was feeling some relief physically as my calcium numbers continued to stabilize. The IV drip bag emptied for the last time. By this point I was numb to pain and I watched in disgust as the nurse removed the needle from the middle of the bright red mass that had once been the back of my right hand. I was released from the ER at 1:45 p.m.

The brutal heat of the July afternoon greeted us as we walked out the door. My full weight resting on her shoulders, Pam guided me to the car. I knew how lucky I was to have her in my life.

Pam worked tirelessly taking care of my needs as the fear of another calcium fluctuation was on both our minds. There was nothing left to do but try and rest. She kept precise records of how many pills I took and when I took them. She bathed and fed me and made sure I was drinking plenty of water. Unable to take care of myself only added to the mounting frustration level I was experiencing internally. In turn my frustration was projected onto the only other person in the room. This only added to Pam's workload and made the whole process more difficult than it needed to be.

Vulnerability and fear raced through my head as I lay sweating in my bed. I was seething inside over the consequences that landed me in this position. The pain of another broken shoulder and the possibility of another nervous-system attack hovered in the air creating thick tension throughout my one-room guest house.

Pam was my sounding board and confidant. She absorbed all my concerns without judgment. Using reason and her eternal optimism she was able to talk me down from the onslaught of several panic attacks. Throughout this latest ordeal I needed several large doses of reality which she patiently delivered. By asking numerous questions over time she elicited my own conclusions. Eventually I would stop fighting and move on to the next issue.

I'm not sure if I fully understood the mental stress I was under. I know I did not consciously take any measures to address the issue. I was struggling to make sense of what was happening physically. Somewhere along the line my inner compass kicked in and I began pushing feelings and emotions out of the equation in favor of controlling my actions. It would take several months before I realized this was my coping method of choice. I continued to follow what came naturally.

The two functions I quickly focused on were work and rehabilitation. What would get my arm healed quicker, my ass out of bed and the stacks of work off my desk? Pam was still in complete control and although I love her for all the help she was providing I really disliked being completely dependant on someone. Anti-dependency became an obsession as I plotted ways to overcome my situation. It was a constant struggle with the reality that I was unable to perform regular tasks for myself. The desire to get up and fight led to increased time sitting up and later, walks around the yard.

I was overly acquainted with the months of physical pain that lay ahead. My mental makeup had been well suited to fight through it. I had no reason to believe I would need to handle this situation any differently. That was as far as my thought process went. In retrospect, until this point in my life, I had never needed to consider the effects of physical trauma on my psyche. The repercussions would eventually challenge my mental state.

Not being able to lay blame, or point my finger at one specific cause, increased my frustration level. My mood was capable of swinging in an instant. Anger permeated my thoughts as did the constant underlying feeling that I should have been stronger than this. My body should not have allowed these events to take place. I channeled that anger into motivation to get out of bed every day. Soon it would be used to go back to work and later to provide effort during physical rehabilitation. This had worked for me in the past. I found it comforting to follow the same path in the early days after my second and third surgeries.

REVERSE COURSE (DAY 116 – 289)

Saturday, July 7—9:30 a.m. I had an appointment with Dr. Braslow to cover my latest blood test results. My ionized calcium level was at 4.3, a bit below normal. So was my serum calcium level at 8.1. The parathyroid hormone level was 10—at the lowest end of normal. Prior to my parathyroid surgery, the PTH level had remained steadily above 120ml, one of the highest numbers the Norman Endocrine Clinic had seen in a male my age. Dr. Norman and Dr. Politz had assured me, throughout our pre-surgery discussions, that when the remaining three parathyroids kicked in, producing a normal level of parathyroid hormone, I'd feel fantastic, but from all indications, it was taking longer than usual for that to happen.

Not clear at this point what all these numbers meant, Pam had several questions for the doctor. Showing little patience, my main goal was to get the hell out of that office as soon after the doctor's assistant finished removing the stitches from my scalp and the staples from my left arm. I fidgeted in my chair as Pam continued to run through her list of questions.

The doctor explained that we would need more blood tests before making any conclusions about the success of the parathyroid surgery. He ordered them twice weekly for the foreseeable future. It felt like a huge punch in the gut as the reality of my situation sunk in. He went on to fill out a prescription for Percocet and Rocaltrol. He informed me that the Rocaltrol (vitamin D) had a side effect of weight gain. After battling weight issues all my life that was the last thing I wanted to hear. A short outburst of disgust on my part, followed by an attempt at reassurance by the doctor, and Pam and I with prescriptions in hand were ushered out of the office.

96

On the way home, we stopped by the pharmacy. I was too sick to stand at the counter and retreated to the car. Pam never once complained about all the work and caregiving. She always kept her optimistic outlook. Thankfully her skillful management of the situation prevented our polar opposite personalities from clashing.

Having had enough of semi-bed rest, I was determined to go back to work on Monday, July 9th. I was not feeling pressure from The March Group to return, but I would not take no for an answer. I threatened to take a cab to work after Pam refused to drive me. She eventually relented after realizing I would not back down. I was struggling physically, maybe even more mentally, and in my mind needed to get back to work and concentrate on something other than my health issues. I found the three remaining dress shirts that were part of my Bohlke International Airlines uniform buried in my closet. These were older, stained and had seen better days. I had deemed them unfit to wear to work after my right shoulder operation. Now I didn't care. We cut the left sleeves off and they become my new work wardrobe.

Monday morning we checked in with Dr. Braslow and my serum calcium was 8.3ml. He pointed out lower-than-normal blood sugar. Again, there was no explanation for these numbers. We needed to adopt a wait and see attitude while gathering more data for comparison.

Pam loaded me up with food for the day and reluctantly dropped me off in front of Deanna's Restaurant. I was on my own to ascend the twenty-two stairs leading up to the office. I had to pause to rest in between each step. After summiting the staircase and entering the reception area several people came to check on my condition. This was a repeat of the scene that had played out a little over seven months prior—one I never envisioned happening again but here we all were. I worked my way through greetings and well wishes from person after person before reaching my office.

As I sat behind my closed door, I was ashamed of my appearance and already sick of the attention. My injured shoulder was hanging out from the bottom of a cut-off sleeve. The blood soaked bandages were visible. The swollen upper arm was red and blue. A triangular buzz-cut on the right side of my head, with a visible scar in the middle, added to the beat-to-hell appearance, and the fact that my body had been subjected to large amounts of narcotics over the previous three weeks left me with a noticeable wobbling motion whenever I stood on my own two feet.

I tried my best to push all negative thoughts out of my head as I browsed through several voice and e-mails. The lack of short-term memory forced me to repeat each message time-and-time-again in a futile attempt to capture pertinent information. I was deep into the process when a knock at the door interrupted what little momentum I'd gained. "Jeffrey, how the hell are ya?" The familiar southern drawl of George Gifford snapped me to attention. Before I could answer he had sized-up my disheveled appearance and orderws me not to push it. Although this was a complete departure from his usual work-harder mentality, George went on to explain that he needed me healthy for the long run. Perry Sheraw stopped by minutes after George left, followed by Kiril and Melissa. The day yielded little progress.

By midday I'd skimmed through most of my e-mails and made five or six call-backs to various private equity groups and TMG co-workers needing my assistance. When I started feeling the tingling sensation in my shoulders, calves and cheeks, I called Pam and she rushed to pick me up. It's difficult to not over react when your head is tingling and your facial muscles are contracting. I did my best to hide my fear from co-workers as I passed by workstations at the top of the stairs and slipped out the front door.

By the time we reached home, muscles in both shoulders and throughout my upper body were contracting so hard we decided to contact Dr. Politz. Under his guidance, I consumed an additional thirteen calcium pills throughout the course of the afternoon—all in hopes of avoiding another trip to the ER. It was an anxious time and remaining calm was easier said than done. I paced, tried to breathe deep and relax. When she could convince me to sit down, Pam would rub my neck and back. I found it difficult having another person witness the effects of my under-performing nervous system. It was embarrassing that I was not strong enough to stop it.

I was extremely uncomfortable, crawling in my own skin from the low calcium levels in my blood. My right hand was still swollen where the IV needle from the previous calcium drip seared the vein. The Percocet I was taking did little to offset the massive throbbing in my left shoulder, sleeping more than two or three hours was impossible and the heat this time of year on island was only adding to the unbearable situation.

My mannerisms changed quickly and I would become agitated without warning—not wanting anyone else around one second and clinging to Pam the next. I paced back and forth, clutching my broken shoulder trying to block the pain with deep-breathing techniques. Pam tried to help me relax with each mood change I experienced. She would ask me even more questions if I quit communicating. I was not always cordial with my responses. She never over reacted or took anything I said personally. I know it could not have been an easy time for her.

I was depressed. Everything seemed labored and difficult. Daily pill schedules and frequent blood draws only added to my frustration level. Pam made sure I followed all of the doctor's instructions and made every scheduled appointment and laboratory visit. She created spreadsheets to track over thirty pills I was taking each day. It was a daunting task—one I loathed and was incapable of managing on my own.

Part of the difficulty I was experiencing was coming to the realization that the final cure was an outright failure. The parathyroid surgery in Tampa was supposed to have been the last step in my ultimate recovery. Instead, I was left with a malfunctioning nervous system, the head of my left shoulder had been completely broken off the bone, and I was facing a long hard rehabilitation. There were times when I lost my confidence, doubting whether I could ever pull it all together. I quickly squashed those thoughts, fearing they would gain a foothold in my psyche. I had bigger worries to address. The ever-growing realization that Pam would soon be leaving the island was weighing heavily on my mind.

Once again, Pam reluctantly drove me to work at 8:30 a.m. on Tuesday, July 10th. It was hard getting back into the swing of things. I had to remember what pills I needed to take, and when. I was still experiencing high levels of pain from the surgeries but needed as clear a head as possible to conduct business, so I refused to take Percocet before or during work hours. I hadn't been given clearance to start rehabilitation, but as I sat at my desk I pushed forward, exercising the shoulder by moving it with my right arm. It hurt like hell, but the overwhelming desire to get started outweighed the pain. After knocking off some more work-related, low-hanging fruit, I called Pam to come pick me up. I was out the door by noon. My second day back to work had ended much the same as the first. Melissa escorted me down the stairs to make sure I didn't fall. Standing on the sidewalk in the summer heat, sweat constantly pouring out, purging my system of hard narcotics, I waited in my own personal hell for my ride home.

Wednesday, July 11th and Thursday, July 12th, followed much the same schedule. Pam, feeling the need to always inject optimism, kept pointing out what I had accomplished in such a short time. I fought her tooth and nail on any positive points she brought up. I was barely hanging on to what little sanity I had. I'd never felt this sick or messed up before in my life. Thursday night I could only manage two hours of sleep. The rest of the night was spent fighting off pain and sickness. The two just blended together to form the most wicked and relentless of opponents. Pam held my hand throughout the night and told me it was all going to be okay.

The early morning hours were spent trying to ignore how bad I felt, playing cards, pacing the floor and rubbing my arm. In a few hours we would be at the laboratory for a blood draw before dropping me off at work. Pam made sure we were out the door early enough to make the half-hour drive to Sunny Isle, stand in the first-come, first-serve line and rush the doors at 7:00 a.m. Getting through the process before noon meant you had to be one of the first twenty people taking a number. We arrived at 6:29 a.m. and were second in line. When the wrought-iron gates finally opened, the entire line surged into the hallway outside the laboratory door.

After the front door to the clinic was opened, each person in line pulled a numbered tab from a wall dispenser. The seats in the tiny waiting room quickly filled. The line stretched out the door and down the hallway as I heard my number called over the loud speaker. My arm was tied off with a rubber hose as the nurse tried to locate a healthy vein. It was becoming increasingly difficult. They were instructed to only use my right arm because the doctors wanted to protect the blood supply to the left shoulder. Between all the IVs and weekly blood draws my once pristine veins had disappeared. No longer filled with anxiety before the needle hit the skin, I still found it unpleasant to go through multiple punctures in a quest to fill three vials of blood. I was out the door by 7:20 a.m. Forty minutes later, I was standing on the side of the street watching as Pam drove west down Company Street after dropping me off at work.

Two hours later, I was struggling to find a rhythm in my work routine and decided to take a break. I ducked out the front door of the office holding my left arm tight to my body. I walked one block to the west, turned north towards the water and down the hill. I knew my small gesture would only scratch the surface of my gratitude but I wanted to buy Pam a special gift. She was scheduled to leave island the next morning. A gold bracelet had been woven into a mesh that reflected light like the surface of the ocean. It would look beautiful on her wrist. I had the counter lady wrap it in the finest gift box. I got back to work and tried to push ahead with menial tasks. My mind was on Pam's departure and I found it difficult to concentrate. I called Pam to come pick me up at 1:30 p.m.

After arriving home, we spoke with Dr. Braslow on the phone about the latest blood tests. My ionized calcium level was 4.2—below normal. My serum calcium was 7.8—below normal. My parathyroid hormone level was 7—below normal. Validating the reason I felt so run down, these numbers also revealed a startling truth: my three remaining parathyroid glands were not producing PTH in sufficient quantities to regulate the calcium in my blood. The likelihood was—they never would. My condition had officially changed from hyperparathyroidism to hypoparathyroidism. From www.parathyroid.com (Dr. Norman's and Dr. Politz's website:

Calcium is the element that allows the normal conduction of electrical currents along nerves—its how our nervous system works and how one nerve 'talks' to the next. Our entire brain works by fluxes of calcium into and out of the nerve cells. Calcium is also the primary element causing muscles to contract.

Knowing these two major functions of calcium helps explain why people can get a tingling sensation in their fingers or cramps in the muscles of their hands when calcium levels drop below normal. A sudden drop in the calcium level (like after a successful parathyroid operation where the patient doesn't take their calcium pills for the first few days after the surgery) can cause patients to feel "foggy," "weird" or "confused" like my brain isn't working correctly." The brain DEMANDS a normal steady-state calcium level, so any change in the amount of calcium can cause the brain to feel unloved and the patient to feel bad. Likewise, too much parathyroid hormone causes too high a calcium level—and this can make a person feel run down, cause them to sleep poorly, make them more irritable than usual, and even cause a decrease in memory. In fact, the most common symptoms for patients with parathyroid disease are related to the brain, and include depression and lack of energy! After removal of a bad parathyroid gland, most people will feel dramatically better. Some say it's like "someone turned the lights on."

After three straight weeks together it had come down to Pam's last night on island. During her entire visit she took my mood swings, irritability and anxiety in stride. She kept me grounded, and focused on moving forward even when everything seemed to crumble around me. She had nursed me, rushed me to the emergency room, taken on the role of a psychologist and had made my life better in countless ways. I wanted to enjoy her company and have the night last as long as possible. We played cards, and after a nice takeout dinner, I gave Pam her bracelet and told her how much she meant to me. Less than an hour later I was forced to lie down—overtaken by exhaustion. It was 8:30 p.m.

My brother Rod rearranged his busy lifestyle in order to fly down from Oregon, a trip of twenty hours—each way. He would be staying for five days. When or how this plan came together I don't remember, but I cannot overstate the importance of knowing he was going to be on island with me. Not only did it ease my fears about being left alone, it would also allow

102

me to continue to climb back into my work routine. Pam's flight left at 11:00 a.m, Rod's plane landed at 1:00 p.m. It barely gave me enough time to cover up the emotions of seeing Pam walk out the door for the final time.

This was going to be no vacation. Reality for Rod was dropping me off at work each morning, picking me up in the afternoon, watching me fall asleep around 5:00 p.m. and wake up by 7:00 p.m. The remainder of most nights I was in a restless and irritable state. Mix in filling prescriptions, doctor's visits and blood draws, little time was left for enjoyment.

Kathie drove me to the airport to collect my brother and I was never happier to see another human being in my life. Before Pam had left she had written detailed accounts of all the events leading up to his arrival. She gave him the pill schedule and instructions for future blood draws, emergency contacts, physician's names and numbers etc. She had stored countless stacks of magazines, books, clothes, boat parts and tax returns out of sight in plastic bins bought at the hardware store over the previous two weeks. Although I'd found the constant documenting and cleaning up process annoying to watch from my bed, I could not argue with the fact it was nice to have an organized home for my brother's visit.

Even though my health issues left me feeling exhausted and weak, Rod managed to make me laugh and enjoy a few moments each day. The only accommodation I could offer him was a blow-up bed on top of my couch and loveseat pushed together in the corner of my stifling hot one-room house. He made salsa, went grocery shopping and played my guitar and dobro every night. He remembered me talking about not being able to drape my right arm over a guitar for months after my first surgery. I finally got to a place where I could finger pick with the guitar neck straight up in the air. Rod brought me a charango, a much smaller stringed instrument I could play without pain. We had seen several variations of this instrument on our trip to Peru. It is just over two feet long and has ten strings. After teaching me a couple of chords we were soon playing off-key Rolling Stones songs.

The weekend seemed to fly by. Monday morning approached and work loomed on the horizon. I had formulated a strategy to push myself as hard as possible to increase hours spent at the office each day. Knowing this was the quickest way back to a normal routine, I was determined to stick to the plan. In the upcoming week I told my brother not to pick me up until at least 3:00 p.m., an hour and a half past the last time I called Pam the week before. The next week I would stay until 4:00 p.m. Soon I would be able to stretch it out to a full day.

On Tuesday night, I had just enough energy left to attend Trivial Pursuit at Chicken Charlie's Roadhouse. Pat and Kathie joined us and by 6:00 p.m. there were eight teams under the open aired tent vying for top honors. As always our goal was to beat the reigning champions, The Bar Fly's. Having my brother there gave us a good chance. He was able to answer several hard questions and after the first two rounds we were dead even. This was my first social event since I left for Tampa a month prior. The rush I got from being around people again soon faded, and I started feeling exhausted. I tried keeping it to myself as long as possible. A half-hour later I let Rod know I needed to leave. Pat later informed me that after all was said and done, The Conquistadors had taken a distant second place.

After work on Wednesday, July 18th, I asked Rod to drive me to the Ford dealership. I knew I had to change to an automatic if I was going to be able to drive in the near future. Rod had a hell of time handling my four-liter V-6 manual truck. Popping the clutch every time he shifted gears forced me to brace myself for the jolt of pain shot through my upper body. The first couple of times it happened I almost passed out. Rod would just smile, curse my truck and ask why I had bought this piece of shit.

I was wearing a sleeveless shirt. My arm was in a sling with small dried blood patches visible on the days-old bandage. My brother was sporting a five or six day beard, torn up tee shirt and old shorts. Not sure if we were two bums walking off the street to get out of the heat, the salesman reluctantly approached us. The trucks on the lot had over-inflated price tags. I had checked the prices at Florida dealerships earlier in the day. These where almost double the price. The salesman pointed out the added cost of shipping to the island as the reason for the discrepancy. Trading in my used

Ranger became a second sticking point. The dealership would not be able to give me a good deal. It was suggested I would be better off selling my truck outright. By this time, I was so pissed off we got up and walked out.

My brother's visit was quickly coming to an end. He was scheduled to leave the following morning. Just as in Pam's case, I will never be able to repay my brother for his help and support during one of the darkest and most dependent times in my life. Strong emotions built up inside me as his time on island came to an end.

We had one last good jam on my back porch under the Caribbean stars. The neighbor's dogs howled at the high-end pitch of the Charango I unleashed over Cotton Valley. My brother played brilliant accompanying guitar. The joy I experienced at that moment was barely enough to mask the growing sadness inside. By the time Rod left the next morning I was overcome by the loneliest feeling I have ever felt.

How do you get from one day to the next? There is no road map to follow and I sure as hell did not know how all this was going to play out. My illness had taken away so much, but there was no option to just give up. I did what came naturally. I pushed myself harder than ever before.

It soon became apparent that I had to learn to set my pride aside and ask for help. I leaned on my friends and they offered assistance without hesitation. I had to rely on my landlords Tony and Donna, friends Pat and Kathie, Melissa and Kiril and countless numbers of other people for transportation to buy groceries, fill prescriptions, weekly blood draws and doctor appointments. They had already paid their dues when I had my first surgery and it weighed heavily on my mind each time I asked a new favor.

I was scheduled to see Dr. Chase in St. Thomas and begin official rehabilitation at Beeston Hill after getting his clearance. I needed to be able to drive myself. Donna was employed as a CPA at Caribbean Automart. They were the largest dealer on island and had several brands of vehicles under one roof. Donna suggested we attend the upcoming tent sale the following weekend. I was desperate at this point. My heart was set on a new truck but I was only able to make a deal on a KIA Sportage. They accepted my truck as trade but increased the overall price. By the time it was all explained to me, I could have cared less. I was in no position to bargain. On Monday July 23rd, with one functioning arm, I drove myself to work in my new car.

My latest blood draw had come back with a calcium level of 7.8ml and a PTH level of 7ml. I had every reason to be feeling lousy, but instead was thrilled with my newfound freedom. It felt like a huge weight had been lifted off my shoulders. I stayed in the office past 5:00 p.m.

The joy of independence was short lived as my back froze up later that evening. Unable to move without hunching over and applying pressure on my lower back with my right arm, I drove to Dr. Braslow's office the next morning. He prescribed a muscle relaxant—Methocubamol (750 mg). The problem was probably caused by sleeping on an angled pillow meant to ease my breathing. After struggling through an entire day of work, I gladly took my first muscle relaxant later that night, and within minutes I was fast asleep.

I continued to talk with Pam at least twice a day. I reported tingling in my face and arms on a regular basis. She would ask several questions to gauge the severity, keeping meticulous notes of my responses. A rating system had been developed on a scale of one to ten. Our benchmark for emergency intervention was based on my Fourth of July response. Just before leaving for the emergency room I'd told her it was eight out of ten and increasing by the minute.

On Monday, July 30th, I was experiencing a two out of ten. By all accounts this was the least severe symptoms I'd felt in a long time. I had a phone consultation with Dr. Politz and he was pleased with my progress. He vowed to continue working with me to try and figure out the right balance between calcium pills, vitamin D supplements and other drugs.

On July 31st, my blood results showed a PTH level of 13, hovering at the lower end, but a few points higher than previous tests. This validated the improvement I'd been experiencing with my symptoms over the previous two days. I allowed myself to briefly contemplate the idea I was on the road to recovery. Days later, the next set of blood test results showed my PTH levels well below normal. It was a roller coaster ride. Every time my PTH level would bounce back, I would think my parathyroids would finally kick in and I would start feeling good again. This yoyo effect only contributed to my darkening mental state.

The doctors expanded their search for signs of a wider range of problems including additional tests on my next blood draw. Dr. Politz was convinced my symptoms were not all related to my malfunctioning parathyroid glands. The test results provided few clues: Serum calcium 8.8, Ionized calcium 4.6, glucose 132, total protein 8.4, osmolality 281—all came back above normal. We would need to keep an eye on them going forward, but according to the doctors they were not so far above normal to be considered a major contributor to the symptoms I had been experiencing.

Footnote: Glucose "To determine if your blood glucose level is within healthy ranges; to screen for, diagnose, and monitor hyperglycemia, hypoglycemia, diabetes, and pre-diabetes," Total Protein "As part of a general health checkup, to determine your nutritional status or to screen for certain liver and kidney disorders as well as other diseases," Osmolality "A plasma osmolality test and osmotic gap may be ordered when a patient has symptoms such as thirst, confusion, nausea, headache, lethargy, seizures, or coma that the doctor suspects may be due to hyponatremia or the ingestion of a toxin such as methanol or ethylene glycol." www.labtestsonline.com

Wednesday, August 1—severe tingling in my head and shoulders late in the morning at work. I immediately took an additional five calcium pills and drove home to rest. The tingling escalated to ice-pick stabbing sensations lasting for several more hours. Air blowing across my skin intensified the pain, making it too uncomfortable to have the fan on. Sunlight hurt my eyes, giving me an instant headache, so I closed the slats in the window. I sat on the side of my bed rocking back and forth as I prayed to God to put a stop to this. My facial muscles were contorting, causing my mouth and lips to lock up in the rising afternoon heat. My leg muscles cramped and my back hurt. My head was cloudy and my stomach was nauseous. I feared I was having a stroke. I weighed my options and was unable to make a decision to call for help. As day faded into night, alone in my house, I was forced to dig deep into my soul to fight off the overpowering anxiety. Shortly after 9:00 p.m., the symptoms started to ease. It was followed by the worst hangover feeling you can imagine. I did not get to sleep until well after midnight.

Thursday morning I rushed to work filled with a strong sense that I needed to be around other people. It gave me comfort knowing I was not going to be alone for the rest of the day. I called Dr. Politz on his cell phone and left a long message explaining the previous night's events. When he contacted me later that afternoon he reiterated his stance that we would find a balance. "Sometimes it just takes longer with some patients." My case was so rare he did not remember anyone in the past with the severity and strength of symptoms I was describing. He increased my daily calcium intake to twenty pills per day. One week before, he had dropped me down to seventeen from the twenty-two per day. My body was broken and my nervous system was shot. The weekly changes in pill counts did little but increase my anger level.

Tuesday, August 7—I flew by seaplane to see Dr. Chase in St. Thomas. He took x-rays of my arm and immediately commented on what a good job Dr. Mark Mighell in Tampa had done on my shoulder surgery. The reason physical therapy had been delayed was that the head of the shoulder had completely broken off the humerus bone. Such a severe break needed additional time to heal. As he performed all the required mobility tests, by moving the arm and rotating the shoulder, the pain level ratcheted up to new heights. I tried not to pull away or scream out. I failed on both fronts.

After looking at the x-rays and charting my measurements he approved therapy beginning in one week. The longer healing process left us with a shorter amount of time before the scar tissue solidified. I needed to get busy tearing it up. For good measure, Dr. Chase performed the same mobility tests on my right shoulder he'd performed on my left shoulder. I had progressed enough to put my right hand behind my lower back. We both considered that real progress.

Waiting for a cab outside the Paragon Building, I barely noticed the stifling August heat. I had received the green light to start rehabilitation. This was the first positive boost to my morale in weeks. As I ducked into the cabin of the seaplane for the second time that morning I managed to keep my smile while the pain coursed through my shoulder. I stayed late at the office, in part to make up for lost time, but also to enjoy the cool AC.

Wednesday, August 8—My latest blood work was for: ionized calcium 4.5, PTH level 12, serum calcium 8.3, glucose 111, and osmolality 281. After briefly consulting with Dr. Politz, his conclusion was to continue the same pill count.

I had been trying to get a new prescription filled through Dr. Braslow for Calcitriol (generic vitamin D). I'd run out the previous day and had left several messages for both the doctor and the pharmacy. I was becoming extremely annoyed knowing the slightest change to my pill regimen could set off a nervous-system meltdown. By late in the day, at my urging, the pharmacist spoke with Dr. Braslow. He informed them that the Vitamin D I was receiving in my calcium pills was sufficient and I did not need to take the prescription version. This was news to Dr. Politz and he wanted to talk to the pharmacist before making a decision. After his conversation with the pharmacist, Dr Politz decided this would be a good time to try discontinuing the Vitamin D supplement. I was less than thrilled with the idea of taking away the absorption capabilities and reluctantly agreed to test the new theory.

The left hand of my medical team and the right hand of my medical team were not communicating information effectively. As the patient, I was left with the burden of facilitating the line of communication between medical experts. I was less than pleased with health care in general and more specifically with Dr. Politz, Dr. Braslow and the Medical Laboratory. I could not rely on the standing order to fax the results of the twice-weekly blood draws to the doctors. The laboratory always said they faxed them and the doctors always said they'd not received them. I would have to repeat the whole follow-up process time and time again before test results finally fell into the correct hands. It became a daunting daily task to undertake. Pam was with me every step of the way. She tried to deflect as much of the work load off me as possible. She understood that I was growing increasingly frustrated dealing with the day-to-day management of the medical system. In the end there was little choice in the matter.

After several long calls throughout the week, Pam had calmed me down concerning mismanaged communication among the medical professionals, and came for a week-long visit from August 9th through the 16th. She had arranged this trip shortly after leaving island in July knowing I would need help. I started to panic knowing I'd not been able to clean or prepare. I was in no shape to entertain a guest. She reassured me she didn't care. She was coming to take care of me. She was more than willing to clean my house while I was at work. She urged me to relax. All she wanted was to lay low, play cards and take walks every day.

Dr. Braslow had prescribed Ambien to help me sleep. My brother warned me against adding it to the long list of pills I was already taking. I took his advice and had not taken any, but I needed to get some sleep. I was so worn out and knew the body does not heal if you do not allow it to rest. Even with Pam on island for the next couple of days I was still unable to sleep more than three or four hours. After contemplating it several times, and not following through, I took my first sleep aid on August 11th.

Pam drove me to my first physical therapy session after work on Monday the 13th. I was pleased to be officially starting rehab following the surgery to my left shoulder. Everyday tasks including bathing, hygiene, dressing, etc. had become next to impossible. After Pam's scheduled departure, I would be left on my own with the ongoing struggle of only being able to use my right arm. These were functions I had taken for granted all my life. Just as in the past, the continued struggle with the most basic functions became a stark reminder of how far I'd fallen.

My motivation to regain mobility became the fuel that would drive me through the rehabilitation process. Just as with my right shoulder, I would go above and beyond in the effort department. I knew the process, the pain, and the mental ability it would take. The level of effort I supplied would directly relate to the final outcome. I had to be able to shut everything else out of my mind and focus. I had to completely buy into the process.

It had taken thirty-seven physical therapy sessions to rehabilitate my right shoulder. My insurance carrier placed a limit of sixty sessions in a calendar year. That left only twenty-three sessions to break up scar tissue and increase mobility in my left shoulder. We were forced to work with what we had and stretch the sessions out from August through the end of January. It's amazing that an insurance company can determine the number of times you need to see a therapist for an injury. Of course there was no way of knowing I would be injured twice and in need of physical therapy within the same calendar year, but the fact Cigna had a say in it at all was mind boggling to me.

The physical therapists had already prepared a schedule that included two sessions after work and two more self-guided workouts each week. They gave me detailed instructions and encouraged me not to overextend myself. I already knew most of the exercises by heart and the therapists were confident I could handle the individual workouts without incident. I would have to control my desire to see immediate results, an issue they had confronted time-and time-again in my previous rehabilitation process.

I had no internal or external mobility. I was unable to move my arm more than one inch in any direction. I could straighten it out towards the ground at the elbow but it caused the shoulder a great deal of pain. Therapists manipulated the arm during each session loosening scar tissue. Weights, pulleys and bungee cords provided the resistance needed for the tearing process. Massage therapy would keep the tissue supple over a longer period of time. If it was allowed to permanently harden, I would never regain a full range of motion. Electro therapy at the end of each session, and ice packs several times a day, would control swelling. Progress for the first two months would be frustratingly slow and measured in 16ths of an inch. I knew the game, and how it was played, but even having been through it in the recent past did not prepare me enough for the mental strain of going through therapy for a second time.

As my immediate physical needs where being addressed in therapy, another alarming trend was bothering me—the loss of my short-term memory. The doctors had warned me I would experience some loss from the anesthesia, but that should have long since been out of my system. The problem was noticeably worse with each passing day—especially at work. I always formed my questions for the Roundtable guests as they discussed their background, business model, investment targets etc. I might scribble some notes but never needed the full question written out. I would open the questioning round without missing a beat as the questions were right there, parked in my brain to be used when needed. Post-surgery, I could still think of the questions, but when the time came to use them I'd forgotten what they were. One Saturday I found myself driving to town—which usually takes fifteen minutes. I'd reached the turn just past Cheeseburgers in Paradise on the East End Road, when suddenly it dawned on me that I'd forgotten why I was going to town. I continued driving. Two minutes later the reason came to me. By the time I got to Gallows Bay, it had completely vanished from my brain again. Daily conversations were inundated with lapses of memory or searching for the point I was trying to make. I felt the gift of being able to communicate was slipping away. Pam bought me a book called *Mind Games*, filled with puzzles and exercises designed to stimulate the brain. I started reading more and more, anything to keep the brain active. I was battling the fear that I had a permanent brain disorder.

August 16—I watched as the dust kicked up from the back tires of Pam's rental car. I hated seeing her go. The stark reality quickly sunk in that I was on my own. It was followed by the onslaught of anxiety. I was scheduled to play my regular Thursday night poker game at Bud Orpen's later that night. Tingling sensations started occurring in my face early in the morning at work. Later it spread into my intestinal track. The left side of my lower rib cage felt like it was hooked up to the electrode machine at the rehabilitation center. I called and backed out of poker. I took ten extra calcium pills and drank water nonstop. The symptoms did not escalate but remained uncomfortable the remainder of the day.

Pam called to let me know she'd made it back to Cleveland without any problems. I didn't want to burden her with the details of my day. Later I took an Ambein and was able to get to sleep sometime after midnight.

Friday, August 17—I woke up experiencing slight tingling on the left side of my nose and mouth. During the workday it intensified and my facial muscles started to contract. My lips quivered uncontrollably and my jaw felt as if it were locked and did not fit properly in my face. I closed my eyes for fifteen-minute stretches towards the end of the workday to try and relax. Everyone was meeting at the Brew Pub for drinks after work. I had committed to attend the gathering earlier in the week. I caught a lot of flack but I had to back out. I headed home and popped ten extra calcium pills, sat in the dark and rocked back and forth for six and a half hours before I felt good enough to take an Ambien and go to sleep.

I continued icing down my left shoulder to numb the severe pain. Dr. Chase assured me what I was experiencing was normal. I had gone through some of the same pains with the right shoulder, but I felt I needed to explain everything in detail to the doctors. I was never sure where a pain would lead me. What would happen if I ignored it?

Wednesday, August 22—My latest blood work came back from the laboratory. My PTH level was 16 and my serum calcium was 8.1. I was still experiencing involuntary muscle twitching and tingling sensations in my face. The only change in my pill regimen had been the removal of the Calcitriol (vitamin D). I left a message for Dr. Politz on his cell phone. We spoke on Friday, August 24th about the tingling sensation and the continually low calcium numbers. He wanted me to hold off re-introducing the vitamin D and see if this subsided over time. I was apprehensive, but agreed to see if the nervous system would miraculously start to self regulate.

Wednesday, August 29—Blood test results showed much of the same: PTH level 13, serum calcium level 8.2. It had been a week since speaking with Dr. Politz. There were no positive signs. I was lethargic and needed to rest a lot. After returning home from work, I turned out all the lights, closed my eyes, and blocked out all noise and airflow over my skin. This had turned into a nightly ritual.

In the Caribbean, August starts a brutal, four-month stretch of extreme heat and humidity with little to no breeze. At work, the AC provided a break, but at home it felt like I was stuck inside a fully functioning blast furnace.

Thursday, August 30—I drove to the Medical Center at Sunny Isle Shopping center over my lunch hour. I was scheduled for a full-body bone density scan ordered by Dr. Chase. I was tired and had to wait in the front room for over an hour before the procedure began. I had to get undressed and don a hospital gown. Medium was all they had. It barely covered my torso. I was asked to lie down on a table and bend my legs up. After trying in vain to pull cloth over my crotch to save the female technician an embarrassing moment, I gave up and relaxed. There I was—exposed for the world to see. The machine had barely finished passing over me as the technician ran out of the room telling me over her shoulder that I could get dressed. I headed back to work.

Tuesday, September 4—I flew to St. Thomas for a checkup with Dr. Chase. My bone density scans showed I was in the osteopenia range in the three main skeletal (spine, hips and wrist) areas scanned. This was an improvement over the single wrist-bone density scan performed at the Beeston Hill Rehabilitation Center in January. Those results had shown my left wrist-bone density to be at a -2.8 T score—indicating severe osteoporosis.

> Osteopenia refers to bone mineral density (BMD) that is lower than normal peak BMD but not low enough to be classified as osteoporosis. Bone mineral density is a measurement of the level of minerals in the bones, which indicates how dense and strong they are. If your BMD is low compared to normal peak BMD, you are said to have osteopenia. Having osteopenia means there is a greater risk that, as time passes, you may develop BMD that is very low compared to normal, known as osteoporosis.
> www.webmd.com

Some people who have osteopenia may not have bone loss. They may just naturally have a lower bone density. Osteopenia may also be the result of a wide variety of other conditions, disease processes, or treatments. Women are far more likely to develop osteopenia and osteoporosis than men.

www.webmd.com

Dr. Chase took x-rays. His best estimate: the bone was receiving enough blood supply to heal properly and should survive. This was good news and put my mind at ease. There was no great celebration or feeling of elation but I did leave his office that day with a grin on my face. I caught a cab back to the docks and waited for the next available seat on a seaplane home.

Wednesday, September 5—My latest blood work showed my serum calcium level was below normal at 7.4ml. No wonder I was feeling lousy. I spoke to Dr. Politz. He moved me back to sixteen calcium pills daily and I was to continue with weekly blood draws. With the lab only able to process half the tests on site, it meant keeping track of two sets of results. Every time I checked with Dr. Politz he would have one part of a blood test result and not the other. Sometimes he had not received any results. It was a frustrating mess trying to keep track of it all. I had filled out paperwork for the laboratory giving Pam permission to receive my blood work results. She had them faxed to her work and then faxed them to Dr. Politz. I started asking for printouts every week at the laboratory and faxing them to Dr. Politz myself. Even with these measures, the results always seemed to be a week behind and never what we needed in real time.

The tingling continued in my face. As soon as it started I would take four to six extra calcium pills and try and relax for fifteen minutes. When you work in a fast-paced job this presented problems. You're unable to shut it down when your schedule includes five, six, or seven meetings and countless phone calls and e-mails each day.

Thursday, September 13—I was feeling exceptionally pressured and full of anxiety. I'd had enough of the constant run around and called Dr. Politz. I explained that the tingling was not going away. I was taking twenty plus calcium pills every twenty-four hours to offset the symptoms. Having this continue to happen on a daily basis was not acceptable. I went on to explain that three months after parathyroid surgery I was disappointed that my medical condition was not improving. He told me to increase the number of calcium pills to eighteen from sixteen and keep taking extra when I felt bad. He was convinced everything would calm down. My case was one of the rarest he or Dr. Norman had seen in a male patient. It was going to take time to balance out. These pep talks helped boost my moral temporarily, but I was really starting to become depressed. I could not sleep without taking an Ambein, and with it, I was only able to get three to four hours a night.

Wednesday, September 19—Blood test results showed my serum calcium at 6.8ml, lower than when I passed out in Tampa and broke my left shoulder. There was no PTH level because the blood was hemolyzed (cells disintegrating) during transport to the laboratory in Florida. I felt demoralized. The illness was winning the battle.

Pam was feeling the brunt of my growing frustration. The anger she heard in my voice prompted her to book a flight to come see me on September 21st. To divert my focus away from health-related issues, Pam drove us around the east end of the island as we looked at lots that were for sale. We liked a couple, but I could not bring myself to contemplate anything other than medical issues and work. We agreed to discuss them at a later date. On Sunday, with the help of Pat, we went sailing for three hours on *Folly* expending all the energy I had in reserve. We laid low and played cards the rest of the afternoon. Without taking a sleeping aide, I was out cold by 9:00 p.m. Pam's stay was short but effective. She had calmed me down and was leaving me more relaxed with a clearer head. She flew back to Cleveland on Monday, the 24th.

Tuesday, September 25—The workday was especially jam-packed with meetings and deadlines. In the middle of it all, Dr. Politz, armed with the latest half of the recent blood draw, called and started me back on one Calcitriol pill per day in hopes of helping calcium absorb into my blood stream.

That night I experienced symptoms that were a mirror image of when I passed out in Tampa. I felt the doctor had been a little late reinstating the

Calcitriol I'd suggested earlier. My mouth and lips were cramping severely. I was experiencing ice-pick stabbing sensations and was left praying this was not a stroke. Afraid to be alone, I called Pam and she stayed on the phone with me for hours. I took fourteen extra calcium pills. The onslaught lasted all night. I rated the symptoms at a nine out of ten. We debated the need to go to the emergency room. It was touch and go, but I wanted to avoid heading to the hospital at all costs. Pam continued trying to calm me down and encouraged me to ride it out. I was exhausted, but could not lie down because the tingling in the back of my head intensified in the horizontal position.

I'd hung up the phone with Pam shortly after midnight. I was feeling a little relief in the fact I no longer felt my muscles were crawling under my skin. The hours of continuous rubbing of my jaw and face, trying to unlock them, finally yielded the desired results. Eventually the cramping throughout my body subsided enough for me to fall back into the comfort of my pillows. The clock on my cable box read 3:00 a.m. Blood work at the laboratory was scheduled in four hours.

I felt horribly hung over as I drove to the laboratory. I arrived late, and paid the price—being last in line. I was barely aware of my surroundings by the time the needle was stuck in my vein. It was 10:30 a.m. when I finally arrived at work. I struggled through the day and headed to my rehab session at Beeston Hill after work. I took twelve calcium pills and still felt tingling in my mouth, lips and the back of my head. I completed physical therapy and made it home around 7:30 p.m.—every bit the walking dead!

The tingling continued at an elevated level every day for the next week. I was scheduled for a trip to our Coral Springs office to conduct some training with the group of employees I managed. I was looking forward to the hotel room with AC so I could get comfortable and hopefully experience some much-needed deep sleep. I flew out on Monday October 1st. We were moving in a more customer-centric focus from our past practices. Several new steps, including cross-selling all TMG clients, needed to be implemented. I had been lobbying for this change since the team was formed and needed to be on top of my game when discussing it with the group. A new salary and bonus structure was constructed and my boss, Sara Sheldon, flew in from California to spend some time with me. The week was filled with long work days, packed with meetings and group training. To offset my symptoms I took extra calcium each day and got some much needed sleep each night with the help of Ambien and AC. I had minor tingling but nothing that rivaled the previous week. I flew home on Friday, October 5th.

Dr. Braslow became increasingly difficult to reach. He didn't get back with me about blood results and other medical procedures. It became impossible to speak with him. When I finally got hold of him he explained he had family issues in the states and was in the process of closing his practice.

The only choice I felt comfortable with was switching back to Dr. Frank Bishop. He was a throwback to earlier days when doctors actually took time to explain each issue to a patient. This much-sought-after doctor patient relationship added to the long wait times in his office and was the cause of my seeking out Dr. Braslow in the first place. Most of Dr. Braslow's patients made the same choice, increasing Dr. Bishop's already overloaded patient log.

Wednesday morning, October 24—I was standing over the toilet when my body discharged a large, red coagulated mass in my urine. It was followed by a solid stream of blood for three to four seconds. I felt clammy and started to sweat. Only able to reach Dr. Bishop's answering machine, I immediately drove to his office. Walk-in patients are accepted between 7:00 a.m. and 8:00 a.m. on a first-come first-serve basis. The office was full as I swung open the door at 7:10 a.m. When Dr. Bishop poked his head out of the examination room door I took him aside and explained my situation. He promised to see me as soon as possible. The rest of the patients in the waiting room gave me the stink eye, and moaned and groaned as if I had just cut in line. It was 9:00 a.m. before I was ushered into a waiting room. Dr. Bishop had me pee in a cup and we waited to see how much blood settled to the bottom of the container. He explained that blood is heavier than urine. At the end of the test there was about an eighth of a cup of blood in my urine sample. He assured me I was not bleeding out, but it could mean serious issues existed. Dr. Bishop ordered a sonogram of the bladder and kidneys. I went down the hall to the Imaging Center and waited for my name to be called.

I was asked to take my shirt off and unbutton my pants. The technician used a handheld sonogram device similar to one used to check pregnancies. There were no blocks or obstructions that could be seen. Dr. Bishop also ordered a sonogram of my prostate. According to the technician they were booked and I would have to schedule that procedure another day. I returned to work before noon and stayed late into the evening to make up the time lost earlier in the day.

Friday, October 26—I had an appointment for the prostate sonogram before work. I went in thinking that they would rub the handheld sonogram wand over my belly and call it a day. My first signal that this was a different procedure was when I was asked to undress and don a hospital gown. The technician moved quickly. He didn't go into great detail about the proce-dure—except that I would need to bend over. He proceeded to take a gloved, KY Jelly covered finger and start feeling around in my anal cavity in search of my prostate. Although uncomfortable enough to cause me to bite down on my folded-up shirt, we managed to finish that exam. I was thinking it was time to get dressed. It had been an unpleasant experience but I would survive. No such luck. I was asked to lie on a table on my right side. I saw something out of the corner of my eye that frightened me. It was a wand six or seven inches in length with a knob on the end. There were electrical wires trailing out the back leading to a diagnostic machine. The technician pro-ceeded to probe all the way up my anal canal with what I prefer to call the wand of discomfort. The disposable paper sheet covering the metal table was firmly clinched between my teeth as I began fixating on a weapon of choice to use on the all-too-eager technician. Moments later I had settled on the ball peen hammer I used to beat the rust off my dilapidated boat trailer. Unaware of the raging assault being directed at him within the con-fines of my head, the technician leaned over my left shoulder and said, "It really would benefit you if you held still. I am trying to make this as comfortable as possible." If I ever got this wand out of my ass I was ready to do battle. The technician explained this was necessary to get a good look at the prostate. He recommended that I get this procedure done every year going forward. He told me a story about how this procedure had saved his father's life by detecting prostate cancer less than a year before. Somewhere along the way I let go of the anger. My thought process had morphed from what I first perceived as an unnecessary violation, into a helpful intrusion. By the time the test was finished it felt as if he had just done me a favor. I actually thanked him after all was said and done. I was allowed to clean the half pound of lubricant from my backside and get dressed. Several people at work commented on how quiet I was throughout the day.

The blood continued to seep out into my underwear and flow through the urine stream. Dr. Bishop called a week later with the results of the prostate sonogram. They were negative and everything seemed clear. They had checked everything out and found nothing. There was no true explanation, but his best guess was it was not serious. "These things happen and they generally clear themselves up." He wanted me to continue to monitor the situation and give him updates. I continued to have noticeable blood in the urine and seepage during the day at work for the next seven days.

Needless to say, this was a stressful time. I thought I had surpassed the limits of my coping capabilities only to realize this was the beginning of a much larger fight. The barrage continued with the most unlikely of symptoms. My tongue started to feel like it was on fire. The pain started in the morning and intensified early in the afternoon, continuing into the evenings. The burning sensation kept me from sleeping. I tried everything to make it stop. I started eating copious amounts of ice cream. It only gave me short respites from the pain. The air running over my tongue felt like winds spreading a forest fire. I examined my tongue in the mirror the first couple of days and there was no discoloration. I called Dr. Bishop and spoke to his nurse. She promised to pass the message on to him. Three days later Dr. Bishop returned my call at 7:30 p.m. He'd heard of a condition that can be related to nervous-system disorders called Burning Mouth Syndrome. He didn't believe I had Thrush because the color of my tongue was normal, and my gums and teeth didn't hurt.

Some research suggests that primary burning-mouth syndrome is related to problems with taste and sensory nerves of the peripheral or central nervous system. Secondary burning mouth syndrome is a symptom of one or more underlying medical problems. Underlying problems that may be linked to secondary burning-mouth syndrome include:

Psychological factors, such as anxiety, depression or excessive health worries.

There's no one sure way to treat burning mouth syndrome, and solid research on the most effective methods is lacking. Treatment depends on your particular signs and symptoms, as well as any underlying conditions that may be causing your mouth pain. That's why it's important to try to pinpoint what's causing your burning mouth pain. Once any underlying causes are treated, your burning mouth syndrome symptoms should get better.

If a cause can't be found, treatment can be challenging. There's no known cure for primary burning mouth syndrome. You may need to try several treatment methods before finding one or a combination that is helpful in reducing your mouth pain. Treatment options may include:

• A lozenge-type form of the anticonvulsant medication clonazepam (Klonopin)
• Alpha-lipoic acid, a strong antioxidant produced naturally by the body
• Oral thrush medications
• Certain antidepressants
• B vitamins
• Cognitive behavioral therapy
• Special oral rinses or mouth washes
• Saliva replacement products
• Capsaicin, a pain reliever that comes from chili peppers
Surgery isn't recommended for burning mouth syndrome.

www.mayoclinic.com

I would suffer with this condition for the next three weeks before the symptoms diminished. I remained on an ice-cream bender the entire time.

Not only did ice cream help temporarily, it was as if my body craved it. I woke up every morning thinking about ice cream. I ate it for breakfast and again after work. Naturally my weight started ballooning out of control. Although I was working out at the gym for rehabilitation purposes I was not burning enough calories to offset my intake of the ice cream. After moving to the island I'd dropped from 260 to 200 pounds. After my first surgery, when I met Pam, I weighed 220 pounds. Now, after my second shoulder surgery, my weight had crept back to over 240 pounds.

I dropped the ice cream, switching to calcium-rich yogurt and started walking as much as possible on the weekends to offset my growing waist-line. Nothing I did seemed to work and the pounds continued to pack on.

Thursday, November 1—At a time when most people around the office were starting to talk about holiday plans, flights to the states to see family, shopping and parties on island, I was struggling to make it through each day. The tingling sensation reached the point that by each evening my lips and jaw would lock up. I had to mentally talk myself out of going to the emergency room to seek calcium from an IV several nights in a row.

I was determined to push all aside, get through the workday and attend the poker game scheduled for later that evening. I needed to enjoy some-thing. The symptoms continued to intensify as we drove out to Bud's house overlooking Rust Op Twist and the North Shore. My eyes were shut behind my sunglasses as I tried to concentrate on relaxing my facial muscles. As the first hand was dealt, my legs and arms went numb for periods of time and my head was cloudy. The intensity did not reach the ice-pick stabbing sensation so I continued on. I knew I should have stayed home, but did not want to ask for a ride all the way back across the island. I took six extra calcium pills over the course of the three-hour game.

Unable to concentrate, I played poorly and lost over $60.00. As the game came to an end my only thoughts were of making it back home and controlling the symptoms enough to avoid a trip to the emergency room. I kept my ultra-sensitive eyelids shut behind my sunglasses to avoid the headlights of oncoming traffic during the ride home.

It was 10:45 p.m. when I called Pam and explained I was not feeling well. I needed to shut it down before my symptoms escalated. Sitting alone in the dark I rocked back and forth for two hours concentrating on positive thoughts. I was thankful for a strong breeze that had picked up out of the north-northeast. The heat was just breaking at night and the air was dry. We were heading into the best months to live on island. I was looking forward to some time away from work over the holidays. The symptoms were held at bay and I was able to fall asleep some time after 1:00 a.m.

Tuesday, November 6—I took the seaplane to St. Thomas to visit Dr. Chase. He'd asked me earlier in the year if he could use my unusual case in a demonstration he was presenting at a convention of sports-medicine physicians in Trinidad and Tobago. Pictures of my shoulders had been taken and I gave my permission to use my x-rays. He had organized the details from my case file into a Power-Point presentation and proudly showed off the final product. "Immaculate, your going to make me look good this year!"

With the bone continuing to receive enough blood supply to survive and the humerus (head of the shoulder) fusing back together with the help of the five-inch stainless-steel plate holding it together, Dr. Chase felt I was advancing as well as could be expected. I expressed my concerns that my mobility was not where it needed to be. Dr. Chase reassured me that my progress was on schedule. I was not an easy patient to convince. I wanted to be out swimming and hitting golf balls. He expressed the sentiment that I most likely would not be able to return to these activities at the same level I had in the past. My blood was boiling inside over these comments. I wanted to lash out—but refrained. Before ending the consultation Dr. Chase brought up the need in the future to return to a medication that would help increase bone mass. I reminded him of how bad Fosamax had made me feel and had caused memory lapses the first time I took it. There were several alternatives he agreed to look into for me. We still needed to wait and let the break in the bone heal before adding any of these types of drugs into the mix. I caught the seaplane back to Christiansted and headed to work.

Wednesday, November 7—I was busy at work when I experienced excessive tingling in my face. Not having the time to shut down completely I took ten extra calcium pills, concentrated on deep breathing, and continued to push through the workload. The symptoms increased throughout the day but I managed to keep them under control long enough to fight through and make it home.

Thursday, November 8—The tingling sensation had not diminished from the day before. I took four extra calcium pills as soon as I reached the office. Throughout the day I took an additional six pills. It was poker night and I was determined to make the game. I asked Pat if he could drive for a second straight week. "No problem." In my pockets I had ten extra calcium pills. I had taken eight of them as the game wound down. During the ride home my entire head was tingling and my eyes hurt. I knew I needed to shut it down before this episode intensified. Pat dropped me off at 10:30 p.m. Even with the help of Ambien I could not get to sleep.

I became anxious and could not lie down as my face twitched and my lips locked into a whistling position. I called Pam and she tried to calm me down. She was becoming an expert on delivering pep talks. Several questions into gauging the extent of my latest meltdown, Pam had assessed the situation and helped me focus on deep breathing and relaxation. I explained I needed to hang up and try and shut it down on my own. One hour later I was sitting on the edge of my bed rocking back and forth feeling more of an escalation than relief when I called Pam back. I found trying to answer her questions for a second time annoying, but her voice on the other end of the phone had an overall calming effect. She had witnessed the effects of low calcium attacks first hand and understood I was, at the very least, fearful of the outcome. Although I was cognizant of my reactions and worked on lowering their explosive nature, I still felt I was lashing out. As the night dragged on my tone became stressed and curt—even as I tried my hardest to keep my responses in check. Pam reassured me that the symptoms would run their course. She urged me to take additional calcium pills. I felt guilty about keeping her up so late. The clock read 1:30 a.m. The symptoms had finally calmed down enough so I could lay down and get some sleep. We hung up the phone, I eased onto the right side of my body and soon drifted off into a restless sleep for the remainder of the morning hours.

6:30 a.m.—My eyes opened to a cloudy hung-over feeling. It would not change over the course of the next two days. I continued to have periodic muscle spasms in my arms and hands and my eyes jumped and danced in bright light. I took an extra ten calcium pills both days. My mind was racing, especially at night, causing sleep to elude me.

Wednesday, November 14—I had a long discussion with Dr. Politz. In spite of my recent nervous-system attack he believed I could eliminate a few of the calcium pills I was currently taking each day. I wasn't sure about that. I was having so much trouble sleeping. I was experiencing minor tingling and muscle twitching daily. He wanted me to cut two calcium pills from my daily intake effectively lowering the number from twenty to eighteen. He asked that I keep track of the tingling and report back in two weeks. I was also expected to back it up with another blood draw in five days. I brought up the fact that Dr. Chase had been asking me to take Fosamax again. Dr. Politz did not think this was the right time to introduce the bone density drug into my system. He wanted me to wait for a year to eighteen months, giving my bones time to heal and my nervous system time to balance itself out. I was caught between two doctors wanting two different outcomes. It added stress to an already explosive situation. I called Dr. Chase and explained Dr. Politz's theory on Fosamax and he agreed that I could hold off for a year before taking the drug. At the end of another long day of tracking down doctors through their nurses and assistants, scheduling specific times to call back, waiting on hold, taking notes and trying to communicate exact wishes from one doctor to the next, I was wiped out. There had been no major new developments and I continued to suffer lingering symptoms. I was reaching the end of my rope.

Over the course of the next few days I noticed a considerable decrease in the symptoms. Even though the muscle cramps and tingling were still a daily distraction, they slowly diminished and were less prevalent. I had learned to accept small amounts of muscle cramps and considered them part of my everyday existence. I continued having problems falling asleep, not because my nervous system was acting up, but because of an overwhelming anxious feeling. Ambien did not provide relief from the anxiety as I tried harder and harder to relax.

The end of each year is always busy in a Mergers and Acquisitions firm. Several deals ride in the balance after both parties have agreed in principal to the price structure and future relationship after the sale. The negotiations go back and forth balancing on the fate of one or two concessions. Upcoming tax implications for both parties ratchet up their willingness to concede. November and December of 2007 was no different. The March Group closed out ten deals during this period.

Even with the fast-pace at work, my nervous system seemed to be quieting down, but I was not in the clear by any stretch of the imagination. My second toe on my left foot became swollen and turned sideways. The color was bright red and the pain caused me to walk with a limp. I took some anti-inflammatory pills prescribed by Dr. Bishop. I was also having problems breathing, again. Throughout the day, and especially at night when I was laying down flat, I would struggle to fill my lungs to capacity. Several times it caused me to sit straight up in bed and gasp for air. I was convinced it was the calcium pills I was taking, causing an upset stomach and activating my acid reflux. I began taking Nexium once a day when the breathing issue first started but it was not helping stop the constriction I felt in my chest and throat. I spoke with Dr. Politz on December 3rd and he suggested I move down to sixteen calcium pills daily and crush them up instead of taking them whole. Adding the process of crushing the calcium pills seemed like the last straw. I was becoming more and more agitated with the lack of progress. The constant balancing act my physicians were trying to find between pills and my nervous system was never ending. It changed daily and it was frustrating—trying to keep up with it all. What I was looking for was an answer that once and for all would stop the ups and downs of this parathyroid/nervous system roller-coaster ride.

The breathing issues continued to escalate and became alarming. I was struggling at night, especially, and having a hard time getting more than three or four hours of sleep. On December 13th, I had a follow-up appointment with Dr. Bishop. He ordered an x-ray of my foot and another sonogram of my prostate. I'd stopped peeing blood at the start of November and the follow-up test was to make sure there was no blockage forming. We discussed, at length, my breathing issues and he felt it was caused by acid reflux and that I needed to take my Nexium daily as a preventative measure instead of when I felt the symptoms begin. I left his office more frustrated than ever with the addition of another daily pill.

I went down the hall to the Imaging Center to get the x-ray and sonogram. Knowing what the sonogram entailed, I had to concentrate on holding my anxiety in check. I was getting to be an old pro at this. I was just looking for the morning to end. I needed to get back to work. It would be noon before I would reach the comfort zone of my office. Diving head long into another busy day erased the mornings proceedings from memory.

My plans were to stay on island for the Christmas holiday, then visit Pam in Cleveland. I was set to leave on December 28th. This was the first time I'd scheduled a vacation to the states in over two years. I was going to be traveling with a laptop and keeping up with e-mails, but planned on slowing down, enjoying vacation time. The break from work and getting off island was my motivation as the frantic end-of-year pace continued.

Starting in November, I began working on rebuilding my boat trailer. It was long past time when I needed to pull *Folly* out of the water. Metal that has been submerged in the salt water of the Caribbean corrodes quickly and *Folly's* trailer had rusted through in several spots. It was in danger of collapsing under her 3,500 pound load.

The process took a lot of time on weekends and after work pounding on metal with a ball peen hammer and using an electric grinder. Only having the use of my right arm made it that much more difficult. I did, however, find the work therapeutic. I needed to replace large sections of rusted cross beams and shore up some of the arms that raised and lowered the pads that

Folly would rest on. I could not do all the work and would eventually need help to finish the project.

My landlord Tony, an engineer, helped me plan out the new main frame structure. Everything had to be level and in its proper place. The weekend before Christmas a friend brought his welder over. He had procured some angle iron at a fairly cheap rate from a local metal shop. We were in the drive way from 8:00 a.m. to 5:00 p.m. By the time we'd finished, everything looked great. I spent most of the day grinding down welds to make them smoother before primer coating the entire trailer. It was finally completed Christmas morning with new coats of primer and rust-resistant paint. It looked brand new.

Heading to Christmas brunch at the Newman's, I felt a sense of accomplishment as my trailer was finished. The Newmans have guests from Denmark each year and they throw a brunch for family and friends. Crucian Christmas music blares from the stereo, greeting us as we enter the great room of their house. They have a fifteen-foot tree, shipped from the states every year, and there are dozens of presents piled up in every nook and cranny. Champagne and Bloody Mary's flow as the huge forty-five inch, flat-screen television has a continuous video loop of a log fire burning in a brick fire place. It is a strange sensation watching everyone in shorts and short sleeve shirts gather around the TV screen waiting in anticipation for the arm to come into frame and stoke the fire. A big cheer always goes up.

I drank two Mimosas talking with friends around the buffet. Hungry from my early morning work, I ate two plates of food and switched to drinking Coquito, a local made holiday drink similar to eggnog. The greetings, food and drink continued throughout the morning. Captain Llewellyn Westerman and his wife Karen, Judge Deromo, the Danes and several other people mingled in and out of the Newman's house overlooking Cotton Valley and the Caribbean, a beautiful setting for a Christmas-day party. I was in the best mood I'd experienced in months.

Just before noon I started experiencing light breathing issues. It was not serious and I felt slowing down on liquor and food would help ease the symptoms. My system was not use to rum or the rich foods I'd been consuming all morning. Even though there were several toasts still to come, I switched to water and stopped eating altogether in hopes of enjoying the sail to Buck Island we'd planned later in the afternoon. Over the years the afternoon Christmas sail had become tradition. So much had been turned upside down over the past year, I was looking forward to the normalcy the sail represented.

About 12:30 a.m., Pat, Kathie and I gracefully bowed out of the Newman Christmas brunch and headed home to change. Kathie was not going to join us on the sail, but a new couple on island we'd met at the Yacht Club were joining Pat and me. After arriving at the beach on Buck Island we planned to make several cell phone calls to friends and family back in the states.

There was no launch service from the docks on Christmas day. With limited use of my left arm, it was up to Pat to swim out to the boat and motor it into the end of the dock. We were in the process of removing my sail cover when I had to sit down and rest. Pat continued to ready *Folly* and eventually I got up and continued the prep work. I was struggling to breathe and feeling highly uncomfortable as we motored off the dock. The water was choppy and the winds were strong out of the north-northeast.

As we turned into the wind outside the mooring area in Teague Bay and raised the main and jib I was struggling to pull air past what felt like a growing blockage in my chest. Ignoring the pain in my left shoulder, I sat back down and took the tiller, leaning forward, concentrating on deep breaths. About every third to fourth breath I was unable to inhale to full capacity. Kristin and Greg asked if I was okay. I assured them I was. We soon were traveling at hull speed under sail down wind towards the cut in the reef.

As I tightened up the main sheet, using the traveler mounted on the stern deck, and pointed *Folly* towards the buoys, I knew I was in trouble. We skimmed past the green buoy to starboard as planned, heading straight for Buck Island. My head had to be lower than my knees to get a full breath of air. We made it another half-mile and I knew I had to get back to land. I didn't want to ruin everyone's Christmas afternoon, but I could not breathe enough to stay up right. I reluctantly turned the helm over to Pat.

I moved to the front of the cockpit and leaned against the outside cabin wall with my head down and my eyes closed. I apologized to everyone as I gasped to take in air. Pat flipped us around in a stiff breeze and we pointed back towards the cut leading to the three-quarter, mile-long shoot into Teague Bay.

I didn't feel well enough to lift my head or open my eyes. I reminded Pat of one particular coral head and he basically dismissed me. He was sailing for speed and would take the quickest way in. It was faster to sail through the cut before starting my small Johnson kicker motor. We waited to get in between the shore and the reef, turn into the wind, drop sails and lower the motor. Thank god she fired up on the second or third pull. We were still twenty minutes out from the dock and any attempt on my part to help with the work being done to button the boat up was met with even more shortness of breath. Pat is a strong sailor and my boat is simple in design, but it still is a lot of work to raise and lower sails on a rolling platform in breezy conditions alone. The winds were blowing eighteen to twenty knots and the seas were choppy. The twenty-minute motor ride was rough as we rolled from side to side without the weight of the full sails to keep us steady. My shoulder was throbbing as Pat swung us by the docks where Greg and Kristin helped me step off. Pat had to then catch my mooring ball by himself, before swimming to the beach by the clubhouse.

Kristen and Greg sat with me in lounge chairs next to the Yacht Club beach while waiting for Pat to return. I did not feel chest pains, but was getting cloudy in the head and I wanted to get home as fast as possible to lay down. When Pat made his way out of the water, a small argument erupted over me driving home. I assured everyone I was more than capable. I won the argument with the stipulation that Pat would follow me. It is only a five- minute drive, but he could see I was having trouble filling my lungs. I wished everyone a merry Christmas, climbed into my car and drove off.

I was already making plans to see Dr. Bishop first thing the next morning. If his office was not open, my backup plan was to show up at his house in Cotton Valley.

Kathie called within five minutes. She was worried and I promised to call her if my condition worsened. I tried to lie down, but could not fill my lungs with air. Sitting up, I tried to relax every muscle in my body and take deep breaths. I drank water, took a hot shower and continued my own version of meditation. Nothing seemed to work. As the minutes slowly ticked away I started to lose the battle of mind over matter. The anxiety got to me as I was unable to bring air into my lungs for three to four second periods of time. Gasping, I made the call.

As Pat and Kathie raced me towards the emergency room, I slumped over in the back seat—gasping the entire ride. We tried to make jokes about how I was always wrecking everyone's holidays.

There were fewer locals milling about on Christmas eve than in past visits to the emergency room, but dealing with the sign-in nurse proved to be as problematic and lengthy as past trips. The attitude afforded Pat, Kathie and I was much the same as in November 2006. It was as if we were unwanted visitors who showed up unannounced. The two-window system was still in place. There was little communication as the process seemed to completely depend on a patient's ability to convince the admitting nurse they deserved to be seen. I had become adept at pleading my case, and there was real desperation in my voice as I explained the issue at hand: that I could have serious complications if she didn't move quicker. The proceedings rolled slowly forward. I didn't get to enter the actual ER for over forty-five minutes. My breathing issues had increased the entire time and I was now struggling to pull any air into my lungs. Pat ran back and forth between the admitting window and the information window where all the records are kept. When I finally was wheeled to the ER, and placed in the familiar holding area, a nurse told me there were two stab wounds and one gunshot victim ahead of me. It would just be a moment. I was expecting hours of waiting, but to my surprise I was examined by a physician's assistant within minutes. This was a pleasant change from past experiences. He ordered an EKG, took my pulse and listened to my breathing through a stethoscope. As he stepped out of the curtained-off room a nurse stepped in and performed the EKG. Twenty minutes passed and upon his return the Physician's Assistant assured me I was not having heart problems which I had voiced as my biggest concern. A doctor would be in to see me soon.

Twenty minutes later, the doctor on call was standing over me holding my chart and asking pertinent questions. I explained that I had experienced a breathing issue in the past due to acid reflux but nothing to this degree. He went on to explain that I must have panicked when the breathing issues started and that intensified the issue, and the alcohol and rich food earlier in the day had most likely contributed.

He lost me when he said I panicked. I wanted to argue the point. Ten minutes later, after a shot of Ativan, I found myself relaxed and breathing without effort. I was given a prescription for fifteen Ativan pills. Minus the admitting procedure, this visit was the least time-consuming and problematic of all my visits to the ER at Governor Juan F. Luis Hospital.

It was 9:00 p.m. when I arrived home. I thanked Pat and Kathie for their help. Later, alone in my house I couldn't stop thinking that the breathing issue was yet another unresolved health concern. How could acid reflux put me on the verge of passing out? I was so relieved the EKG results were normal, though I was not convinced it was a panic attack or acid reflux. panic attack denoted weakness to me. I was not ready to accept that.

A panic attack is a sudden, intense fear or anxiety that may make you short of breath or dizzy or make your heart pound. You may feel out of control. Some people believe they are having a heart attack or are about to die. An attack usually lasts from 5 to 20 minutes but may last even longer, up to a few hours. You have the most anxiety about 10 minutes after the attack starts. If these attacks happen often, they are called a panic disorder.

Experts aren't sure what causes panic attacks and panic disorder. But the body has a natural response when you are stressed or in danger. It speeds up your heart, makes you breathe faster, and gives you a burst of energy. This is called the fight-or-flight response. It gets you ready to either cope with or run away from danger. A panic attack occurs when this response happens when there is no danger.

Panic attacks and panic disorder may be caused by an imbalance of brain chemicals or a family history of panic disorder. They sometimes happen with no clear cause.

http://health.yahoo.com/anxiety-overview/panic-attacks-and-panic
disorder-topic-overview/healthwise—hw53798.html

The night air was cool and the Christmas winds blew steadily out of the northeast through my windows. With the help of the Ativan I was relaxed and able to have a great sleep for the first time in weeks.

Wednesday, December 26th, was a scheduled day at work. Although there would be no real business taking place with clients, I had to get several end-of-year reports and projects finished before leaving island on vacation. After my arm exercises and stretching I went to use the restroom around 6:30 a.m. The toilet bowl turned red with blood, the inside of my penis felt as if it was on fire. Dr. Bishop had told me this could reoccur. He said this condition happens to men of my age for no apparent reason and there's no way to determine the cause beyond the tests already performed. He believed the blood was from veins around my prostate that somehow were seeping into the urine track. The advice he gave me was to see an urologist to get their opinion if the problem did not clear up on its own. I called his office and left a message to let him know about the latest episode.

The breathing issues were less prevalent during morning hours and I wanted to keep them that way. Pushing health issues out of my mind had become common place. It was my one defense tactic. I knew I could not take an Ativan during the workday because the drug made me sleepy. I would have to suppress any anxiety. I called Pam before leaving for the office and freaked out about being in the ER and peeing blood. My verbal release lasted for only a few minutes. Ever the optimist, she absorbed all of my frustrations. Pam reminded me what the doctors had explained about the blood and the breathing. She asked several questions, and told me she could not wait to get me up to Cleveland.

My immediate need was to focus on work. With that said, I headed out the door with little belief this was going to be the easy, low key catch-up day at the office I'd hoped for.

I'd recently been moved to one of two offices located at the top of the old, great house. The view afforded me was a complete panorama of the harbor below. I could see boats riding at their moorings and waves breaking on the reef outside Gallows Bay Harbor. The stairs leading up to my office were twenty-four in number and very steep. Upon entry, I saw a room partition behind which sat my large, wooden desk facing the windows to the north. None of the natural beauty that was visible on this day had much of a calming effect on me. I experienced breathing problems most of the morning but tried to keep it in check. Throughout the day I made several trips to the restroom at the bottom of the stairs to check on the bleeding issue. In between, I worked efficiently through a tremendous amount of paperwork. I sent out several e-mails, and left several short voice mails, gasping for air by the time I'd finished talking. The day flew by and before I left I wanted to leave a message for Dr. Politz. It surprised me when he answered his cell phone. He was concerned, and asked me to stop taking the green Oscal calcium pill. "Some patients in the past have experienced a bad stomach reaction to the Oscal." He felt that my stomach would be less upset if I were to stick to Citrical and continue crushing the pills.

I still had to attend my regularly-scheduled, one-hour rehab session before heading home. I arrived at the gym just before 6:00 p.m. The session was focused on light-weight lifting routines and arm stretching. I explained my breathing issue to my Physical Therapist. She was reluctant to allow me to continue, but ultimately relented. I started with a twenty-minute fast walk on the treadmill. I knew the workouts were important because I was down to my last three therapy sessions before the insurance coverage ceased. By intermingling physical-therapist guided workouts with my own we'd stretched the twenty-three rehab sessions over five months.

There were so many questions needing to be answered before I was ready to start working out completely on my own. My arm was still tender and sore. I didn't want to do anything that could cause permanent damage. I don't think I could have mentally handled a setback in my development at this stage of the fight. It had to go according to plan.

The weight training began on a total gym machine using body weight for resistance. I performed several exercises until my arms could not take it. My shoulders burned by the time I was done. I was amazed at how weak I'd become. That strength was gone and might never return. Throughout the therapy I learned the proper use of smaller weights, and how to perform the exercises precisely. It took several sessions for me to get the hang of it. Beside strength conditioning weight training is proven to help increase bone density. After my ice down, electric therapy and massage, I was alone in the changing room standing over a urinal and proceeded to fill it with red blood. The high from the workout left immediately. I drove home and took another Ativan to relax and get some sleep.

Thursday, December 27—I woke up, went to the restroom and filled the bowl with bright red urine. I summoned the strength to do my morning exercise routine—stretches and a short round of sit-ups. Mentally, I was drained, but I still had to go to work. I spent the day preparing for any and all potential issues in my absence. As usual, I would be traveling with a laptop, but I would not be available to answer direct questions from my group or the fifty-six business development managers. I left voice mails and sent e-mails making sure my two guests were still planning on attending. The day was long and I struggled to stay on course. I checked the blood seepage throughout the day, revealing growing stains. This only added to my difficulty breathing. Brutal and long, the day was finally coming to an end. I had never been so happy to cross a finish line. All I had left to do was go home and wait to board my flight to Cleveland the next morning.

A Faint Smile Hides Much Pain

The Guest House at Cotton Valley Where the Author Lived for Eight Years

THE NEW GUYS (DAY 290 – 300)

Pam had been suggesting I see a gastroenterologist. I was leery of adding an additional doctor to the mix. She remained persistent. Her father had been a patient of a Cleveland-based gastroenterologist and had held him in high esteem. She called his office on my behalf and was told the doctor was not available during the time I would be in town. They suggested I see another member of their group Dr. Eric Shapiro. His receptionist did not believe they had an appointment available but promised to check with the doctor. To her surprise, Doctor Shapiro, himself, called Pam back. He would be willing to fit me in for a consultation on 1/7/08. He was unsure what he could do for me and my breathing issue with only one visit, but was willing to make some recommendations.

I summoned my last bit of strength and packed before taking an Ativan and collapsing on my bed. Although I was still urinating blood and my breathing was somewhat labored, I fell asleep knowing I was headed to safety. This was my first trip to Cleveland. Pam had parties and people lined up for me to meet—including her family. She was inviting all kinds of friends to a New Year's Day party. Somehow she threw in a wedding reception and we planned to drive to Illinois to see Mother for a few days.

Friday, 12/28/07—My phone rang at 3:30 a.m. Pam was calling to be sure I did not miss my flight. I was on the 6:50 a.m. American Eagle Flight to San Juan, Puerto Rico, and then on to JFK and Cleveland.

To my dismay, the blood in my urine had not diminished. My breathing was labored and my facial nerves were tingling. I'd slept poorly. Part of my sleep issue was health related and part was my excitement to be getting off island. Even with my current state of exhaustion and sheer disgust over what was taking place with my symptoms, I was looking forward to seeing family and friends. In some ways I was hoping I could escape the day-to-day medical grind life had become. I knew Pam would be waiting to take care of me and I would be able to relax.

I checked my bag and cleared customs with time to spare. I sat down and wrote some final e-mails to my team and worked on the end-of-month bonus reports due the first week of January. I buttoned up the laptop just as the boarding announcement was made. The air was cool and a steady breeze blew out of the east. As our group of passengers walked the length of the tarmac in silence, the sun rose over the tops of the eastern hills. It was a beautiful morning. Although I was feeling good about getting off island I was anxious about all the socializing Pam had planned for us. I needed some rest. I felt tired the majority of the time and was quick to fly off the handle. The slightest mistake by a driver, or someone causing a delay in the grocery store would have me be screaming internally for that person's head on a platter. This was not normal behavior for me, but there had been no break in the action. I was too busy fighting the daily issues at hand. Immediately after the door to the plane closed, the flight crew announced a short delay. I felt the anger boiling to the surface. We were waiting on the final crew member who had not arrived on time. It was going to make my connection in San Juan very tight. Not a good way to start a relaxing holiday.

When American Eagle finally touched down, I literally had to run to catch my connecting flight. American Eagle flights from the islands arrive at the lower level of the airport. You have to go up one floor and all the way across the airport corridor to get to your gate for the larger jets. The escalators were not working and I was carrying my alpaca bag from Peru, laptop computer, two books, passport carrier and pill bag. I started running and wheezing, gasping for air the whole length of the airport. I made it to the gate just as the final boarding call was being announced. I was out of breath and feeling exhausted as I collapsed into my cramped seat. I asked

138

the stewardess for a glass of water and took two crushed calcium pills and an Ativan. I'm six-feet-two and have a difficult time getting comfortable on commercial airline flights. I'm never able to sleep on a plane, but my head hit the tray table just after the wheels left the runway and I was out. I woke up when the pilot announced we were preparing to land at JFK. God bless Ativan!

St. Croix is on Atlantic Standard Time. We never change our clocks. Six months out of the year we're equal with Eastern Time and six months during the winter we're an hour ahead. Armed with two books and several pills I was ready for the long layover at JFK. David Halberstam had written my favorite book, *October 64*. I'd not read it in three or four years and planned on re-reading it on this trip. The book chronicles my favorite baseball team, the St. Louis Cardinals, and their epic 1964 season that culminates with a World Series win against the New York Yankees. I love the book because, in the end, I know the good guys win. I also carried with me *Over the Edge of the World* by Laurence Bergreen. It is a tremendous book about Magellan and his crew's circumnavigation of the earth in the 1500s. I love to read and hadn't had much of a chance over the past year. I was determined to finish these two books before the end of my trip. I thought that concentrating on something other than myself or work could help ease my growing negative disposition.

As we broke through the clouds on our approach to JFK it was grey, raining and there was white snow on the ground. It hit me that I had just left 82 degrees and sunshine to spend almost two weeks in cold, grey wet weather. I didn't even own a coat.

Right after landing, I purchased water and took another set of crushed calcium. I was experiencing facial tingling and some muscle cramps as I entered a restroom and found an empty stall. I had been peeing blood for four straight days. My deepest wish that this would end before seeing Pam had failed to come true. I had to clean myself up, and make sure all the blood had flowed, before buckling up. I found a quiet chair in an empty gate and began to read *October 1964*, by David Halberstam:

In the fifth game the Yankees saw the real Bob Gibson. On this day McCarver thought, he had everything working for him. The advantage of pitching in the shadows of the stadium and against a background of the center-field bleachers made it all the more difficult for the hitters to pick up his ball.

After reading several chapters, I opened the laptop and went to work answering e-mails, and made a few cell phone calls to co-workers. Everything seemed to be going well at the office. The holidays are a slow time, but we still had to represent our clients. I encouraged my AMDs to take as much time off as possible. It takes two to three months for the investment world to wake up from their holiday hangover and start to think about buying platform or add-on companies again. Our clients, business owners wishing to sell, are also distracted this time of year. They have just gone through the holidays, taxes and re-financing rounds. Their focus tends to be inward as they plan the year ahead and set new goals.

Running the risk of having potential buyers fall through the cracks, my plan over the holidays was to continue to sign in and answer e-mails every morning and make as many calls as needed. I cut out all but two buyer strategy meetings with new customers. Checking for and approving all changes to our confidentiality agreements needed daily attention because it could delay a potential sale or prevent it from happening all together. If I did not stay on top of the e-mails I would have returned to hundreds that needed immediate attention. There was no getting out of it—this was a working vacation.

It was finally time to board the flight to Cleveland. As we climbed out over New York City through the dark night you could see the white snow covering the ground. The plane I was on was a small regional American Eagle Jet. I barely fit into the seat but it was only an hour-and-a-half flight. I started reading Laurence Bergreen's *Over the Edge of the World*:

A week after leaving Seville, the fleet reached the snug coastal town of Sanlucar de Barrameda, the final point of departure for the Ocean Sea. 'You enter it on the west wind and depart from it on the east wind,' said Pigafetta, repeating the lore he recently learned. On arrival, the crew found a windswept seaport, seemingly poised on the edge of the world, and reverberating with a sense of adventure.

As the captain announced our final approach into Cleveland Hopkins Airport, I was riveted to the book. Magellan was still looking for the strait across South America. It was only a rumor that it existed. He needed to get to the new ocean and find the Spice Islands. The wheels touched down. It was dark and wet in northern Ohio, and cold in the jetway. As I walked off the plane, through a long hallway and down some stairs, my mood was upbeat and relaxed.

I had been focusing so hard on the illness and recovery, I had become isolated. Just a few short months ago I had been carefree, social and fairly easygoing. Now I was on an hourly pill count, weekly blood draws, rehab assignments, workouts, doctor's appointments, ER visits and suffering constantly from nervous-system fluctuations. To a large degree I had lost a level of enjoyment for life. Pam gave me some of that back. She stood by my side and refused to let me fight alone. As we hugged in baggage claim I took my first really deep breath of the day. As I exhaled my shoulders dropped, releasing the tension.

I could make out the outlines of the flower beds and gardens in the snow as we pulled into Pam's driveway. Her house is a neat split level in Richmond Heights. I was impressed by the size and number of trees in her neighborhood. My house is surrounded by Tan Tan and Kasha bushes. They hardly look majestic and stately like the hundred-year-old Oak in Pam's front yard. I noticed everything was spotlessly clean. "How do you live without piles of boat parts and a quarter-inch of Sahara dust on your floor?"

She just laughed. I found it all to be a great change of pace.

The elephant in the room was the blood that continued to seep out of me. I used Pam's restroom and the bowl turned bright red. It was late and I took an Ativan to fall asleep.

Saturday, 12/30/07—I woke up feeling better than I had in months. Pam and I had a few quiet days together before the social events began.

We ate well and got reacquainted. Pam had all my favorite foods in her refrigerator and we watched movies and played cards.

Every couple of hours she would disappear and I would find her decorating or cleaning in preparation for the New Year's Day party she was hosting. The holidays are split between the siblings in her family and Pam has Christmas and New Year's Day. She explained that the New Year's Day party includes family members, and this year she was inviting co-workers and friends to come meet me as well. Pam's older brother JR, who lives in Iowa with his wife, was in town but was leaving before New Year's Day. On my second night in Cleveland we went to Pam's sister Robin's house and I met Pam's three siblings for the first time. JR is a wine connoisseur and opened several bottles before the evening was over. Robin likes to play cards and we bet round after round of 65 and Cabbie. I never felt nervous and her brothers were easy to talk with.

The snow had piled up in the front yard by late afternoon the day before the big party. Pam was in full decoration mode. Her house looked fantastic. She collects Christmas ornaments and I had brought her a new one from St. Croix. Pam placed it front and center on a tree covered with hundreds of ornaments. There were poinsettias lining the living room and the wave of wonderful smells emanating from the kitchen really brought back memories of holidays with my family when I was growing up. Pam cooked a turkey for me because I don't eat red meat. She also baked a ham and several other dishes for the party. She really worked hard to get ready for the big day. Before I knew what happened my pessimistic outlook of the year's holiday season was gone and I was full of holiday spirit. I was happy to help vacuum, dust and clean up. The smells from the kitchen and the non-stop holiday music were fantastic for my psyche.

It continued to snow all day on New Year's Eve. Pam and I stayed in and had a movie night. We had a great fire in the downstairs TV room. I woke up the next morning and shoveled the driveway and sidewalks before guests started to arrive. I shoveled left handed allowing my right arm to perform all the heavy lifting. Although I live on a Caribbean island I still had that midwestern mentality that winter is a great time to be outside. I didn't find it overly cold—even without a coat.

As the snow continued to fall, the final touches were being applied inside. I was impressed with the preparation Pam put into her party. Around one o'clock, Aunt Flow, Aunt Irene and Uncle Joe pulled up to the house. Pam had invited them over early so they could have some time to meet me before Robin, Jackie and a host of Pam's friends from work were set to arrive. I immediately took to the Aunts and Uncle Joe. They were high energy and threw me some barbs about my thinning hair and the amount of meat on my bones. The two Aunts cut to the chase—asking if I played cards. After telling them of my weekly poker game they made short order with their intentions to take every last penny I had. I felt up to the challenge. Pam's uncle Joe was quieter. I learned that he had played in the St. Louis Cardinal minor league system before World War II. He was a third baseman before being called away to the war effort. I'm one of the biggest Cardinal fans on earth and we had a good, long conversation about players he knew and facing big-league pitching. I told him about the book I'd just finished reading. He actually knew some of the scouts that were mentioned in it. The day progressed and everyone moved to the dining-room table. In between eating and greeting new guests, a card game broke out. Flow and Irene were trash talkers and it made it easy to want to beat them. I felt right at home.

Money flowed around the table for a couple of hours. More guests started to arrive and I would stop for a brief moment and say hello and shake a hand but then it was right back to the game. Before I knew it, we had been playing for five straight hours. Pam had been in the kitchen most of the day making sure everyone had the food they wanted. She was busy with guests and only played a few hands at the table. Robin, Irene, Flow, Joe and I rarely left what had become an all-day card session. Pam would later bring this up to me several times. She wished I had more time to meet all her friends that popped in for half hour here and there. By the end of the day, piles of coins had been won and lost by everyone at the table. There was no big winner and everyone went home happy.

The party wound down about nine o'clock. I walked Aunt Flow, Aunt Irene and Uncle Joe out to their car. Pam was cleaning up and I soon joined in. We were leaving for Mother's house the next morning—a seven hour drive. We needed to wrap things up and get a good night's sleep. I was worn out and slept well without the need of a sleep aide.

It was bitterly cold on the drive through Ohio, Indiana and Illinois. To pass the time I had bought four new CDs to listen to on the trip, and Pam picked six CDs from her collection to bring along. Pam will listen to anything I like to play and not say a word. I found it hard but did my best to tune out the modern country music she loves so much. We found our middle ground with old soul and Motown groups. We stopped for gas on the Indiana border and the sign at the truck stop read minus thirteen degrees. The wind went right through me. It continued to snow a good portion of the drive.

Mom lives in the same house I grew up in. Several years after my father's death, she married JK Reed. JK is a World War II veteran, farmer and metal sculpture artist. He has three children who are all married and live within an hour of Charleston. JK and his family are wonderful people and I always enjoy their company. They would all be at Mother's for a large dinner in two days. My brother Tim was coming up from Oklahoma, but his wife Tami had to stay home because of a project she was working on for Oklahoma State University. Brother Rod, his wife Theresa, niece Rory and nephew Jasper were on a train ride from Oregon to San Antonio, Texas. They were scheduled to stop in Illinois and join the late holiday festivities.

On Doctor Politz's suggestion, I had started crushing my calcium pills and stopped taking Oscal. At first I tried the back of a spoon, a hammer and frying pan. None of these methods produced good results. The pills would fly off into oblivion, or worse, onto my bug sprayed Sahara dust-coated floors. I purchased a small mortar and pestle at Gallows Bay Hardware store. It was still a workout to get the calcium ground to a fine powder. Over the holiday, Pam and I visited a store in Cleveland at the mall near her house. I purchased a larger mortar and pestle and it took little effort to crush and grind the pills. I was more pleased with this purchase than any in recent memory as I was crushing sixteen calcium pills per day.

After checking in at the hotel we quickly drove across town to Mother's house. My brother Tim had already arrived from Oklahoma. We had a running bet on the yearly Illinois vs. Purdue basketball game. At one point Purdue had won nine straight and Tim was getting tired of receiving new pocket knives for a payoff. This year we had agreed to change it up. With Illinois finally winning a game, the tables were turned and a homemade dinner of stuffed manicotti fulfilled his debt. I was thankful Pam had the opportunity to meet him without all the family around. Tim is a Ph.D of Economics and a professor at Oklahoma State University. Over the course of the past year, despite a busy schedule, he always took time to stay in touch. Much to my dislike, the topics of conversation revolved around pain management, growing frustration with the medical profession and how to make it from one day to the next. None of it was fun, and little of the content reflected humor or joy. The people closest to me hung in there and took the brunt of my growing negative disposition. Tim was no exception.

Listening to my brother try and explain what he does for a living was hilarious to Pam. He's a college professor, a professional risk-management consultant and runs a grad program for economics students. Translating all that takes time. Mom is the same way. She was a music teacher in the public schools before going back to college after my father's death and receiving her Ph.D in Education. She then went on to become a tenured professor at Eastern Illinois University. She is also an accomplished piano and organ player. JK, my stepfather, is a farmer and was once a Director of a bank. In his spare time he creates metal sculptures. Many adorn my mother's house and yard. The conversations are always interesting around my mother's table. It never fails that I seem to take the brunt of several jokes. I admit I do hand out my fair share of jabs at both brothers. I'm a lucky person to have the family I was born into. The rare times when we all get together are special.

I was getting tired as evening turned into night. By nine o'clock it was time for Pam and me to head back to the hotel. The next day would be busy.

Mom and Tim were headed to Mattoon, Illinois, to pick up my brother Rod and his family from the train station later that night. We said our goodbyes and walked out into the cold.

Pam made sure I had taken all of my calcium and other pills over the hours of catching up with family. Once again I was wiped out. We found a movie on television and sat up laughing at the day's events before falling asleep. It was the second straight night without needing to take an Ativan.

There is always a moment, a split second when you feel nervous before meeting your better-half's family. Pam's came in the morning. She spent what seemed to be an eternity getting ready. I asked her if she was nervous, and she said no, but then in her usual manner, she went on to explain how it's okay for her to want to look good and make a good impression. She did not want to be rushed, and she was going to take her time.

We made our way to Mom's house around 9:00 a.m. My niece and nephew were still sleeping in the basement bedroom but my brothers and Mom were eating breakfast. Pam jumped right into the conversation. It felt like she already knew everyone even though she was meeting most of them for the first time. Later we went for a walk downtown to a coffee house/art gallery. JK had some of his metal art pieces on display. Rory and Jasper came along with my mother, Pam, Tim, Rod and sister-in-law Theresa. My arm was sore but I had borrowed an old coat from the rack in the basement and Pam had brought me gloves and a hat.

Later that afternoon I was feeling tired and started to feel tingling in my face. We lasted another hour or two and then called it an early night and headed back to the hotel for some much needed rest.

The next day was the big family gathering with my stepbrother, step-sisters and their families. Mom had a huge spread laid out by the time we reached her house around 10:00 a.m. The card games started early and then the guests arrived. What a group! All fifteen of us gathered around the table for lunch. Mom had a new tradition she wanted to start. She passed a ceramic pig around the table. When the pig was passed to you, you were supposed to tell everyone what you were thankful for in the past

146

year. When it came to me the only thing I could think to say was, "What does not kill you makes you stronger."

After we ate, I was feeling worn out, and had to go lie down for a while. Pam joined me downstairs and we watched some TV by the fireplace. When we caught our second wind, it was time for the delayed opening of Christmas presents. They were stacked up everywhere. Mom had saved them for us to open even though Christmas had passed. Everyone had a great time. We were scheduled to drive back to Cleveland the next morning and did not leave my mother's until after 10:00 p.m. It had been a long day and I was experiencing facial tingling, muscle cramping and my left arm was sore. I needed an Ativan to knock me out.

The next morning we checked out of the hotel and stopped by Mom's for breakfast. We stayed for an hour. It was hard saying goodbye to everyone before hitting the road to Cleveland.

The drive home was spent reminiscing about our time with family and friends. Pam was sure that one day she would get my stepfather to make her an art piece to hang in her living room. She seemed to like everyone, and got along with the entire group.

Monday, 1/7/09—I was apprehensive about adding a new doctor. At the same time I held out hope of moving in the right direction. I knew I needed to get to the bottom of my breathing issues along with taming my anger attacks and clearing my mind, so at 2:30 p.m. I found myself in an unfamiliar doctor's office, reaching out for additional help.

Dr. Shapiro turned out to be a wonderful doctor. Before he even finished his exam I had a good feeling about his abilities. He had me do some breathing exercises as I explained all the troubles I was experiencing. It is a long story to tell and I never want to leave out any details. He listened to everything and reassured me that he could help with the breathing issue. He would later make some good suggestions about other problem areas as well. The first step was increasing my Nexium from one to two a day. He believed I had an upset stomach due to acid reflux. The second part would be another visit and a procedure called an endoscopy. Basically they would be going down my esophagus and into my stomach with a camera. He left the details for me to arrange, but sooner was better than later.

Cleveland is world famous for its medical institutions, including The Cleveland Clinic and University Medical Center. After seeing how easy and convenient it was to get in and see quality medical professionals the seed was planted to start seeing doctors in Cleveland for all my major issues. Logistics would be a challenge. However, I felt much more comfortable taking care of these issues in Cleveland than on St. Croix.

1/8/08—With a sense of sadness I traveled back to St. Croix. I missed Pam immediately. At the same time she was tracking me on her computer. She called me as soon as my plane touched down. I thanked her for the wonderful holiday season!

After my arrival, it took just under an hour to realize my luggage did not make the trip back home. I would have to go to the airport the next day and pick it up. I was tired, but felt good about the progress on my breathing issue. I was eager to get the endoscopy procedure out of the way. It was as if my body took a deep breath allowing me to sleep without the need for any pills or long, drawn-out mental exercises. As I dozed off, I knew I was headed down the right track.

Wednesday, 1/9/08—During my first meeting of the day I was told I needed to reconfigure my spreadsheets for December. The brain trust at The March Group was trying to position my team to perform at higher standards and bring in more quality Confidentiality Agreements that would lead to more signed Letters of Intent. These legal documents, in turn, would lead to more sales of our client's businesses. Not long into the process I was called into the conference room. The battle continued to rage over the operating systems we had purchased for the telemarketing branches. We had started out with Sales Logix and when it under performed we switched to Sales Net. Months and months would go by before I would get the opportunity to work with the new system designers.

The latest news was a huge setback as I was told to gear up for our switch back to a new and improved Sales Logix. This would put us another six months to a year behind schedule.

On top of the new operational system change, we had to convert our phone systems back to Packet 8 for the second time. Packet 8 was sure that with increased services their system could handle our needs this time around.

Back Row—The Author's Brother Rod, and the Author
Front—Their Mother Helen, and Brother Tim

RENEWED HOPE (DAY 301 – 367)

I decided to kick-off the New Year by focusing my thought process on positive change. It gave me a sense of renewed hope. 2007 had been spent battling health issues and following instructions from doctors that led to minimal results. I was looking forward to overcoming the lack of progress and finding some solutions in 2008. I threw my belief into the idea that forming a cohesive medical staff in Cleveland, to oversee all my medical needs, would be a positive first step towards ending what had become a nightmare. I felt empowered making the decision. Now all that was left was to put it into action.

Thursday, 1/1/08—Pam contacted Dr. Bishop's office requesting the latest prostrate sonogram and foot x-ray results. The receptionist said she would have the doctor call back by the end of the day. My throat was constricted at work, making it increasingly harder to breathe as the day came to an end. I did not hear back from the doctor as promised and my frustration level began to mount. I decided to play poker later that night as I had a need to be among other people in case I stopped breathing altogether. The game was fantastic but I continued to struggle. In the past, when I'd experienced these breathing issues, they seemed to take over my thoughts and I was left mentally drained trying to calm myself down and relax. This time was no different. With my mind racing, my only recourse when I got home was to take a Lorazapam (generic for Ativan). It helped my throat muscles relax and I got some needed sleep. My new year's resolution to incorporate positive thinking was already being tested. I was fearful and felt lucky to have gotten four hours of sleep over the course of the night.

Sunday, 1/13/09—I had been experiencing strong tingling in my face and cramping in my leg muscles since Friday. It did not let up throughout Saturday and by Sunday night I'd become worn out. There was no chance of getting a good night's sleep as I struggled to inhale. Time seemed to sit still. By 9:00 p.m. I absolutely felt I could not take it anymore. I'd tried everything. I turned off all the lights and rocked back and forth on the edge of my bed. The symptoms continued to intensify. My head was going numb and my face was locking up making it difficult to unclench my teeth. I called Pam. I was unable to produce more than a mumble. Pam did all the talking as her voice was the only thing that kept me from going over the edge. I was in bad shape and needed to find solutions soon. I fought the urge to go to the emergency room. I took one of my four remaining Lorezapam pills. Pam and I hung up after 11:00 p.m. Around 1:30 a.m. the breathing issues eased just enough to allow me to fall back in complete exhaustion. At 5:00 a.m. I popped straight up in bed unable to fill my lungs fullly with air. I stumbled through my arm exercises and got ready for work.

Staring another workday with little sleep, I was no longer willing to accept my current breathing issues without taking further action. I called California and informed my boss that I was going to Cleveland for the test with Dr. Shapiro who was was willing to fit me in on short notice. The date was set for 1/29/08. I breathed a little easier the rest of the day knowing this test would help me find some solutions.

Tuesday, 1/15/08—I went to Dr. Bishop's office in search of another prescription for Lorezapam. I couldn't sleep without them and I'd run out. In his usual guarded response, he prescribed fifteen pills. Dr. Bishop also gave me my prostate sonogram and foot x-ray results. It had been important to measure the size of the prostate and see if it was inflamed. He assured me the volume was fine. He did find a cyst in the prostate that he felt was caused by a previous infection when I was younger. He said the cyst could cause irritation, but more than likely was not the cause of the bleeding. He didn't recommend trying to get the cyst removed at that time. The x-ray taken of my foot showed no calcium deposits. The tendon, however, was inflamed. He explained that I was unable to take the proper anti-inflammatory medication until my throat constriction was cleared up. I would have to live with a sore and swollen toe on my left foot for the immediate future. It hurt so bad I walked with a visible limp. To help with the breathing issues he told me to eat smaller amounts of food while increasing the number of meals I ate per day. He recommended bland foods only. Dr. Bishop is good at taking the time to explain each detail. He brought out models of the male anatomy and explained what the results meant. In the end there was not a whole lot of reason for the bleeding in the urine or the breathing issues. Somehow I felt better knowing it had been checked out. However, I did not believe there was no viable reason for these issues to occur. The fact I would need to live with the symptoms whenever they came back irritated me to no end. I left his office feeling the need to continue the search for answers on my own.

Thursday, 1/17/08—I made the final arrangements with Dr. Shapiro's office for the endoscopy procedure. I'd caught a cold bug. By Thursday I started coughing up green phlegm and was tired after work. I had to get out of the house, so I pushed my endurance limit and went to poker at Bud's. By the time I came home I was completely wiped out. I felt horrible all day Friday, and stayed in bed the entire weekend. January is the best time of year on island. I'm often out sailing, hiking or swimming, but I could not pick my head up off the pillow.

Monday, 1/21/08—I went to work, but barely hung on to finish out the day before collapsing back home in bed. I started throwing up on Tuesday, 1/22/08. I went into the office and got a lap top and came home and worked from bed. I was past tired. I'd reached total exhaustion. For the next three days I felt miserable and did not leave my house. I was too sick to get excited as I packed late Friday night.

Saturday, 1/27/08—My flight path had been changed. Instead of going through JFK, I was diverted to Dallas and then through Chicago because of a winter storm in the New York area. This made the second leg of my flight last over five hours. I experienced massive breathing problems while in the air. When I landed in Dallas I paced up and down the corridors and called Mother and then Pam. I had taken a Lorazapam and it was not working. I was having difficulty calming down. I walked for over an hour. When my plane was ready to board, I took another Lorazapam. It was the only way I felt I could make the flight to Chicago. Standing in line to board, I got a warm feeling in my head and my entire body relaxed. The second pill was kicking in. I'd never taken two in the same day. I was wobbling from side to side as I sat in my seat. I put my head against the seat back directly in front of me and was out. I woke up when the wheels touched down in Chicago. I was still flying high on the Lorazapam as I staggered into the massive terminal. Collapsing into an empty seat I fell asleep next to the loud speaker at my next gate. Forty-five minutes later I was awakened by the announcement it was time to board. I was seated alone in the back row and curled up across both seats with my legs hanging out into the isle. It was the last flight of the night and I was out cold before the plane took off. We did not touch down until after 10:20 p.m. in Cleveland. I was still pretty messed up from the second pill, but I was relaxed and feeling no pain. I had a minimal response when I found out my luggage did not arrive. I filled out the forms and they promised to deliver the next day to Pam's house.

Sunday, 1/27/08—Pam and I stayed home, built a fire and watched movies. The only work being done was keeping the fire going. Pam had cooked me a turkey and I ate well. I was over the cold and finally regained some energy, but I experienced breathing trouble late that night and had to take another Lorezapam to relax enough to fall asleep.

Monday, 1/28/08—My 42nd birthday. I'd aged substantially over the past year. I was much heavier and knew I needed to get the weight under control. Thoughts of my father's heart issues crept into my mind.

The day started with a call to Mother. I congratulated her on a job well done. She sang "Happy Birthday" and promised the check was in the mail. Every birthday she sends me a check for double the amount of my age. I joked with her that I might actually be able to afford something this year.

Truth be told, all my money was going towards paying off prescriptions, doctor bills, rehab charges etc. Even with insurance I spent over $20,000 dollars out-of-pocket on medical bills in 2007. 2008 was also shaping up to be an expensive year for health. I was extremely fortunate I was fairly well compensated for my work. I also was fortunate that I had the flexibility to perform my work from Pam's house when I needed to go to Cleveland to see a doctor. The added expense of travel aside, in my mind it was going to be way easier to get results from tests and move forward with a plan of action in Cleveland than continue to struggle to get results on island.

In preparation for the test I couldn't eat or drink after midnight as the procedure required I be put under anesthesia. I was told in advance that the endoscopy can take between one and two hours to complete. I would be hooked to an IV and needed to have a ride home after the procedure.

Tuesday, 1/29/08—Pam and I arrived at the hospital just after noon. Dr. Shapiro carefully went over the procedure in detail. Pam was able to stay with me and watch the proceedings—start to finish. After lying on my right side, hooked to an IV, the procedure began. I wasn't bothered at all by the needle in my vein. After I was unconscious a tube was inserted down my throat. Dr. Shapiro was able to maneuver a small camera down the tube and into my esophagus, intestines and stomach. When I woke up Dr. Shapiro and Pam were sitting right next to me. He explained that I was fine. I did have gastritis, but the biopsy of tissue taken from my intestine had already come back from the hospital laboratory clean of any cancerous cell formations. He went on to explain that my stomach was inflamed. He believed the large amount of calcium I had to take each day contributed to the inflammation. He told me that I should see improvement with the breathing issues if I continued taking two Nexium each day. Prior to being checked out, I was sure there was a major problem either with my heart, lungs or stomach. Finally some good news! I was a little leery that no major cause had been found, but at the same time I was relieved. Dr. Shapiro reassured me that everything looked good as we said goodbye.

Following my parathyroid operation in Tampa, my health went from bad to extremely bad. There was no break in the action from that point forward. I found myself ill prepared and definitely not in control. My body was failing me and there is no road map in these situations. I did have things to be thankful for, but I rarely felt good. I finally came to the conclusion the doctors had been correct in their assessment that I was suffering from anxiety. The nights left praying to god, promising everything and anything if I could just make it to the next morning, had taken a toll. I had tingling in my face and head on a daily basis, and could not breathe easily. To top it all off, I was urinating blood. I was a train wreck. Pam just continued to provide a positive calming influence. We discussed what steps should be taken next. There was a lot to think about.

Work, during the next three days, was on my laptop and cell phone from Pam's living room. It was great being there when she came home at the end of the day. We played a lot of cards, and ate well and had fires in the basement each night. Growing up in Illinois, we cut our own firewood to heat the basement during the winter. Around the basement fireplace was where we hung out as a family. Sitting in front of Pam's fireplace really brought back some great memories. I felt so comfortable at her home that it was difficult leaving on Saturday morning. As my plane pulled out onto the tarmac I was feeling lucky to have such a wonderful person in my life.

The following week, work was hectic and the feelings of stress soon crept back into my head. I found myself in a dark mood. I was feeling worn out and all activities were labored. Friday night I went out with people from work to the Brew Pub, but I began feeling tired and left early. I always caught grief from my co-workers when I cut out early. They didn't understand. I definitely didn't want to drink more than one or two beers because it would negatively affect my nervous system and stomach. It was constantly in the back of my mind that there was a threat of another nervous-system attack. Sleep did not come easy and I experienced tingling in my face throughout the night. I refused to take sleep medication while I was having a nervous-system attack. One had caused the muscles in my right shoulder to contract so hard they had broken a severely weakened bone. Maybe if I'd been awake I could have stopped it. I did not want a repeat performance. I sat in the dark without fans turned on and rocked back and forth. I was finally able to relax around midnight and fell asleep close to 1:00 a.m.

On saturday I reluctantly forced myself into an early morning hike to Jacks and Isaacs's Bay. On the way home I drove up the ridge line off Questa Verde road and looked at some property for sale. When I came back home and got cleaned up, I laid down immediately. I did not get out of bed until Sunday morning, when I woke with new energy and found myself determined to go sailing. I met Pat at the Yacht Club at 10:30 a.m. and we took the launch out to *Folly*. At first sight I could tell she was a mess. I'd neglected her over the past year leaving her in the salt water far longer than usual. Her teak cockpit was dull grey in color and she showed some rust on her fittings. Although covered by a sunbrella sock, the tiller was delaminating. I had not been able to swim or kayak out and scrub her bottom every week like I'd done in the past. There was two to three inches of marine growth covering the hull. Everything still worked fine, but I knew I needed to pull her out of the ocean and do a major overhaul.

We sailed out past Buck Island and kept on going. The color in the waves went from clear turquoise in the shallows to rich blue over the deep crevasses in the sea floor that run along St. Croix's northern edge. Riding up four to five foot waves and rocketing back down them never seems to stop being fun. Several turtles and flying fish crossed our path and I kept a watchful eye out for dolphin. The winds were blowing fifteen to eighteen knots out of the east-northeast. It was a long reach heading back past Buck and through the cut in the reef. *Folly* was making her familiar noises and the hull powering through the water was overtaking most other sounds. What a great day. Our sail had lasted four hours. There had been no problem breathing out on the water. I felt tired but I had a wonderful feeling of accomplishment.

Monday, 2/25/08—I woke up and went to the restroom. I was shocked at the amount of blood that came out of my system. It felt like I was taking five steps backwards for every ounce of enjoyment I could squeeze out of life. The pain at the end of the blood stream had been ratcheted up. This was the third episode I'd had within the previous four months. I was devastated and really didn't know what to do. I'd had this checked out by every means on island and there were few reasons why it was happening. Dr. Bishop believed the vessels around my prostate were seeping blood into my urinary track. There was no concrete evidence this was the cause, but everything else had been ruled out. I would spend the next seven days monitoring the amount of blood and finding stains in my clothing. Because of the pain I needed to take it another step further as suggested by Dr. Bishop. It was time to have a urologist examine me.

Wednesday, 2/27/08—I had my blood drawn at the laboratory on St. Croix and received the previous test results. My serum calcium was 8.5ml. I started experiencing stomach pains while the needle was in my arm. I ran to the restroom experiencing diarrhea and found I was also still urinating blood. Both issues continued throughout the day. I was exhausted by the time I made it home after work. Later that evening Pam called and I expressed to her that I'd reached my limit. I could no longer take the stress related to my body failing me. In her usual calm, inquisitive voice she proceeded to gather all information and showered me with encouragement.

2/28/08—Pam called Dr. Shapiro on my behalf. She left him a message explaining what was happening with the blood in the urine and the diarrhea. He took the time out of his day to call Pam back. He urged me to see a urologist and get a good endocrinologist, or a really smart general internist. He thought that urinating blood was just not right for someone my age and that this could signal a larger problem. He recommended a urologist he knew—Dr. Frederic Levine. Pam called their office and got two possible dates to come up to Cleveland and see him. She had taken the responsibility off my shoulders and allowed me to focus on work. I absolutely could not wait any longer. I had to get this taken care of. It was becoming mentally challenging every day.

Pam had made a quick friend in the receptionist at Dr. Levine's office.

She was sympathetic to my cause and understood why I needed the first available opening. Dr. Levine agreed to squeeze me in on the afternoon of 3/5/08. He was set to check my bladder, kidneys and prostate. I'd not spoken directly with the doctor, and had no idea how this was going to be accomplished. To be perfectly honest, at this point and time, I did not care. I booked my flight and arranged to work from Pam's the next two weeks.

My contact with Dr. Politz in Florida continued. He was concerned about the bleeding and my stomach was upset, cramping and diarrhea. Dr. Politz said it was understandable for me to be looking at the calcium as part of the problem, and it might or might not be the cause. He had not received my most recent blood results and I explained to him that I was worn out from having to take care of making sure all the results were distributed to all my doctors. He thought, if he gave it a try, they would send the records over with more regularity. He sensed the urgency in my tone and understood I was feeling stressed. Dr. Politz wanted me to drop down to ten calcium pills per day for a week and then get my blood drawn to see where my parathyroid hormone (PTH) levels were. He wanted me to repeat the blood draw for eight straight weeks. This was my fifth day of urinating blood. My forehead was clammy day and night, and I generally felt lightheaded when I stood up. I also had tingling sensations in my head, and my tongue started to feel like it was on fire again. I was at an impasse. The next day I boarded, what I regarded, as an emergency flight to Cleveland.

3/1/08—Flying to Cleveland did not stop the busy work week ahead of me. I continued to log the hours working on my laptop and cell phone. During the full day of travel the blood continued to flow making me uncomfortable.

The March Group was wonderful in understanding my need to see specialists, supporting me one hundred percent. I was granted any amount of time I needed. I always made up whatever hours I took off for any doctor's visits or travel time, and I felt like I got more work done alone in Pam's living room than in my office. This time I scheduled additional days to allow for follow-up tests if they were deemed necessary. I still held out hope there would be one final cure for all that ailed me.

Seeing Pam at the airport my body exhaled. Falling into our routine of playing cards and watching movies helped take my mind off the issues at hand. We walked every day and did exercises in her basement. We also built a couple of fires in her family room. There was still snow on the ground in Cleveland and it rained several days in a row. I enjoyed the change in weather. It suited my mood more than bright sunshine every day.

Sunday, 3/02/08—It was my seventh straight day of urinating blood and the volume was starting to abate slightly. I actually wanted it to continue through my appointment on Wednesday so Dr. Levine could see what I was dealing with. I began to worry that he wouldn't have anything to look at if the blood stopped altogether.

On Sunday we went to the Fox and Hound to shoot pool after seeing a movie. I have had to alter my stroke to accommodate the lack of mobility in both shoulders. I shoot pool left handed and therefore had to elevate the pool cue to a point where my left shoulder did not experience pain. We played for close to three hours. The day was a great escape, and I was able to set aside my medical problems and enjoy time with Pam.

Monday, 3/3/09—The next day I was scheduled for a CT scan prior to Dr. Levine's visit and felt the need to make up time before I took the next two afternoons off. I put my nose to the grindstone and worked on several projects. I was looking into a website called Elance where people post their services to be out-sourced to companies like TMG. I had been given a small budget of $5,000 to run a test for foreign- based callers. I worked with our research department to figure out which foreign countries purchased the most United States-based companies. As the dollar declined in monetary value, foreign-based ownership of U.S. companies was increasing. TMG saw this wave of foreign ownership as an opportunity to market our clients to an untapped buyer pool. In the past, our marketing campaigns had not brought in the desired response from Europe or Asia. Most of our clients did not have enough yearly revenues to generate interest from foreign buyers. Further study of M&A trends showed the companies being sold to foreign buyers generally produced a specific product or serviced large clients—including the U.S. Government. Tapping into this wave of purchases would force us to gather information on what these buyers were looking for and bring in clients in the future that more closely matched their interests. This was my new task.

After receiving the list from Research, I could determine which countries to target on the test calls. I could then post the parameters of the project on the Elance website for potential bids. If things went well, I felt there was a great chance for out-sourcing lots of work in my department and saving TMG increased employee costs by outsourcing foreign-based calling.

I had no idea the difficulties involved. The project was still in its early stages and I'd not picked the outsourcing companies yet. I'd posted the project and received bids. I'd received several phone numbers of applicants on the website and needed to speak with them in person. My contacts for the week included three men in Hong Kong, one in India and two in Spain. All of this going on almost made me forget that Monday was my eighth straight day of urinating blood.

Tuesday, 3/4/09—At noon Pam picked me up and we drove to Spectrum Diagnostic Imaging which was located in a nearby strip mall. I had a CT scan performed on my abdomen and pelvis. Dr. Levine had ordered the test done without contrast. I could not eat or drink past 8:30 a.m.

> Computed tomography (CT) is a medical imaging method employing tomography. Digital geometry processing is used to generate a three-dimensional image of the inside of an object from a large series of two-dimensional X-ray images taken around a single axis of rotation. The word "tomography" is derived from the Greek tomos (slice) and graphein (to write).   http://en.wikipedia.org/wiki/CT_scan

Although I'd been subjected to a CT scan in the past, I didn't remember much about them. What I did remember about them was a CT scan takes less time than an MRI and you are not confined in a tube. The entire procedure was just over an hour. They gave us the results before we left and I was able to take them to Dr. Levine's the next day. Scheduling the CT scan on St. Croix would have taken weeks. I would also have to waste a half-day in the Imaging Center waiting room. Getting the results to the doctor would take another two to three week delay. Everything in Cleveland was much more efficient compared to what I was used to dealing with on island.

Wednesday, 3/5/08—After submitting the CT scan films and filling out the usual half-hours worth of insurance paperwork, I was called back into a waiting room. Dr. Frederic Levine joined me within twenty minutes. I found him to be knowledgeable and possessing a presence of confidence. The end of the previous day marked the 9th straight urinating blood. He believed the bleeding was most likely caused by a benign prostate node. He explained that the CT scan was free of abnormalities. After donating a urine specimen I thought the exam was over. I was sorely mistaken!

I was asked to drop my pants and sit on the examination table. There would be no long explanation why, limiting what surely would have beena negative reaction on my behalf. It was a smart move by a doctor who has performed these types of examinations countless times. I wondered later what it was about my personality that had made him choose the sneak attack approach. Whatever gave it away he was correct in choosing that tactic.

At the time I remained fairly calm, watching curiously as the events unfolded. He rolled over a cart, with a metal box on top of it, from across the room. As he inched closer and closer, all I could think was what is in that box? When the top of the box was opened by Dr. Levine, I realized this was no sonogram machine. Wait a minute! Why was there a quart sized container of liquid with an electric pump and a long tube? I was still trying to put two and two together as I pushed further and further to the back corner of the examination table. Dr. Levine asked me to lie back in the middle of the table. He explained the need to see what was inside my prostate and kidneys. The only way in was to auger through the opening in the penis. I needed to remain very still. Did the word auger really need to be used? At this point I sat up on my elbows. "Oh shit." He told me to lie back down. I almost jumped through the roof as Dr. Levine fired up the machine. He might as well have been pull-starting a five horsepower Briggs and Stratton roto-tiller. Although I'm sure the electric motor was barely audible, I was hearing what sounded like a pack of chainsaw wielding lumber jacks headed for my privates. As the contraption churned to life he was trying to explain how uncomfortable this was going to be. No shit! I took one more glance over my chest. The doctor was sporting a headset with a tube coming out of it and was holding something in his hand. I thought it best that I not look anymore. Liquid and a probe were being inserted up my penis and into my urinary track. I had no say in the matter and better yet I had to pay a hefty co-pay fee for the privilege.

It was extremely uncomfortable as the doctor had previously warned. I clenched my fists and gritted my teeth trying not to flail around. Instantly the probe made me want to urinate. I did my best to hold back from allowing that to happen. The camera on the end of the probe was feeding a live picture back to the doctor through his headset monitor. Occasionally an "um ha, um ha" came from the doctor as he watched live footage of my inner plumbing. The exam lasted what seemed like an eternity, but in actual time it was less than ten minutes. I was allowed to clean up and use the restroom when the probe was finally removed.

Dr. Levine said my prostate was enlarged and that blood vessels located near the prostate were the source of the blood in my urine. He also said that I had some tiny stones inside the prostate. He assured me that was nothing to worry about. He thought it would clear up and go away on its own. He did not believe the amount of calcium I was taking every day had any correlation to the bleeding. He did mention stress as a potential cause. For the time being, he did not want to put me on medication to shrink the prostate. He wanted to give the body a chance to heal on its own. He did cover the possibility of surgically scraping the prostate and removing the small stones. He went on to explain the scraping was not a good idea at my age and did not want me to consider that as an option at this time. The doctor was making good sense. No pills, no scraping. He said I should not force bowel movements and I might notice bleeding after heavy lifting. Other than that, there were no new restrictions placed on me. At the end I knew I'd been checked out more thoroughly than I ever could imagine. I was relieved and able to relax the rest of the day.

During the ride home Pam asked me why I was being so quiet, "What are you feeling? Is there anything wrong?"

I had just been examined in a way that was difficult to explain let alone talk about. I gave up a few details and for some strange reason we both burst out laughing at the same time. I felt relieved and was happy knowing the bleeding was not caused by a major illness. I'd thought it could have been a cancer. The explanation that this condition just happens never really felt right. Finally hearing it from a urologist gave it merit and eased my concerns.

I had been in contact with Dr. Politz in Florida ever since my surgery in June. Like most doctors, he's difficult to get a hold of, and I found it increasingly more difficult getting the blood test results to him in a timely fashion. I appreciated all the extra time he spent consulting with me, but I felt I needed to have one doctor that I funneled all information through, one who had a wider vision and was more accessible. It all seemed to make sense. Now I needed to find the right person for the job.

Thursday, 3/6/09—Pam called Dr. Eric Shapiro's office and spoke to his assistant. She wanted to know if Dr. Shapiro could refer us to a general internist. Dr. Shapiro had been spot on when he recommended Dr. Levine. As much as a doctor's visit and subsequent tests go, he was one of the best doctors that had treated me. True-to-form, he took the time out of his busy schedule and called back on Friday, saying he thought it would be best for me to have a full physical. He was concerned about the numbness in my left arm and legs that I'd spoken to him about. He recommended Dr. Joel Weisblat. Before the end of the day I was scheduled for a full physical at Dr. Weisblat's office. I was amazed at how easy and convenient dealing with the medical organizations in Cleveland was. I was given instructions to fast for at least twelve hours before my 2:00 p.m. appointment. I started to get my hope and optimism back. I needed some relief and I was getting some answers and gaining the confidence that my medical issues could be dealt with. I knew that I was never going to be the same, but still felt a need to search for a cure. I had to get to a place where I could just live life and not feel so overwhelmed and sick all the time. I was hoping Dr. Weisblat would help me take the next steps in the right direction.

At one point, I asked Pam why she was so good at being a patient advocate. She talked about her father and his illness. She was with him every step of the way. She took notes and organized his doctors' visits, tests and surgeries. She is ultra organized and it really carries over from her work to her personal life. She amazes me in that regard. I am the exact opposite. I do have organizational abilities but they are quite different from Pam's. She files all mail, papers, magazine clippings etc. I am more of a pile it up and when it collects enough dust, throw it away, person. Several years earlier I'd taken a number of personality tests including Myers-Briggs while working at Cincinnati Bell Telephone. I was a confusing mixture of both type A and B. I choose to push myself hard with little patience for delays. I do see the big picture and give instruction well. At the same time the analysts found me to be laid back and easygoing. I never bought into all of these theories too much, but the difference between me and Pam is like night and day. The two of us together really do make a great team because we cover the entire spectrum.

I wouldn't have advanced this far into the process without Pam's help, encouragement and guidance. I could have easily continued throwing my energy into working more and ignoring my illness as much as possible. Unfortunately my illness, and the subsequent health issues, were too big to dismiss. She forced me out of my comfort zone by encouraging me to get more tests and seek out new doctors.

When I first woke up with a broken shoulder, I had no idea how to take care of myself. If I could have, I would have avoided doctors like the plague. Unfortunately none of my issues could have been handled with home remedies or self-medication. It took me over a year to realize I needed to face all issues head-on and get the most professional help available. I needed someone who could make sense of all the test results and take an active roll in the direction of my treatment. Although it sounds so simple, the process of reaching this conclusion was complex, and it took several conversations with Pam to convince me I needed another doctor in the mix. I am forever in her debt.

Monday, 3/10/08—Ironically the blood in the urine started again on Monday morning. I was scheduled to meet Dr Joel Weisblat later that afternoon. The blood was coming out at both the start and finish of the urine stream. I'd gone to great lengths to get to the bottom of this issue. I still found it disturbing as I concentrated on Dr. Levine's words, "It is something that will take care of itself over time." This was my fourth episode urinating blood. At least the blood was not accompanied by the burning pain prevalent during the third episode. It's the small victories in life that offer solace.

Early the next morning I was working from my laptop in Pam's living room, making up time in advance for the hours I would be at the doctor's later that afternoon. The morning work occupied my mind straight through lunch. I was glad to be busy. It kept me from thinking about eating. Pam came home from her work and picked me up at 1:30 p.m. We drove fifteen minutes to Dr. Weisblat's building. His receptionist had me fill out the usual insurance papers and then she gave me literature to read. The handout provided information about services offered by Dr. Weisblat and his wellness staff. Dr. Weisblat and his team offered a different approach compared to your usual family doctor. The list of services included on-call phone consultations, availability to see the patient when needed, addressing all concerns thoroughly and using cutting edge technology to help make that happen. Each visit is allotted at least a half hour and they work on scheduling to eliminate long waiting times.

They offer additional special services through a membership program. There are three plans to choose from, Basic Member, Wellness Club and E-Wellness Member. I chose the E-Wellness plan. For under $200 per year I had several services available to me, including:

> ...doctor available by phone in case of emergency, prescription refills
> called/faxed to your pharmacy without an appointment, test/referrals

scheduled on your behalf, doctor reviews test results with you without the need for a separate appointment (can be by phone or e-mail), phone consultation with doctor or nurse to follow up on problems addressed at a recent office visit, weekend wellness clinic, doctor and nurse available for preventative visits, urgent concerns and free blood pressure and weight checks two Saturdays per month, discounted visits with a dietitian and access to a personal trainer.

I appreciated the preventative aspect stressed in the literature. I held out hope that joining this program would eliminate some of the scheduling and communication frustrations I experienced on island. Living on island meant I would need to communicate with the doctor without having to see him in person. Dr. Weisblat's ability to communicate via a secured website was a good solution. It all seemed to fit nicely with my needs as a patient.

I was prepared to give my complete story, but it was difficult to think about it. As I sat in the examination room, hitting the high notes of the previous year, I realized just how much crap I'd waded through. I gave the fullest account I could of what had taken place. Dr. Weisblat immediately took out pen and paper and took notes, never once cutting me off. The doctor's few questions and responses during my oratory gave the impression he was tuned in—not egotistical. He seemed open to communication, and he put a lot of thought into his analysis of the situation before speaking. I immediately got the perception that he was intelligent and willing to help define a long-term treatment plan. There was no chance one doctor's visit was going to make me start feeling normal, but I needed to catch a break. I wanted to know someone was going to be on my side and help design a plan that would produce positive results. I'd been reacting to the symptoms far too long. I wanted to go on the offensive—take charge of this illness. Dr. Weisblat agreed.

He asked several questions. I answered as accurately as possible. He waded through the stack of medical reports gathered over time from doctor's offices and laboratories in St. Croix and Florida. He needed all of them to get a full picture of my illness. Even with our best efforts, the file

166

Pam and I collected was incomplete and a massive effort still lay ahead of us. I'd arranged for Dr. Politz to call Dr. Weisblat to speak, in person, about my history. I was thankful Dr. Politz was willing to take the time out of his busy schedule on my behalf. I'd left a message for Dr. Bishop to contact me at his earliest convenience so I could direct him to do the same, and I would have to rely on him to send the most recent medical records from St. Croix. The trouble was going to be getting the laboratory and the imaging center on St. Croix to send all of my past test results. They had sent about half of what I'd requested. To this day the project is incomplete.

During the visit, Dr. Weisblat performed a complete physical that included an EKG. After the physical he retired down the hall to his office. We had spent over an hour and a half together. He was taking the time to go over all the information on my case and collect his thoughts before delivering his prognosis to Pam and me.

Other than my shoulder injuries, Dr. Weisblat did not think I would have any permanent damage. I had expressed my concerns that the low calcium and parathyroid hormone levels in my blood had caused some permanent damage to my nervous system. He believed that most of the tingling and muscle cramps are not irreversible and could partially be explained by stress and anxiety. Hearing this made me uncomfortable. I did not believe I was buckling under anxiety or stress. I silently disagreed as I allowed his prognosis to continue unquestioned. He quizzed me about the acid reflux and I agreed that taking two Nexium per day had helped with the breathing problems. Dr. Weisblat believed I was experiencing panic attacks. I broke my silence stating that I did not believe I had panic attacks or anxiety. It was disturbing to hear that from a doctor. Panic attacks and anxiety sounded like weakness to me.

Dr. Weisblat wanted me to make a change from Lorazepam, a replacement for Ativan, and start taking Xanax. Choosing his words carefully he explained that Xanax would take the edge off when I started to feel the stress build up. Stress, not panic attacks. I agreed that I carried it around with me in abundance. There was no more talk of panic attacks. He prescribed the smallest dosage .25 mg. He said Xanax was less habit forming and wouldn't make me sleepy if I needed to take it during the day. He thought I should take it any time I started experiencing breathing troubles.

My attempts to prove the doctor's prognosis wrong were in vain. Many months would pass before I finally accepted the fact that I was experiencing panic attacks brought on by my health issues. I thought I would fill the Xanax prescription and park it in the pill bin along with the large bottle of Percocet I chose not take after surgery. I was pretty sure I didn't need pills, or any help, to beat anxiety or panic attack disorder. Now that I knew, I would be able to use relaxation techniques and stop it, and to some degree, I'd already been trying this—so far nothing was working. Dr. Weisblat said Paxil and Zoloft are stronger medications which prevent anxiety but he did not believe I needed them right now, but maybe they were something we could look into down the road.

Knowing my family's DNA increased the likelihood of heart-related illness had been on my mind since childhood, I could not shake the notion that some of my medical experiences were heart related. I'd read in some research on parathyroid disease that calcium controls muscle contractions which can lead to problems with your heart, though the Electrocardiography (EKG) found no damage to the conductive tissue in my heart muscle, and according to the doctor, none of the issues I was experiencing were heart related. Instantly my shoulders relaxed and my breathing eased. He said I did have a high cholesterol level at 232 mg., and he wanted me to work on getting it under 200mg. He prescribed Lipitor. I was not happy about introducing another pill into the daily regimen. Dr. Wiesblat listened to my concern and said he wanted bloodwork after the first month of use. We would monitor the new pills effect and see where it took us.

The last area of concern was the toe on my left foot. He had suspected my problems were related to gout, as the CT scan had not turned up any structural damage. My uric acid level in the blood came back at 7.9 mg—just above normal. High uric acid in the blood leads to gout. Dr. Weisblat prescribed a drug called Colchicine for any future flare-ups. At least I didn't have to take this pill daily. My toe would swell up at the first knuckle and turn to the left. It hurt miserably, would last for days at a time and then disappear. Dr. Weisblat told me to stop taking anti-inflammatory for the toe as he wanted me to avoid irritation to my already inflamed stomach.

He also urged me to return to full exercise. This was enlightening news. I had been asked to stop working out when I started urinating blood, and I needed daily strenuous exercise to blow off frustration and help me sleep. Dr. Weisblat encouraged me to see the dietician on staff through his E-Wellness program. I needed to drop several pounds. I passed on the dietician, but kept it open as an option for my next visit to Cleveland.

Dr. Weisblat's prognosis for the future included eventual system stabilization. What amount of time it would take was anybody's guess. Eventually, I would be able to reduce the amount of calcium needed in my daily life. The hope was that in the future I would experience less anxiety and fewer panic attacks. My blood pressure was elevated—150/94. The normal range is 120/80. My weight was 242 pounds. I'd gained back twenty-seven pounds and was trending upwards each day. This fact was not lost on me, and I vowed to get my weight under control and lower my blood pressure and cholesterol level.

I felt good about Dr. Weisblat, and understood the need to regain a healthy body weight. I may not be able to control the illness inside of me, but I could focus on getting myself in better shape. I needed to stop the daily ice cream and get back to my workouts. I'd given up over the past four or five months, and been forced into a more sedentary lifestyle. I'd lost my drive to exercise and became consumed with thoughts of how bad things had gotten. Facing these issues head-on, instead of trying to push them aside, was my only way out, and getting back to a regular workout routine was paramount in moving forward.

Tuesday, 3/11/08—Blood continued to flow in my urine. Much more of a nuisance than a shock, at this point, I just wanted it to end. I contacted Dr. Levine as instructed, and he wanted me to come in to his office and give a urine sample. I didn't have a car and felt I needed to work all day to make up for some of the extra time spent at Dr. Weisblat's the previous day. Pam agreed, without hesitation, to take me to Dr. Levine's the next morning before heading to work. It was a half-hour drive in the wrong direction for her.

Wednesday, 3/12/08—It was a quick in and out at Dr. Levine's office. Later that day he called to say there was nothing different about this specimen than the specimen examined one week before. It turned out to be just another inconvenience, in a long line of inconveniences, that did not yield any great breakthrough. He was not overly concerned that the blood was now visible at the start and end of the urine stream. He encouraged me to hang in there and my body should heal itself. In the event of any episodes in the future, he wanted me to give him another call. As far as I was concerned, this was standard doctor rhetoric. I wondered if I would ever get a definitive answer on any of my health issues.

When searching for answers you tend to lose your objectivity and cling to the first opportunity that comes your way. You can trick yourself into believing the one magical treatment that cures you is waiting right around the corner. The truth is—cures are few and far between. I'd jumped at the first solid opportunity to end it all when surgery was performed on my parathyroid glands at the Norman Endocrine Clinic. Although it was probably the right decision, I will never again enter into a medical situation without knowing what the consequences of each action could be. Dr. Weisblat faced a seasoned patient and several hard questions about the new medications and their side effects did not faze him. He was upfront about the fact that he alone was not going to solve the mystery my illness had become. What he brought to the table was the ability to help me make better informed decisions going forward. It had become apparent to all involved that the method being used to treat the illness to date was not working. This was a new beginning.

For the most part, I'd pushed aside the fact that previous treatments had failed. I was too busy following instructions and fighting the daily battles. I subconsciously buried the lack of detailed discussion I now knew I should have had prior to my parathyroid surgery. I did not take the time to thoroughly probe them about consequences if the parathyroid surgery went wrong, or the remaining parathyroid glands did not work as advertised. As these thoughts began to surface, my frustration level increased. It was not that I did not inquire about the risks, but the confidence level projected by Dr. Norman and his belief that I was going to wake up and feel like a new human being the day after surgery blinded my practical side. I had ignored the warnings about complications brought on by removing any body part. One of my massage therapists spoke to me at length prior to my surgery about being sure this was the right step. I purchased what Doctor Norman was selling hook, line and sinker. Dr. Norman believed that he was telling me the absolute truth, but little or no time was spent discussing what would happen if things went wrong. Dr. Norman and Dr. Politz did not acknowledge the chance of failure, and when the three remaining parathyroids failed to function properly, there was little they could do about it.

Any thoughts about long-term plans increased my frustration. I was living hour-to-hour, day-to-day and had little patience for forward thinking of any kind. Dr. Shapiro had pointed me in the right direction at a time when the thought of seeing another doctor or talking about finding a new one produced an angry outburst, and disgusted me. Thanks in no part to my decisions, I'd landed in good hands. I was directed to a quality urologist, and now to a wellness center that looks at treating the overall patient and believes in preventative maintenance. I needed a set of fresh eyes and Dr. Weisblat was the first member of my new team.

The situation forced me to think about how the healing process works. At the time it was a painful thought. After many hours, the answers finally came: work out as hard as possible, educate myself on my particular illness and question all future medical professionals until I understood exactly why I was to follow a specific plan of action. I needed to know the risks involved before diving in headfirst. If you sit back and believe that pills prescribed by doctors or surgeries alone will cure all ailments, your lack of involvement might extend the effects or increase the severity of what ails you. You really have no choice but to research your illness. Know it inside and out. It is paramount for the recovery process to understand what it is you're dealing with. Weighing all options and risks is essential. Before jumping into my parathyroid surgery, I briefly considered a dietary change. There is a belief that through nutritional variations the parathyroid can be brought back to normal function without surgery. Weighing the two options, I felt the risk of another fracture in the near future gave the edge to the more expedient solution. I now wish I had explored the nutritional option. It is one of my deepest regrets. The quick fix offered seemed to be the perfect fit. I'll never know what would have happened if I'd gone to an all greens diet—including seaweed, which reportedly helps with the parathyroid and thyroid functions. The quick surgery removing my rogue parathyroid eliminated any other potential cures.

I knew I had to become more active in combating my illness. It's not all up to the doctors. Understanding key triggers for symptoms became paramount. Never having dealt with a long-term illness I found this to be one of the most important and difficult issues to grasp. Know what your system feels like twenty-four/seven. Commit to memory what you were feeling before your last attack. Don't over-react every time you feel the slightest difference in your body or you will end up with a mental illness called hypochondriasis. Understand what the symptoms mean and how you're supposed to respond to them. It was a constant balancing act. I'd been doing my best to just sweep everything under the rug—ignoring all the symptoms as much as possible. To move forward, I decided I needed to take more control of the situation and be better prepared. I would no longer be the victim.

I couldn't run home and shut down every time my face tingled or twitched a bit, as it was literally happening every day. I simply had to be able to distinguish the difference between a minor issue and the first signs of a low-level calcium attack. If the symptoms include muscle cramps, facial twitching and contortions, then I needed to shut down. I didn't need to push myself to the limits to prove I was stronger than the illness. Staying as calm as possible, not overreacting, was important to the final outcome. I knew it helped to be in the dark and have as little noise around me as possible and no flowing air over my body. I also need to be sitting up. Taking those preventative steps would help me avoid a full-blown attack and know when to seek immediate medical assistance. The only way I'd gotten to this point of preparedness and understanding was through trial and error over countless nervous-system attacks.

As stress and anxiety are part of my illness, coping with them is significant in managing my symptoms. Looking at the daily struggles from a point of knowledge would help with the levels of anxiety. The internet is an unbelievable tool. It was as if I was going back to college to study a new subject. I learned extensively about hyperparathyroidism, hypoparathyroidism, bone density and the role calcium plays in the body. Very few men my age ever need to research this information. Along the way, I have received an education in medical administration, operational efficiencies and insurance practices. I could do it. I could manage the stress and anxiety.

The next two days were spent working in Pam's living room and spending time with her in the evenings. We had a lot of fun and I felt relaxed and relieved. I was happy with the progress made during this trip. I was encouraged by the new-found approach of Dr. Weisblat and that the most recent test results had not revealed any new issues.

I was scheduled to fly out of Cleveland to Chicago at 6:05 a.m., and on to Miami where I would take the only daily direct flight on to St Croix at 12:05 p.m. Pam dropped me off at the airport at 4:30 a.m. and we said our goodbyes. It was getting to be harder and harder to leave her. Making matters worse, the half-hour drive from Pam's to the airport had been shrouded in fog. I was hoping that it would not delay my flight.

When I arrived inside the terminal, the electronic departure board lit up with the word DELAYED in big red letters. The airline didn't know how long, but they would get us out on the first available flight. I used the restroom at the airport and found I was still urinating what seemed to be a large amount of blood. This was the sixth day in a row.

After many false starts, my flight eventually departed for Chicago at noon. When I landed at O'Hare, I scrambled to the American Airlines hospitality desk. There was no way to make it to Miami in time for the daily flight to St. Croix. They went to work on getting me into San Juan and catching an American Eagle Flight home. While I was in the air, they would work on securing me a seat. When I landed in Miami I scrambled again to the American Airlines desk. They gave me some bad news. I would have to spend the night in San Juan. My frustration level shot up. I chose to spend the night in Miami, instead. I'd stayed at the Marriott at the Miami airport in the past. The direct flight from Miami to St. Croix left at 12:05 p.m. the next day. I had to go down to the luggage carousel, retrieve my checked baggage then catch a shuttle bus to the hotel.

I checked in and quickly dumped my belongings in my room. I went downstairs and out the front doors for a much-needed, two-mile walk. Sweating, and in shorts, I held my dinner—picked up at a roadside stand. I stood out from the well-dressed business travelers on the elevator ride back to my room. From my balcony, the sky was vivid orange and blue as the sun disappeared in the distance. I took several deep breaths. Overall, I was feeling much better than when I'd I left for Cleveland. I'd lost some of the stress built up over the previous months by speaking with Dr. Weisblat. I looked forward to working with him in our quest to get through these health issues. The travel complications were more of a nuisance than anything. I was still going to get home on the weekend and not have to miss any more time away from the office. The only thing that continued to bother me was leaving Pam.

Sunday, 3/16/08—I woke up in a freezing room. Even though it was early spring, I'd cranked up the air conditioning the night before. Living without AC on St. Croix always led me to take full advantage of hotel units.

I soon discovered the amount of blood I was urinating was cut by half. It was my seventh, and hopefully, last day. The bus came to pick me up, and the plane took off as scheduled. I arrived on St. Croix at 3:30 p.m.

TRYING TO DO IT ALL (DAY 368 – 469)

By the time I'd started working at The March Group in 2005, private debt and the financial services sector companies that packaged and sold the debt were the biggest earning institutions on Wall Street. Manufacturing in the United States had shrunk to a mere thirteen percent of the U.S. gross domestic product. Financial Services represented twenty-one percent of the GDP. Watching how the marketing and sale of the handful of current TMG clients, who could be categorized in the financial sector, progressed and performing further investigations into related companies became a top priority. We wanted to increase our financial services sector clientele list. We needed to know what types of deals were being made and how they were being made.

Three years later, as the credit strain worsened, it had a profound negative effect on most markets, including the lower-end of the middle market. The fish were not swimming downstream as we had hoped. Offer prices for companies started falling. Our clients began backing out of deals at an alarming rate, choosing instead to sit on the sideline until more credit flowed and better offers were made.

As a company, we needed proceeds from the sale of our client's businesses to survive. The growing difficulty we were having with closing deals was only the start of the financial services sector's complete collapse a few short months later. Our goal was still twenty-five to thirty closings in 2008, no matter how many deals fell apart in the process. The mood remained optimistic, but was becoming more guarded by the day.

Monday, 3/17/08—Seven straight days of blood in the urine had mercifully ended. I headed off for what turned out to be a long day in a long line of days at work. We were in the process of adding accountability through tracking measures. I'd always provided monthly reports for my team's progress. However, the reporting capability required in matching the new accountability measures meant spending money with the software designers from Sales Logix. These were lean times, and spending money of any amount made everyone nervous and put the spender directly in the crosshairs. A good outcome was necessary—or it could mean my job. My group was so intertwined with the marketing department and research department that my requests needed to coincide with the other groups within our company. Everything needed to mesh. It was a daunting task spread out over the course of several months. This was the number one project on my plate. It turned out to be the most difficult in a long line of changes that awaited us.

The next two weeks were blurs. The entire time, I had discomfort in my stomach—accompanied by battles with diarrhea. My face tingled daily and I couldn't sleep without taking Ambien. My mind was racing each night with so many work issues that even taking Ambien did not always guarantee sleep. I was still trying to exercise, but my weight was going up fast. The resolution to fight this illness with renewed hope, made just a few short weeks before, was slowly fading.

Sunday, 3/30/08—I'd neglected *Folly* for far too long. I needed to get out on the water and remember why I lived in the Virgin Islands. I really did not have the energy for it, but gathered up a crew and we headed out for a sail. Ordinarily, I would get a sense of relaxation and a chance to enjoy Mother Nature when I was on the water, but I felt anxious during the entire six-hour trip. I love riding the waves and looking for turtles and dolphins, dropping anchor at Buck Island and swimming and hiking, but I just did not get the usual enjoyment out of this sail.

When I returned home I called Pam. We had talked for about an hour before I tired and needed to rest. After I hung up, worries started creeping into my mind. I was not enjoying anything at this point. Anxiety soon set in. My mind was racing at breakneck speeds. Several thoughts and ideas were flowing at the same time. My jaw began clinching and my shoulders pulled up towards my neck. There was no chance of getting comfortable. Lying down was out of the question. I paced back and forth in my guest house for hours. There was no stopping the discomfort. My stomach was upset, my face was tingling and my mind was racing. I had to force positive thoughts into a head filled with to-do lists, daunting tasks and negativity. Nothing like this had ever happened to me before this illness. I was having a horrific time overcoming this episode. There had been others, but this one seemed to really dig in. When morning arrived, I felt emotionally drained. I replayed the events in my mind over and over. What was happening to me?

For the next week, my jaw continued to produce pain on a nightly basis. I tried taking Ibuprofen to alleviate the discomfort but nothing seemed to help. Sleep was next to impossible, and I was in a constant state of irritability. I was thankful to make it to the weekend and collapse onto the bed and stay there until Monday morning. It was a Herculean effort to go to the grocery store or try and get some exercise. My mind was focused on work. I needed to rest during the other parts of my day to be able to function for the next go-around.

Tuesday, 4/15/08—My friend Hal Goplerud was scheduled to visit me from Los Angeles. Hal had come down before and we took a trip to Tortola, staying at Cane Garden Bay at Rhymer's Hotel. Although I was looking forward to this visit I knew my physical condition was poor and the slightest taxing of my nervous system could prove disastrous. I was involved in so much at work that I was getting anxious over taking a couple of days off. I'd developed tunnel vision. A break from my work and health routine was going to be difficult.

Hal arrived at 9:00 p.m. from Los Angles. Twenty hours of traveling had pretty much wiped him out. It was great to see my old friend and I was glad neither one of us had energy to head out for any nightlife. We stayed up late talking music and making plans for the following week. I explained I could only afford to take a couple of days off work because I risked falling too far behind. Hal understood and we decided he would precede me by a couple of days and leave in the morning. I suggested we stay in the U.S. Virgin Islands and visit St. John. The next morning, I got Hal to the Seaplane dock early to catch the first flight out headed for St. Thomas. A ferry boat would carry him to St. John later that morning. I immediately went back to work knowing I needed to get a lot done before taking time off.

On Wednesday afternoon my cell phone rang. Hal did not think St. John was going to be the place he wanted to spend his time. There was way more to do on Tortola. He wanted to know if I cared if we changed plans. Usually, there would have been no problem, but my reaction was one of frustration and irritability. I barked out my displeasure in making changes to the plan. I told Hal he would need to make all the arrangements and let me know where to go the next day. This response on my part took both Hal and me by surprise. After I hung up I wondered if I'd gone over the edge. I continued to push through work, but I was still thinking about my over-reaction. Later that night, I spoke to my friend and apologized.

4/17/08—Early the next morning I packed for travel and had a head full of new perspective as I left for the office. I arrived around 7:00 a.m. to cram two full days of work into five hours. When I finally left at midday , I was relieved to be getting out of there and looked forward to a break. I decided to increase my calcium intake by four pills a day to offset the change in routine.

I boarded the seaplane feeling some slight tingling in my face as the twin turbo props revved up before takeoff. A few minutes later, we were launched off the surface of the water. Over the course of the twenty-five minute flight I concentrated on deep breathing to help take the edge off. I had to switch gears from work to vacation mode.

After landing in St. Thomas and catching a forty-five minute ferry ride to Tortola, I was in Road Town by 1:30 in the afternoon. Deep breathing had offset the tingling in my face. The symptoms did not intensify. As the cab climbed over the mountains and we started our descent into Cane Garden Bay, my stress level declined further and I relaxed, releasing the day's tension that had built up in my shoulders. Hal was already at Rhymer's Restaurant and Hotel and after checking in we headed down the beach for our first drinks of the day.

Tortola and the rest of the BVI island chain have the ultimate in beautiful beaches and laid-back nightlife. Unfortunately, we did not have the time needed to explore the islands by sailboat. I was a little relieved because I knew I was not up to the task. I was feeling tired and rundown, and my left arm was still sore. Hal hadn't done a lot of sailing, and I did not want to shoulder all the responsibility. We went ahead with a plan to rent a powerboat for the next day. We stopped by the beach shack where the rental company was headquartered and put the plan in motion.

Friday, 4/18/08—After breakfast at the bar next door to our hotel, we walked down the crescent-shaped beach and found the man responsible for renting the power boats seated at Quito's Gazebo Bar. We waited for him to finish his morning coffee before he came downstairs to the rental shack. We had paper work to fill out and a cash deposit to put down on the boat. We bought a case of water and a twelve pack of beer to fill the cooler.

After getting used to the twenty-nine-foot twin-engine power boat's handling, we headed out through the cut in the reef on the far eastern side of Cane Garden Bay. Along with the full ice chest, we also brought a miniature guitar we'd purchased in Road Town the day before. Our intention was to play at all the beach bars in White Bay on the south shore of Yost Van Dyke. Once we headed out into the channel we pushed west towards St. John. I opened up the throttles and the ride became bumpy. The chop in the pass was pretty big and the boat was not steering as smoothly as I'd hoped. I was forced to throttle down. After an hour of cruising Drakes Passage we headed east for the entrance of White Bay. We wanted to start our two-man jam session at One Love Bar. At the other end of the bay is where you can find the Soggy Dollar Saloon. In between the two are seven or eight other beach bars and snack shacks. The atmosphere in all is laidback.

Pulling into White Bay is fairly easy if you follow the buoys through the cut in the reef. We arrived mid-morning and I knew we would be surrounded by boats before the afternoon came to an end. The waves were rolling directly into the bay out of the north. I pulled the boat in and asked Hal to drop the first anchor about twenty-feet off the pristine, white sandy beach. The boat rotated and the bow was pointing out towards the cut. I swam the smaller anchor off to the side of the stern and placed it firmly in the sandy bottom—about fifteen feet to the southeast. I was not able to swim with a full stroke, but I was able to kick around and dive on both anchors to make sure we weren't going to drift off the anchor and come ashore. Hal grabbed the small guitar in its box and we started to swim for the beach.

My swim was difficult with one semi-good arm. As I approached the beach I could see the water breaking on the sand with force. It proved to be difficult standing up. After two or three attempts, while protecting my left arm, I was able to get forward momentum enough to make it to my feet. Fighting the water rushing back down the beach into the ocean, I made my way clear of the surf. Hal was holding the guitar in its cardboard box as he made his way towards my location. Looking back over my shoulder, I could see he'd only made it about five feet from the boat with the package over his head before the guitar went completely underwater. The box disintegrated and the remainder of the pieces washed up with the relentless morning waves. Hal used the miniature instrument for a paddle until he road a wave and tumbled his way up the beach. We were on our second drink before picking up the last pieces of cardboard that littered the white sands.

Sitting inside One Love bar in front of a bartender named Jean and her dog Zeus, the first tunes were pounded out on the cheap, salt-water logged plastic stringed guitar. She gave us a free beer hoping we would move along and allow her to start her day in peace. No such luck. I was playing my usual blues and Stones numbers. Hal played his own music. The guitar, by this point, was literally falling apart as the salt made the glue come undone. There was no chance of keeping the plastic strings in tune. The back pine wood panel came completely detached from the sidewalls and we patched it back together with a Cruz Bay St. John's bumper sticker. The tone was poor, but we were determined to continue our one-day, beach-shack concert tour. Our next stop was Jewel's Snack Shack and then we were off to Ivan's Stress-Free Bar. I had long since stopped drinking beer and switched to pain killers. It almost made the noise we were creating bearable. We stumbled through some Bob Dylan and Tom Petty numbers before heading down the beach to the next bar. The charter boats started to fill the bay and a couple of hundred people jammed into the seven or eight beach shacks. As the captive audience settled in for a long day of partying, we created a noisy diversion. We played in the sand paths between the bars and under coconut trees where people tried to take a siesta in the bright afternoon sun. Our music generated no applauses, and I'm quite sure we would have been asked to stop if it were not for the fact that everyone else on the island was intoxicated. It was already 1:00 p.m. I knew I had to get us back to Tortola, and my nervous system could not handle much alcohol. I quietly switched back to water.

Around 3:30 p.m., in the middle of a lively game of ring toss at The Soggy Dollar Saloon, I realized it was time to head out to the boat so we could get back across Drakes Passage and into Cane Garden Bay in time for our 5:00 p.m. deadline. Convincing Hal it was time to go was not easy. The day had been fun and there were plenty of new people still arriving. The party there would be raging all night long. We still had to fill up at the fuel dock on Tortola and we didn't want to pay a late fee. Our final tune was Honky Tonk Women.

Swimming back out to the boat was much easier than making landfall had been. We clamored aboard and got set for the trip home, but after several attempts, the engines would not turn over. I squeezed the handball that forces fuel into the carburetors. Nothing seemed to work. I was starting to get advice from people in cockpits of nearby boats. My frustration level started to rise. Finally we decided to let it sit for ten minutes and give it another try. The third attempt finally resulted in two fired-up sputtering motors. We pulled anchors and were off.

Arriving across the passage just before the 5:00 p.m. deadline, the owner directed me, over the radio, to the fuel dock. The water was extremely choppy, and the steering on the boat was very loose. When I approached the outside of the dock, a young boy ran out and directed me around the back of the dock. Inside the dock there is a fifty-foot-wide channel that runs along a cement enforced wall. I was not thrilled to be maneuvering a twenty-nine foot boat in a fifty-foot channel. The boy motioned for me to turn it around and pull up. We hung four bumpers over the side, hovering just above idle. I made my turn alongside the cement wall where we proceeded to run out of room and went straight into a pillar. I was thankful there was no damage. The young boy looked on in amazement. The gas bill was over eighty dollars. We had run the engines for no more than three hours. I was glad we didn't decide to go island hopping and visit Virgin Gorda or any of the other islands. We vowed to be back sometime in the future and sail the island chain.

Saturday, 4/19/08—I woke up and walked down the hall to the large terrace overlooking Cane Garden Bay. There was a small crowd of four or five people gathered watching the sun come up over the Caribbean. The pastel colors bouncing off the water and the sides of the green hills were worth the effort. The beauty of the sunrise was quickly dashed when I ducked into the hallway bathroom and discovered I was urinating blood again. The pain and burning sensation accompanying the blood was at an all-time new high. It was impossible to set aside the fact that I was bleeding, especially when it caused enough pain to make me sweat for half an hour each time I used the restroom. This was not something you tell anybody. so I went back out on the terrace overlooking Cane Garden Bay and called Pam on my cell phone. Pam told me there was nothing I could do, and that I needed to enjoy the next two days as much as possible. She went back over what Dr. Levine had told me. Urinating blood, accompanied by intense burning dominated my thinking. Being able to enjoy the remaining vacation was going to be impossible to pull off.

After breakfast at Big Banana Bar, we hired a cab and visited some other spots on Tortola. Our first stop was Apple Bay, home to the famous Bomba Shack. Later in the day we ended up in Road Town for a late lunch. We did have a good time and I was able to take my mind off the physical problems. I drank only water. Before we left Road Town, I had to use the restroom. The pain was really ramping up and I was visibly sweating when I came out of the stall, feeling tired and weak. After returning to Cane Garden Bay, the rest of the day was spent relaxing on the beach. I continued to drink water, hoping to clear my system. Sunday was our return ferry ride to St. Thomas and then the Seaplane flight back to St. Croix.

We arrived back on St. Croix just after noon. Hal had never visited the North Shore and the rainforest, so we took a drive west from the seaplane parking lot, visiting several scenic areas and stopping at Cane Bay. We drove into the rain forest to the Domino Club. Wild boars are kept in a special fenced-off area outside the bar. We fed cans of O'Doul's nonalcoholic beer to the pigs. It was after 5:00 p.m. when we finally returned to my house. I was exhausted and needed to relax before starting work the next day. Hal was leaving Tuesday morning so he would be on his own for most of Monday.

Monday morning I was not surprised to find blood in my urine. From past history I knew this condition would last for several days. I had to set this aside and make sure that my guest was set up for the day. Hal planned to catch a ride into town and then maybe take a cab all the way to Fredericksted on the west end. I knew I would be in for a long day with a lot of catching up to do. All the projects I was involved with seemed to be moving forward at the same time and I had five meetings before the day was over.

After work, I met Hal on the boardwalk downtown. He'd spent the day in Christiansted visiting the fort and hanging out at the restaurants and bars. We stopped at Green Cay Marina and had dinner at the Deep End Bar. The next morning Hal would be leaving, so we stayed up late and played songs on my guitar and talked past midnight. I would drop Hal off downtown the next morning and he would catch a cab to the airport before his noon flight.

Pam was coming in on Friday. I had little time to unwind. I knew she was perfectly happy visiting while I had to work, and that she loved going to all the stores and floating on a raft in the ocean every day. Still, I was feeling guilty. I started to have a pain in my chest after work on Wednesday. The pressure was building and I called Dr. Weisblat. He explained it was most likely stress-related and didn't think I was having heart issues. He suggested I take some Mylanta on top of my Nexium.

By the time Pam arrived on Friday afternoon, I was still experiencing a lot of pressure in the center of my chest. I was concerned, and when we got home and settled in Pam rubbed my chest for an hour. It seemed to help. The next morning I had diarrhea. That seemed to relieve the pressure, and I felt a lot better, however I was still urinating blood. The never-ending medical issues were taking their toll.

On Monday, 4/28/08, Pam went with a realtor to look at several properties. We had been discussing buying a property together—with plans to build a home in the future. She narrowed the list to her five favorites. After work and on the weekend, we drove around and looked at all of them.

We eventually put in a bid on a half-acre lot at the top of a ridge overlooking the Reef Golf Course and the Yacht Club. The elevation was over 300-feet, insuring strong easterly breezes year round, and the lot had a second ocean view on the northern boundary. We were excited to enter into the investment together. Several talks about the lot and future house designs ensued. I'd never bought property and thought our offer was a done deal.

On Monday morning I contacted a land surveyor service and they agreed to make two different types of surveys on the property for $1,000. I thought this was just a formality. The realtor was proposing a thirty-day close date after the agreement had been reached. He was certain the owner would accept our offer. The survey would be done in two weeks. Everything seemed to be in order. We read over the codes and restrictions thoroughly. In the weeks that followed Pam and I talked daily about our future plans.

The bleeding stopped and the pressure in my chest relented. I was starting to feel better just as Pam's visit was coming to a close. As with all her visits, I was sad to see her leave. Work continued to be hectic, and

I was waiting for the property survey and looked forward to finalizing the purchase. Although excited, I continued to feel tired. I had daily tingling in my face and the back of my head.

Sunday, 5/04/08—I spent the day packing. I was leaving for The March Group's Coral Springs, Florida office on Monday morning. I had to attend some meetings that were being held by my boss from California. I was also going to be performing some training for the three Associate Managing Directors on my team.

Monday, 5/05/08—I took the direct three-and-a-half hour flight to Miami, rented a car and drove the thirty-five miles to Coral Springs. I was looking forward to living out of a hotel for a week. I was happy to be getting off island and visiting with my counterparts in the Florida office, but the long hours were virtually unavoidable on these trips and this one proved to be no different.

I completed the training with my team and attended all my meetings as scheduled. I kept up my day-to-day responsibilities and had not collapsed by the end of the week. Part of my increased energy was sleeping well each night with the aid of AC and Ambien. Friday morning I conducted the Private Equity Conference call from my departure gate inside Miami International Airport before boarding the 12:30 p.m. flight home.

It had been a strenuous month entertaining Hal and Pam, and continuing to work and travel to Florida for a week. Things tend to fall through the cracks when life is moving fast. I continued a high-level of performance at work but had started to slack off on the exercise and training regimen. I was gaining weight, and was performing only a few arm exercises each day. I needed to re-dedicate, once again, to my health. Working out more was the first step.

Tuesday, 5/14/08—I scheduled a physical therapy evaluation for my left shoulder to determine where I was in my recovery. The calendar year had rolled over, meaning my insurance allowed sixty new physical rehabilitation sessions. The main purpose of the visit was to get refocused and receive some expert direction. My progress was becoming stagnant and I needed guidance to help move beyond my current limitations. The physical therapist at Beeston Hill performed all the measurements and determined I was further along than they had envisioned. They didn't want me injuring either shoulder by overworking them with heavy weights or improper form. I was never going to get the outward rotation back in either arm, but I was able to show them I could lift small weights and put both hands above my head. I was eager to prove the physical therapists' prediction wrong. I was convinced I could regain normal function in both shoulders.

I went to the gym for five straight days. My workout routine alternated between the pool and the weight room. Sixty-to-ninety-minute workouts were coupled with a vigorous forty-five minute cardio warm up in hopes of shedding some of the recently accumulated weight. The response from the therapists seemed to suggest I'd already peaked and gone beyond their expectations. Though, with only seventy-to-eighty percent mobility in either shoulder, I was motivated to get back into a regular workout routine.

The yearly Three-Ball-Three-Club Tournament was held Sunday, 5/25/08. The day before, I attempted to play a practice round at the Reef Golf Course using all my clubs. I was unable to perform a complete back swing. Both shoulders wouldn't rotate through impact, abruptly stopping the swing three-quarters into the back swing and again in the follow-through limited my effectiveness. I'd fought through six-months of rehabilitation on the left shoulder just to reach this point. I was excited to be out on the course again, even if it was in a diminished capacity.

I felt pain in my left shoulder after the practice round. It was different from the usual pain my shoulders gave me. I looked at it as a test. Do I push ahead or run the risk of re-injuring my shoulders? I had been warned by everyone from Dr. Chase to the entire staff at Beeston Hill that I ran the risk of pushing too far, too fast. To me, moving forward meant passing the current test.

The rules are simple. You can only play with three balls and only have three clubs in your bag. If you lose all three balls, you are out of the tournament. I played with my driver, six iron and wedge. I'd completely modified my swing to accommodate the lack of mobility in my shoulders.

By the time we'd finished nine holes of golf my left shoulder was inflamed and the tissue around the metal implant was sore. I was happy to have been able to play again, and did not dwell on the burning sensation. I've never been a great player. but the fifty-four I shot was an all-time high score.

It was fairly evident that the surgically repaired bones would never allow my shoulders to function with the same mobility. On this day, just like hundreds of times in the past, I pushed the thought aside as soon as it popped into my head. Other times I would allow it to linger for a few split seconds, using it as motivation. I chose how much reality to let in and when.

Ignoring the pain in my left shoulder, I stuck to my new workout commitment and went to the gym the following morning. Later, after an hour and half of water-based resistance therapy, the pain had advanced to a constant dull, throbbing sensation in both shoulders. Later that day I took the launch out to *Folly* to pump out some fresh rain water in her bilge. I was shocked at how dilapidated and worn out she was looking. In many ways our lives were headed down the same road. Her painted surfaces were faded and cracked. The teak was grey and dried out. Some metal fittings needed replacing and there were patches of fiber glass work to perform on the deck. She needed new sails, halyards, sheets, and a ladder system. I sat in her cockpit rocking back and forth with the waves.

Tuesday, 5/27/08—I found myself unable to unwind after a long day at work. Problem solving, trouble shooting, flow charts and client marketing schedules raced around in a jumbled mess inside my head. I couldn't stop it. 10:00 p.m. came and went. With the torrent of thoughts continuing to flow there was no possibility for natural sleep. Up until this point, I vowed never to take the Xanax Dr. Weisblat had prescribed. Taking the pills was admitting I was weak and could not take what life was dishing out. My views had not changed much, but I needed a break. After tightening the childproof lid back on the bottle I sat and waited for the drug to kick in. The .25mg pill did little to ease the racing thoughts.

11:30 p.m.—The left side of my mouth started to lock up and there was numbness and tingling in the rest of my face. I immediately took extra calcium pills. My left arm felt weak and I started to experience burning-mouth syndrome. It was a repeat nightmare performance I'd lived through several times. I had never wavered in my belief it was all caused by low calcium. The culprit was easily identifiable at this point in the game. I just could not control it. I dialed Pam's number.

Cramping in my legs kept me upright pacing the floor. Back and forth, back and forth. Clutching the phone to my ear, I apologized for waking her, and did everything I could to not allow my irritability to come out during our conversation. I clung to the sound of her voice at the other end of the phone as I sat on the edge of my bed and rocked back and forth in the dark. Minutes later I was up pacing again. Breathing became labored as I developed a headache. The attack was increasing in strength and I needed to go it alone and concentrate on remaining calm. As we said our goodbyes she told me to call her at any hour. Fortunately for me she meant it. There had been, and would be, several calls at night in the future.

Dr. Politz had been telling me for months that he did not believe all of my symptoms were reactions from low calcium in the blood. He tried his best to help me come to my own conclusion about anxiety and stress. Quite frankly I thought he was full of shit. The numbers proved I had low calcium, but I heard a similar prognosis from Dr. Weisblat. He phrased it differently, believing the low calcium symptoms brought on an anxiety disorder, and he had gone as far as prescribing, after my refusal to accept his prognosis, Xanax as a way to decrease my breathing issues. Dr. Politz wanted blood taken during these episodes to test the calcium level and prove, one way or the other, what was happening. Because the episodes kept happening at night, and the symptoms left me in no condition to drive, his request was impossible. If I would have stopped and looked at all the clues, I might have been more understanding. Instead I stood my ground and refused to admit to the perceived weakness. I marched on more determined then ever to prove them wrong. I paced my floor until after one o'clock in the morning and finally collapsed due to exhaustion.

Wednesday, 5/28/08—I woke to a hammering headache—the type you get after drinking an entire bottle of tequila. In my case it was not that easily explained. Confusing the morning further, was a physical therapy session scheduled for 7:30 a.m. It was in direct contrast to my desire to unlock the doors and be the first in the office each morning. I felt I had something to prove at work and, although I understood the importance of these rehabilitation sessions, they stood in the way of me sticking to the strict schedule I imposed on myself.

The rehabilitation session consisted of a series of weight machines and core muscle-building exercises. The amount of weights was kept very low in part due to my lack of strength. The physical therapists took their time showing me the correct form. The exercises consisted of using free weight dumbbells while resting my shoulders on a large ball, squat thrusts with weights in each hand and a complete set on each of the new weight machines recently purchased by the gym. The session ran over its one hour time frame. I rushed to get to work, arriving at 9:30 a.m. I felt sicker than ever before as I climbed the stairs to my office.

I had just settled in when I received a phone call from Pam. Our offer on the Cotton Valley lot had been rejected. We briefly talked about it, and decided to up our offer. Pam was going to take care of calling the realtor. I would have to run over to their office and initial all the new paperwork later in the day. It was the last thing I needed piled on top of an already busy schedule. The owner of the lot had five days to get back to us. I was still waiting on the survey results to be returned and was increasingly questioning if it was worth the trouble.

To top everything, my boss was on island from California. I was thankful that for once I was not the focus of her visit. I greeted her with enthusiasm when I got to the office. I was tired but felt a need to keep up a façade of having plenty of energy. She was here for other meetings with other groups she managed. My only responsibility while she was on island was one scheduled meeting and a dinner on Thursday night.

The day dragged on and on as my energy level fell lower and lower. It

189

was as if I was a disposable battery on its last leg. Not sleeping the night before, and feeling hung over left me feeling physically weak. Cramps started forming in my stomach and I had to use the restroom several times experiencing diarrhea. I was never so thankful to see a day come to an end. I headed straight for home.

I needed some extended sick time off from work but that was not going to happen. I have held a job, sometimes two or three at a time, since my first paper route in the fifth grade. The only time I'd ever taken a day off for illness, besides my present situation, was when I was in my twenties and was sent home because the doctor had diagnosed me with walking pneumonia. Although The March Group had never mentioned it to me, I was sure I had used up all of my personal leave and sick time, and I was already planning on taking vacation time at the holidays. I did not want to have to take time off before then. My stomach problems continued as my energy fell to new lows. I was thankful to be in the privacy of my own home.

Thursday, 5/29/08—I arrived at the office at 7:30 a.m. and dug into my workday. Pam heard back from the realtor about our property and gave me a call around 9:30 a.m. The owners had accepted our second offer. We had a thirty-day window to close and needed to perform all of our due diligence before the deadline. At lunch I called the survey office. They assured me the work would be done on time. The surveys included a boundary survey and showed the property had a small utility building on the southern boundary, and the remains of a small barn and a cistern used for goat and cattle farming. The structures had been destroyed by hurricanes, the walls overgrown with weeds and bougainvillea flowers. We needed a survey to tell us what they were and their size. We could then determine the cost of removal and factor that into our negotiations. Although the additional work came at the most inappropriate time, this was all welcome excitement.

1:00 p.m.—I was sitting face to face across the conference room table from Sara Sheldon. She felt I was stretched too thin with the amount of work I was performing on both the marketing and the business development side of the company. I agreed and again expressed a need to hire an assistant. As one of four directors of the company, Sara could have easily fast-tracked my request when I originally made it six months prior. "I thought we just agreed how thin I was being spread over two departments?" She reminded me that money was tight, but she was always willing to get help if I really needed it. We agreed to discuss it in the future. In the meantime I would need to chart out all my responsibilities at work, with detailed notes of my time that would help explain the need for a new assistant. Something with this request did not feel right as I walked out from behind the mahogany double doors and ascended the twenty-two stairs to my office.

There were several toasts made that night at the company dinner. Everyone was all smiles as the topics of conversation were kept light and enjoyable. At the end of the evening we received the "Let's work harder and Smarter" speech from Sara. It had turned hot early this year and as the group disbanded out of the AC into the night, we realized it was still in the mid-eighties. Everyone mentioned how this did not bode well for the upcoming storm season as we walked our separate ways.

By the time I reached home, my mind was racing and the diarrhea I'd been experiencing was back with a vengeance. The rest of the evening was spent getting up and using the bathroom every twenty minutes, and trying to shut off the flow of thoughts in my head. I didn't lie down for good until 1:00 a.m. I woke up just before five with bad cramping and had to rush to the restroom, I proceeded to rub my stomach and drink Mylanta until 6:30 a.m.

Despite my exhaustion, I was able to get a lot of work done in between restroom breaks at the start of the day. At 10:30 a.m. I hosted the Private Equity Roundtable Conference call and soon after was called into back to back meetings with George Gifford and Sara Sheldon. I felt unprepared as they ran through a long list of questions. This had to be on Sara's schedule and I felt more than a little betrayed by her not giving me advanced warning so I could prepare.

Everyone agreed that we needed a functioning buyer database to improve our sales efficiency. How that database was designed was the reason we were having a rather one-sided conversation. The owner of our company, George Gifford and I were on opposite sides of the spectrum when it came to the design and functionality. Although the database would be used mainly by me and my team, I had limited say in the outcome. He was trying to resurrect an idea we had agreed to dismiss six months earlier. Sara knew my thoughts on the plan, but did not stand up to the owner and let him know he was making a mistake.

One portion of the plan was to have each Associate Managing Director own their individual database. They would only contact leads from that database. In my view, that limited my group's effectiveness. Sales Logix was not flexible enough to handle this proposed procedure change, and designing the system to handle the change would cost the company many thousands of dollars. I spent the next two hours explaining, off the top of my head, why I believed this was going to be a difficult transition, hoping the powers-that-be saw things my way for a second time in less than six months. I was assured I would have the resources necessary. Before being dismissed, they both looked me in the eye and told me to make it happen. Finally, mercifully, the workday came to an end.

I had to summon all my strength to drive west to Beeston Hill instead of heading straight home and going to bed. I'd been cleared to continue physical therapy until I met with Dr. Chase on 6/10/08. As usual, a therapist moved with me from station to station giving instructions on form and technique. We concentrated on several exercises that isolated the shoulder and the back muscles. I was also concentrating on building core muscle strength in the stomach and lower back. I put every last ounce of energy in my body into this workout, and was able to keep my concentration and finished strong.

Looking forward to a quiet night at home in front of the fan and TV, my stomach started to feel better as the pressure of the work week finally came to an end. I'd just laid down when the power went out. There was no breeze, and it was extremely uncomfortable inside my small house.

9:00 p.m.—I was outside leaning against the side rail of my front porch for support. Bud and Sadie sat by my side, panting in the thick, night air. We passed the next three hours waiting for power to be restored. I'd fallen asleep in the sitting position at the top of the porch stairs when the whirl of the ceiling fans startled me back to consciousness. It was after midnight.

The following two days were spent resting in bed. Thoughts turned to my overall health situation, but I could not wrap my mind around the big picture. Dr. Politz kept promising that my parathyroid would eventually produce regular amounts of PTH hormone, but blood-test results showed my remaining three parathyroids were barely in the normal range and there were tests showing they were not functioning at all. The best I'd felt since having the rogue parathyroid removed was the first day following surgery, almost a full year earlier. It was as if the medical gods had teased me with a twenty-four hour respite before unleashing the pain and suffering, and the lingering effects that never seemed to let up. The reality of these thoughts left me feeling depressed.

I didn't write a checklist of what needed to be accomplished and when, but I knew I needed to see an end to the medical hardships. With Pam's help, I'd taken the first positive steps in this direction. Developing a cohesive medical staff that could be a part of the solution was the correct move. Eventually I would need to incorporate an Endocrinologist, and possibly a Neurologist, to speed up the healing process. Trying to reach the correct balance between pills and parathyroid function, allowing the symptoms afflicting my nervous system to abate, was the right course at the present time. Deep down I still held out hope I could be cured once and for all.

I needed to change the subject quickly before I went over the edge. I had to get my mind off the medical issues and focus on something enjoyable. Where this respite was going to come from, I had no clue. The answers eluded me as I lay motionless on my bed in the sweltering heat.

Monday, 6/02/08—I arrived early at work, in part to escape thinking about my health situation. Physical therapy was scheduled after work Monday, Wednesday and Thursday. I knew I'd better use up what little energy I had early in the week, because I would be drained as the days flew by.

8:30 a.m.—I received a call from the survey company. They had finished work on Plot 206 Cotton Valley. At noon I walked the four blocks to their office. When they showed me the survey, the actual size of the plot was .47 acres, below allotted covenants and restriction requirements to build. This was the last remaining open lot on the ridge top. As the other houses were built over time, small pieces of land had been used to complete driveways and expand boundary lines to meet building restrictions.

The lot had actually shrunk from its original size of .54 acres. On the south boundary of the lot there was a shed the neighbor had been using and believed was his. He had lived in the house for over twenty years. The survey showed the boundary line running right through the middle of the building. The neighbor had a legal claim to that building because he had been using it for so long. We had been told the shed and the other structures on the property were all included in the price. We wanted to remove the shed and everything else to make room for our house and the yard we planned. I knew Pam would be less than pleased with this news. I thanked the survey company and got back to the office as soon as possible.

I took my frustrations out during physical therapy after work. I was in the pool instead of the weight room and really pounded out my exercises. I could move both my arms around behind my back and above my head. I was able to hold my weight up with two paddles under each hand and my arms straight out at the sides. I performed three sets of pull-ups with my body in the water, grabbing handlebars three-feet above the surface.

My therapist sensed I was throwing everything I had into this workout. She told me to try and swim a lap. Although my left shoulder was on fire, I was able to rotate my arms just enough to complete a few strokes. Neither shoulder functioned like it used to before the surgeries. There was a hitch at the top of the rotation. I was unable to get the same forward arm extension I once had. Never the less, I did swim ten feet. It felt fantastic!

The consensus among the therapists was that the fractures in both shoulders would prevent me from ever swimming again. I was proving them wrong. This was a big boost to my morale. I'd been busting my ass working out and attending every physical therapy session. I'd forced the issue and demanded another round of therapy sessions after the new calendar year. It was a relationship I benefited from greatly. I had worked out on my own for several months, and was starting to lose my momentum. Being able to swim ten feet was a sure-fire indication that we were on the right track.

Later that night I talked to Pam and shared the good news. It didn't seem like much, but to me it was a huge accomplishment. The conversation quickly switched to our property. We had two weeks before we had to commit. We had put down an amount of money that kept the property from being sold to another buyer. The money would be recouped if the deal did not go through. By the end of our conversation, Pam had her checklist of what she was going to look into, questions she was going to ask and various people she was going to call to get to the bottom of this. She was sure this could be worked out. We both really wanted this lot. It had amazing views and I could see the Yacht Club where *Folly* rode on her mooring from what would eventually become the front porch of the house. Up to this point everything had seemed to be moving along and we both had believed we would be property owners within two weeks.

Wednesday, 6/04/08—After work I went to physical therapy. Back in the weight room I plowed though my required sets. To be honest, I didn't like the weight room workouts nearly as much as the pool. They seemed to be harder on my shoulders and I struggled with technique. By the time it was all said and done I was experiencing a fairly high level of pain.

At the end of my therapy session, Dr. Menzie invited me to meet him in the office. He wanted to perform another bone-density scan on my left wrist. The previous scan at Beeston Hill was performed in January 2007. The wrist bone scan takes readings from the exact same bone each time. Dr. Chase and other physicians had explained that the wrist-density machines are less accurate than full-body bone density machines. They do give useful information with two test results. The whole process lasted less than ten minutes, but I had a hard time keeping my left arm still. My shoulder was throbbing by the time it was over. I'd just completed a weight-lifting routine and needed to have ice on the shoulder soon to take away the pain. My results showed my bone density was moving in the right direction. I had a -2.5 reading in the left wrist. In January of 2007 my reading had been a -2.8. I was still in the osteoporosis category, but moving in the right direction. I asked Dr. Menzies to be sure those results were sent to Dr. Chase, Dr. Politz and Dr. Weisblat in Cleveland. He gave me a copy so I could fax the results to all three doctors.

Dwelling on test results became an obstacle that I had to overcome. It would be much easier if I didn't overreact to each set of new numbers as my blood calcium and parathyroid hormone levels changed on a daily basis. It was such a roller coaster ride.

Over time, the numbers became less important than how I felt. All the health problems added difficulty with keeping a workout routine. I would get started, then have to stop for a couple of days because of soreness or not feeling strong enough to get out of bed. I've always been addicted to routines. For three years before my first surgery I worked out four to five days a week. I'd pushed myself to reach a level of fitness I'd been missing while living in the states. I'd lifted weights, there, but I did very little cardio work. I moved to the islands for a fresh start—and a new commitment to losing weight and maintaining a healthy body. The weight gain and the sedentary life I led outside of therapy was disappointing, but I felt so lousy all the time. I was always chasing the next ailment. For a year and a half, there never seemed to be a smooth patch where I actually felt like working out. The longevity of my disorder was wearing me down.

Since my surgery, I hadn't experienced more than five good nights of sleep in a row. I'd had bouts of insomnia prior to breaking my right shoulder, but I always felt there was a physical reason this was happening because when these symptoms occurred I'd feel poorly for days. I never had this checked out or asked a doctor about it. I think it would have been a long shot to have hyperparathyroidism diagnosed from my sleeping problems, but it was a symptom that might have helped with early detection.

After surgery, I went an entire year without getting the sleep needed to revitalize and rejuvenate. I was leery of sleeping pills and refused to take them when my nervous system was flaring up. To me, the fear of breaking other bones while sleeping under the aide of a drug was greater than the benefit of the sleep it provided. I already had two broken shoulders and my hips and spine could be next if I wasn't careful.

Thursday, 6/5/08—I woke up at 4:30 a.m., and by 6:30 a.m. had rushed off to the safe haven behind my desk. I needed extra time to reluctantly work on my new project. I was not scheduled for a therapy session, so I was sure I could go home later that night and take a sleeping pill to catch up on my rest. It's an unimaginable hardship to not be able to drift off to sleep naturally. Planning for sleep and having to take a sleep aide does not provide the same benefit. I tried relaxing, deep breathing and reading. Nothing worked. As I would lie in bed with the lights out, I would get more and more frustrated and end up taking the damn pill. Sleep deprivation became every bit the problem my broken bones and malfunctioning parathyroid had become. Lack of sleep, on many occasions, was the precursor to a rough low calcium nervous-system attack. They went hand-in-hand.

Friday, June 6/06/08—After work my insurance mandated re-evaluation was scheduled at physical therapy. All mobility, including abduction, outward and inward rotation etc. would be closely measured and compared to past numbers. This meeting would be followed by a consultation with Dr. Chase in St. Thomas where he would gather much the same numbers and take a fresh set of x-rays. Together these two would gauge my progress and report back to the insurance company.

I was firmly under the belief I could still benefit greatly from extended therapy sessions. However, my thoughts on the subject did not count when it came to the business side of healing. The therapists had already begun to let me know they had helped me progress about as far as they believed they could. I was facing a similar situation to when my allotted number of insurance visits had run out at the end of 2007. I needed the rehabilitation group, along with Dr. Chase, to be in agreement that I would benefit from continued sessions. They could prescribe more sessions but would be staring at an uphill battle from the insurance company. It would mean extra work on both their parts. At the very least they, would have to prove the benefit to the insurance company with hard data on lengthy evaluation forms filled out at more frequent intervals.

Most experts agree that you have about twelve months after surgery before the repair to the bone and the remaining scar tissue have hardened and you lose the ability to regain additional mobility. The one-year anniversary of my second shoulder surgery was quickly approaching. Hard fought lessons had been learned on the rehabilitation of my right arm. I had higher hopes for my left arm. I was not going to tear up any more scar tissue, but I felt I could still strengthen the muscles and increase mobility. I was desperate to do anything to make that happen.

My right shoulder had regained about eighty percent mobility from its original form. There were times when it hurt like hell, and I had discomfort when the pressure in the weather changed, and while performing motions above my head or in a rotational manner. That would never go away. I understand the left shoulder would more than likely fall short of having one hundred percent mobility but I needed to try everything in my powers to make it happen. Physical therapy sessions and working out on my own time gave me the best chance to recover to the fullest extent.

Saturday, 6/07/08—Sleep continued to elude me. I played a round of golf and could not hit the ball any further than one-hundred yards. The Reef Golf Course is a short course, a perfect place for a person who can not swing a club with any rhythm or speed, to hack away and still feel like they hit a few good shots. After returning home I rested for the remainder of the afternoon. I finally took an Ambien and went to sleep around 10:00 p.m. I woke at 1:00 a.m. feeling extremely tired. I was unable to fall back to sleep until 4:00 a.m., and woke again at 6:30 a.m., and started my Sunday morning workout routine.

Monday, 6/09/08—I began house sitting for my friend Rick Hassen. His home is at a high enough elevation that he and his family can experience constant breezes. He had a nice pool and deck—which I planned to use daily. In return Rick owed me a fishing trip on his 34-foot fishing boat. It was a fair trade.

This was the third or fourth time I'd had the pleasure. Walking his dogs every day on the hills surrounding the house would help my ongoing battle to lose weight. Their wraparound porch faces Buck Island and the British Virgin Islands to the North. The views are incredible and provide a clear view of my boat riding in the waves on her mooring at the Yacht Club. I could not stop thinking about the work needed to be done on *Folly*. I found myself looking at her through binoculars from Rick's breakfast table, making mental notes of things that needed to be fixed. I called Brian's Marine to see when he was available to pull her out of the water.

Tuesday, 6/10/08—I caught the first seaplane flight to St. Thomas, and arrived at Dr. Chase's office just after 8:00 a.m.

"Immaculate. How are you doing?" Dr. Chase ran me through all the measurements and bent my arm in all directions. We went over x-rays and talked about pain levels. At the end of the visit, he told me that my range of motion had exceeded the point he believed I was capable of reaching, and that it was as good as it was going to get at this point. I had regained inward rotation but my outward rotation was not going to return. He wanted me to continue to work on gaining back strength in the muscles. I needed to continue the weight program to help increase bone density. He sent his findings and recommendations on to the Rehabilitation Center. I would receive the combined final analysis at a scheduled re-evaluation at Beeston Hill on Thursday, 6/2/08.

After taking the cab ride back to the seaplane dock, I found that the next available flight was not until two o'clock. The government was flying all the senators and their staffs to St. Croix. I explained my situation and the fact I had to get back to work. Because I was a regular flyer they would see what they could do. They squeezed me in on an earlier flight and I was able to get back to the office just before 1:00 p.m. It was a lost day.

I got to Rick's house just in time to catch the sun going down off the deck overlooking Teague Bay. As I sat on a pool chair, I could not shake how unhappy I was with the doctor's evaluation. As the sun settled below the Caribbean, I was not content knowing Dr. Chase and the therapist had been impressed with the movement I'd regained. I wanted and expected more.

Wednesday, 6/11/08—After a restless night, the vibrant colors of the sun rising in the east bounced off the still waters as I drove to the gym in the early morning hours. A strange calm took over my thoughts. I was no longer worried about never regaining the full use of my arms. I really believed I could improve mobility with continued hard work. The workout seemed effortless that morning, and I was able to push through the really hard repetitions in the weight room, knowing I would get so stiff after the hard workout that reaching for the keyboard on my computer, or trying to raise my arm above my waist, was difficult. Sometimes my arms would visibly swell up and I would need to ice them down all evening long.

Thursday, 6/23/08—I witnessed another amazing sunrise off the balcony at Rick's house. His dogs were eager for a walk and we hit the surrounding hills for a quick half-hour hike before I headed to Beeston Hill for my final re-evaluation. I still wanted some guidance and preferred to continue to meet with the physical therapists at least once a week if for no other reason than moral support.

I was escorted back to a waiting room and asked to remove my shirt. They proceeded to put me through the same battery of tests they had performed earlier in the month. They measured abduction, inner and outer rotation of the shoulder and various other mobility and flexibility tests. Nothing had changed and the consensus was that they had delivered me as far as they could. I would be left on my own to improve what was now about seventy-five percent of original mobility in my left shoulder. They assured me that I had the knowledge to advance my progress. They thought I could gain an additional five to ten percent if I stuck to the program. I countered with my misgivings on striking out on my own. I wanted to have at least a couple of new weight routines that I would be able to build on. They agreed to meet with me for two more sessions.

Rehab had become such a physical grind. It was a thousand times easier to stay at home and miss a day, but as long as there was a scheduled appointment I knew I would never allow that to happen. Going forward, the motivation and determination would have to come from within.

Pain, a rundown condition and nervous flare ups ended up knocking me off my routine in the coming days, weeks and months. Regrouping and finding the willpower to continue my daily rehab became an ongoing struggle. I'd held the therapy specialists in the highest of regard, but quickly turned them from hero to villain in my mind. I viewed the final severing of ties as a slight against me and used it time and time again as motivation to keep the forward momentum.

With each passing day I felt more run down and was in need of rest. I was not sleeping and my calcium level continued to hover below the normal range. Headaches started recurring on a daily basis. They were usually centered over the left side of my head, concentrated on the crown just above the eye. Reading signals from my body helped determine my course of action. I continued to have tingling in my face, hands and the back of my head but I felt I could manage the nervous system with increased dosages of calcium. This was the longest, drawn-out fight of my life.

No one seemed able to wrap their heads around my nervous system and calcium level imbalance. I continued to consult with the doctors through an increasingly frustrated point of view. None of the prescriptions, or changes in the numbers of pills, seemed to help. It was a never-ending battle.

Saturday, 6/14/08—I hosted an afternoon pool party at Rick's house. Pat and Kathie, Melissa and Kristin and Greg came over. I had some yellow-fin tuna steaks for myself, beef steaks for everyone else and baked potatoes. I mixed up a big green salad and everyone else brought desserts. The party was relaxing and we had a wonderful time in the pool. I was conscious of not overdoing it, so I chose to go upstairs and lie down for twenty minutes or so during the afternoon. No one seemed to mind my absence and the party was still going on when I returned. I needed the time to close my eyes and concentrate on my breathing. The last thing I wanted was a nervous-system attack. I only drank one beer the entire day and tried to save my energy for cooking dinner. About 5:30 p.m., I got out of the pool and left Rick's dogs to entertain the group. They loved floating on rafts and being pulled around by everyone. I started up the grill and tossed the salad in a big bowl. When dinner was ready, we ate while watching the sun disappear below the hills to the west of Cotton Valley. The colors, seemingly rising off the ocean surface to the sky, were orange with blue pastels. The day had been a success and I felt good about my effort. Just a few months earlier, I wouldn't have had the energy to pull it off. I also knew I would need to rest most of Sunday to recover before going back to work on Monday.

Monday, 6/23/08—6:30 a.m. I was at Beeston Hill, eagerly looking forward to the first of my last two physical therapy sessions. The therapist showed me two new weight routines. They included more exercises designed to strengthen my core muscles. These exercises included working with various-sized rubber balls, dumbbells and stretching with free weights. I was instructed not to increase weight on my lifting exercises but instead increase the number of repetitions. I was to continue mixing in pool workouts between different arm and leg weight training sessions. I soaked up all the knowledge I could. It was all going to fall on me to continue and there would be no one else to place blame on if I fell off the wagon and got lazy and didn't continue to fight.

Wednesday, 6/25/08—My last day with the physical therapist was spent discussing how to tune into signals my body was giving me. I needed to be able to read my physical state daily and react accordingly. I was told to not push through the pain if it reached a specific level. We talked about holding back and avoiding burnout. It was not going to be easy to maintain the same level of enthusiasm for working out. I knew from past experience that it was a lot easier to stop going to the gym than it was to start back up. By the end of the session I was encouraged to strike out on my own.

DISASTERS (DAY 470 – 600)

Ever since Carlos Scow's tractor lost its battle with rust, Brian's Marine was the only option to have *Folly* hauled out of the water. Two months after I'd originally contacted him, Brian finally called back. He had plans to be at the Yacht Club at 9:30 a.m. the next morning. The short notice left little time to secure Pat's help, remove excess gear and scrub the bottom.

Once *Folly* was out of the water the biggest re-fit of her life would begin in earnest. The long project list was brought in clear focus. There was so much work to be done that my head started spinning just thinking about it.

Saturday, 6/28/08—At 9:30 a.m. the tide was on its way out of Teague Bay. Add that to the fact the ocean level is lower in the summer months, and we were facing a real problem getting the trailer deep enough for *Folly* to float over. Standing on the beach watching the surf, the discussion between the three of us ended with Brian guaranteeing he could get the job done. I had my doubts, but hoped the roller system I'd installed when I overhauled the trailer would help increase our odds of success.

Brian backed his truck down the beach and slowly ventured into the surf as far as he could go. His tail pipe was below the water line, creating a gurgling sensation. The twenty-five foot extension was attached to the hitch on the back bumper with my boat trailer attached to the other end. There's a deep hole just off an old dinghy dock. It was our target resting area for the trailer. As soon as Brian was in position, I caught a ride on the launch to my mooring and brought *Folly* in using the Johnson kicker motor. I cut the motor about ten feet before the back of the trailer and ran forward tossing Pat, who was standing chest deep in the water, a bow line. I watched from the deck as he tried in vain to walk *Folly* up the center rollers. We were about a foot too shallow. I jumped into the water and with several minutes of pushing and pulling we got her centered. As *Folly* slowly rose out of the water we could see her keel did not rest flat but instead balanced on the middle roller, dipping forward towards her bow. It was not the best outcome but would have to do.

I spent over an hour scraping sea weed and ocean growth off her bottom before moving her off the beach. Her final resting place was three, boat widths from a power pole along the front driveway leading into the club. I had some long extension cords that would reach, allowing me to use my power tools during the re-fit.

Folly sat untouched drying out from the end of June until mid-August. I had every intention of getting right to work on her, but I got busy with TMG related projects and didn't feel up to it physically. I would pump out rainwater, and survey the projects to be done, but I did not have the energy to take the first step.

My friend Bud Orpen, diagnosed with cancer, sold his house and moved to Texas to be with family. In an e-mail he stated that he was coming to visit St. Croix at the end of February. I invited him to go sailing when he was on island. In true military fashion, Bud immediately replied with the date of March 10th. Bud was going to be accompanied by a friend of his and wanted to know what kind of sandwiches he could bring. It was seven months in the future and Bud had pinned me down to a day and a time. This was the inspiration I needed to get started working on *Folly*. I was confident she would be back in the water by Christmas at the latest.

Wednesday, 7/2/08—Pam arrived on St. Croix for a ten-day visit. I'd taken Thursday off and we were set to fly by seaplane to Puerto Rico. I wanted to show her Old San Juan and take a few excursions into other parts of the big island. Within the walls of Old San Juan lie several interesting buildings and three forts that have protected this section of the island since Ponce de Leon had them built in 1508. The Spanish ruled this territory for centuries and inside the walls of Old San Juan are blue bitch cobblestone streets and row after row of Spanish Colonial buildings. Today the buildings house shops and restaurants.

Pam and I had become very close. She has a giving personality and always wishes to help me get past the issues I'm facing. Unfortunately the seemingly endless stream of medical problems continued to expand since the day we met. I had become reliant on her eternal optimism to see me through some dark times. When things start to go south for me, Pam is the first person I reach out to. She brings a sense of calm and understanding to a stressful and chaotic situation.

No doctor ever explained what I needed to do to prepare for these attacks. Pam instructed me time and time again to remember what the previous attack felt like, and to read the signals my body was giving me. With her guidance, I became an expert at interpreting my nervous system signals and understanding what the next several hours would be like after an attack started. She re-enforced these coping methods by asking several questions geared towards making me remember what we had done to survive the previous experiences. She did everything in her powers to keep me calm. Several times I lashed out at her verbally in the frenzy of having a system meltdown. She did not back up one step. She proved loyal and willing to face major complications without getting rattled. I wanted this trip to be special in part as an attempt to repay her. It was a small gesture for all she had given me.

Prior to the Old San Juan trip, I had become lazy in my daily workouts. I was still doing regular arm exercises but little cardio work. My weight had been on a steady incline for the past month. I was feeling poorly, struggling just to make it home every day and collapse into bed and watch TV. I had given up reading, a regular pastime when feeling good, and I stopped working on the plan for *Folly's* refit. I really had hit a wall. I was in a major rut and was in need of a kick in the ass to get myself motivated. The lack of sleep continued to be a major factor in my outlook on life. I wanted to get back to having a carefree personality but those days were seemingly gone. As this illness and its effects continued to drag on, I'd turned dark and brooding. I wouldn't characterize the mood as feeling sorry for myself but more pissed off that I was in this situation. As much as sleep continued to elude me, breathing issues continued to plague me. My doctors believed it was stress and anxiety related. I was a walking train wreck, but I tried to hold it all together and enjoy this trip with Pam.

We had bid on another plot of land overlooking Teague Bay. This one was located below the ridge top on the eastern wall of the valley. The lot was over an acre in size so there would be no chance of the survey showing it below buildable size requirements. Before bidding on the overgrown lot, I'd taken a machete and cut my way from one corner of the lot to the next. It would be difficult terrain to build a house on. We would be facing a major excavation project. In the middle of the lot is where the house would sit and there would need to be a switchback driveway cut down the steep incline from the road above. When I blazed my trail across the lot and found the orange markers denouncing the barrier lines, I crossed a fairly deep ravine that ran the width of the lot directly below the midway point. I found one map that mentioned this as a water gut. We proceeded to bid and the owner turned down our offer. We believed that was the end of our involvement and had moved on. It was a great lot, and in the perfect neighborhood, but we could not agree on price.

Thursday, 7/3/08—After landing on the calm surface of the ocean, we taxied to the seaplane dock, located three blocks from our hotel, just before 10:00 a.m. in the morning. We went to the Sheraton and deposited our bags and took off walking. We explored the shops and buildings located on Old San Juan's cobblestone streets for hours. We made our way up the hills and across the town to El Moro, the largest of the three forts protecting the walled-in city. The main fort complex is massive. It stands six stories tall. The front lawn stretches over several acres of open land. We could really not see the enormity of the fort because it is built on the side of a rock face leading to the Atlantic Ocean. After touring the fort we headed towards the hotel taking in the sights. We passed several historic churches

206

on the way, including Cathedral of San Juan Batista which houses the tomb of Juan Ponce de Leon.

We had a great day and it was shaping up to be the perfect getaway from St. Croix. I didn't want to be cooped up in my small house the entire time Pam was visiting. I'd planned this trip, start to finish, in hopes of getting out of our normal routine. Pam had asked me what I would like to do most in Puerto Rico. I said I wanted to hike the rain forest. This was not Pam's number one choice, but she arranged for us to spend a day with a guide hiking on Friday, July 4th. I was excited. I'd spent a lot of time in San Juan and the surrounding areas, but I'd never visited the rain forest.

After checking in at the hotel, we decided to eat at an outdoor restaurant located below the massive twenty-foot high stone wall that protects the city. Earlier in the day we had stopped at this restaurant for drinks. Pam is partial to white wine and Cruzan Single Barrel Rum. The owner was behind the bar on our earlier visit and said he had a bottle of Single Barrel at his home. He would bring it back with him if we ate there that night. True to form, the bottle was there and Pam was happy. We listened to the jazz band under the towering stone wall in a beautiful flower garden. Pam was impressed. We took a slow walk through the street performers with the smell of vendor's fare floating in the air. The night was perfect. Old San Juan was every bit as romantic as I'd remembered it. I wanted this trip to be perfect for Pam—and it was off to a great start.

We headed back to the hotel before midnight because we had to be up and ready to meet our rain forest tour guide at 8:00 a.m. Pam had hired John Druitt of Tropic Tours & Transfers. His slogan on his business card reads "Inspired Walks in Beautiful Places." He had explained that the hiking tour would take five to six hours and cover eight miles. He assured us, if we were in reasonably good shape, we would have no problems with the hike. There would be some difficult hill sections, but the forest temperature was cool and we would find it an invigorating break from the oppressive summer heat.

According to John Druitt, we did not want to stop at the waterfall trails most tourists liked. If we really wanted to get the full experience we needed to continue up and over the mountain where we would find the cloud forest. Over 3,500 feet in elevation, the Puerto Rican rain forest is one of the highest elevations in the Caribbean. In comparison, I'd spent a night at 14,500 feet in the Andes Mountains in Peru. I was sure 3,500 feet would pose no problems for me physically.

An ancient Carib Indian legend states, the good spirit "Yuquiyu" sat on his mighty mountain-top throne, protecting the people of Puerto Rico. The actual sub tropical rain forest occupies little area on the windward side of the El Yunque mountain range. This range crosses the northeastern section of the island. The sub-tropical rain forest lies at the top of the mountains where the rain falls in copious amounts year round. The streams, rivers and water falls that attract most tourists lie at lower levels of the national park. We were going to the top and back down the other side. Pam had set this up but as she heard more about the hike, she had apprehensions, but kept them mostly to herself. She knew this was going to be my favorite part of the trip and she wanted it to be perfect.

I had looked up the website long before our trip, and found the temperatures are cool and the ground moist. The winds can be strong, but what remains is a forested jungle and a variety of plant species and few animals. At the top of the mountain the entire area is shrouded in fog.

I knew I had the strength and will to handle the physical exertion the hike would demand, but this was a test. If I failed I would be discouraged. Mentally I was prepared to fight my way up the trail. My only worry was if I would incur breathing problems along the way.

After a good night's sleep, 8:00 a.m. came fast. Outside the Sheraton Casino, a busy street facing the cargo docks had four cruise ships in port for the weekend. Traffic whizzed by and hundreds of people milled about. We were sandwiched between several modern buildings. On time and in place, John Druitt waited for us in his conversion van across the street. I'd flown over the area several times, but never drove that far south and was unsure how long it would take. In the Caribbean, even short drives can take several hours depending on road conditions, animal interaction and traffic flow. John assured us that it would take less than an hour and a half before we'd be on the trail.

During the van ride, it became apparent that John Druitt was no ordinary tour guide. He had performed foresting operations in South America and sailed to Puerto Rico in the late 1970s. He had barely escaped when his boat was sunk during a hurricane. Shortly after that experience, he started his land tours. At one point he had been a commander in the biosphere project and lived inside the dome for a year.

Pam and I expressed our desire to learn as much as possible about the plants and birds of the forest. John launched into a long descriptive list of what we possible could see. Traffic was held up several times as we wound our way along the beachfront roads leading to the small town of Palmer. We made a stop to buy lunch from a local bakery. Before disappearing into the crowded mass, John gave me ordering instructions. When I reached the counter, the lightning fast Puerto Rican Spanish was more than I could grasp. Out of nowhere John reappeared and saved the day.

With Palmer behind us, we drove up route 191 towards the entrance to El Yunque, passing a handful of small souvenir shops on the way. We drove along a river, and watched as families swam in the cool water and dove from the large rocks on the banks. These scenes provided a stark contrast to St. Croix which is devoid of lakes, rivers or even a year-round running stream.

As we passed through the entrance gates to the El Yunque National Forest at 9:30 in the morning, cars filled every parking spot as we drove up the side of the mountain. By the time we reached the nearest trail heads, people lined the side of the road and vehicles were half submerged in the ditches. We had to make a concerted effort to weave our way through the moving mass. John assured us that these people were all headed to the waterfalls. Our trail to the top of the rain forest and the section known as the cloud forest would be less traveled. The excitement level was growing.

After parking, it was a short walk to the Mt. Britton Trail head. The morning heat had set in and I started sweating immediately. Surprisingly, there seemed to be only a few bugs as we entered the thickly forested trail.

Under the canopy of trees and green plants the temperature cooled and we settled into a comfortable uphill hike. Half a mile up the trail there was a large stone fortress built by the park service. We continued onto the Mt. Britton Spur trail. This led us across a ridge to the El Yonque Trail that would eventually lead us to the top of the mountain in the cloud forest. We were fortunate to see several new plant species John took the time to point out and explain in detail. There were plants that protected themselves by folding up when touched, an umbrella tree that when pelted with rain turns up its leaves changing the forest from green to white and several unique flowers.

Further up the trail large rock formations appeared for the first time. It was getting close to 1:00 p.m. and we were set to stop for lunch. John had promised us a unique setting. He was spot on. It turned out to be one of the most beautiful views I've ever seen.

Near Los Picachos, a point on the El Yonque Trail, we took a small rock-strewn path only big enough for one person to pass at a time. The trail dipped and as we climbed the upside we were greeted with a view of the entire rainforest valley below. The trail deadheaded into a rock formation that jutted out over a cliff. There was only a twelve-inch trail on the right side of the rocks. Once the trail ended, you had to scramble up the rock face to get to a small, flat rock overlooking the valley 1,000 feet below. Pam is not a big fan of heights and she was tentative climbing out onto the rocks. When all three of us were finally seated on a six-foot by six-foot square piece of rock it was one of the most peaceful experiences we could have asked for. Behind us, the rock formation fell off over 500 feet to a ledge half way to the forest floor.

As we settled in for lunch, clouds seemed to form off the top of the trees below. A light cool rain began to fall. The clouds were blown right over the top of our heads. It was a mysterious, cleansing experience. I was proud of Pam for being a trooper and not overthinking the climb out on the ledge. We ate in silence and awe of the natural beauty that surrounded us. My thoughts had gone back to the Amazon Rainforest and the cloudbanks that had rolled over my brother Rod and the group of guys who had gone mountain biking in the Andes. We had stood on a cliff at 14,500 feet and experienced the clouds rolling right through us at midnight in Peru. This experience with Pam was every bit as stunning. Nature is truly an amazing element in life and experiencing it first hand is always exciting to me.

After lunch we carefully climbed off the rain-soaked rock, keeping a good foothold on the path while leaning into the rock face to avoid falling back over the ledge.

Successfully navigating the thin path back to safe ground, we made our way to the main trail and continued our climb. Reaching the crown in the cool cloud forest at the top of El Yunque felt like a triumph. We stood at 3,496 feet. The forest was wet, cool and eerily silent. We had heard some bird calls on the way up, and John was sure we'd heard a parrot or two but we were not lucky enough to spot one in the wild. At the top of the mountain the trail goes behind a large communication tower signaling the end of your rain forest experience. It was close to an hour of straight down walking on a service road. I was glad to finally see parking lots ahead and know we were close to the van. Our experience had covered close to eight miles and lasted about five hours. The entire hike was wonderful and having a professional guide along made it all interesting. I'd remained on my regular calcium regimen and was not feeling any adverse effects.

Back at the Sheraton we were in no mood to walk the streets of Old San Juan. Our legs were spent. Pam and I ate at the hotel. We briefly donated some money at the casino and went across the street to a local watering hole for a few after-dinner drinks. When I started feeling some tingling in my face, we called it an early night. When we got back to the room there was a message waiting for me on my cell phone. It was our realtor on St. Croix. The owner of the second lot we'd bid on had changed his mind and accepted our last offer he'd previously declined. He wanted to purchase a sailboat and cruise the world, and needed the money. We spent the rest of the night discussing what we had thought was a dead deal. We finally decided to sleep on it and make our decision in the morning.

After numerous discussions, we decided to move forward with the purchase. Building on this lot was going to be more involved than the previous property because of the incline. Besides the building issues, we had a lot of talks related to what owning a piece of property would mean for the two of us. Our relationship had progressed rather quickly and even though we lived over 2,000 miles apart, we both understood that one had the others back at all times. Pam had helped me through the most trying times in my life. I was still struggling to overcome the effects of hypoparathyroidism and working full time. Pam understood that she would need to take the lead on the property deal. Lots of time would need to be spent contacting government agencies, realtors, banks etc. Although the previous lot we'd bid on was within eyesight of the new one, they had different homeowner's associations. Investigating the different requirements would fall on Pam's shoulders. In the end, we agreed that I would take care of the survey and we would move forward accordingly.

Later in the afternoon, we called the realtors back and agreed to move forward. We wanted a sixty-day grace period before closing. This was important for us because of our past experience. The owner wanted a thirty-day close and was unwilling to back off his demands. This did not leave us feeling good about the process but we reluctantly agreed. We kept a guarded enthusiasm about moving forward. While on vacation in Puerto Rico, we had agreed to buy a dream lot on the Caribbean Island of St. Croix. We were excited about the potential purchase and our future together.

Saturday night we walked the entire length of Old San Juan and ate dinner at a romantic outdoor restaurant in the middle of a flower garden. Again we listened to jazz music and stopped at several street performances on the way back to the hotel.

Sunday morning, we walked the half-mile to the seaplane and boarded our flight to St. Croix. As the engines revved up, we went hurtling across the water. I was consumed with a satisfied feeling. I had a wonderful girlfriend, a good-paying job and I lived in paradise. The one constant issue was my poor health. If I could just get that part of my life under control I could reach a new level of happiness.

On Monday I headed back to work and Pam was free to roam the island for hidden treasures. I felt bad returning to work while she was still on island, but she was not leaving until Saturday the twelfth, and I could not afford to take the extra time off. It was going to be hard enough returning after the four-day weekend. The company was involved in several deals, and we had new clients coming on board every week. My schedule was jammed packed with meetings and my group needed more and more guidance with the additional clients.

By noon on Monday my lips were quivering and my facial muscles were contracting. A bad headache had invaded my skull and I was feeling lousy. Fighting through the distractions I finished the day and a good amount of work had been cleared off my desk. As I drove home, I tried to project a happier persona. She was waiting for me at the door. I believe she sensed my growing tension and suggested we go for a walk.

Sleeping continued to be a problem, so letting off some late evening steam with a walk was a good idea. Even with exercises, I was unable to fall asleep without aide of a pill. I knew I needed to keep my strength up or I could suffer the consequences. My usual routine was leaving work and immediately coming home and lying down in bed. I tried to read for at least an hour every night intermingled with several hours of watching television. This was not the lifestyle I envisioned after moving to the islands.

Balancing a houseguest, work and health concerns was not easy, but having Pam with me every night was good for my mental state. She was always willing to listen to my issues and offer solutions. I was still feeling overwhelmed and for the most part, unwilling to acknowledge by how much. Pam forced me to face my most pressing issues and figure out how to proceed. The last thing I wanted to do was find another reason to speak with a doctor, give blood or anything else. I was way past the point of tolerating the medical system. After allowing me to blow off steam, Pam would bring me back to a rational thought process by asking me questions.

The work week finally came to an end on Friday. Pam was scheduled to fly out the following day. I was hoping for a big dinner in Christiansted, but I think Pam sensed I was pulling from my last reserves. We stayed out east and went to Chicken Charlie's. We played some 65 after dinner and went outside and looked at the stars. We continued to tell each other that things would be different in the future.

The weather had turned and the heat was starting to rise as it always does in mid-July. There had not been the usual number of hurricanes the previous summer, but the weather pattern was extremely hot and humid heading into the 2008 season. The rains started to fall a couple of weeks later. I was constantly running to the Yacht Club and pumping *Folly* out. I did not want the water to stand in her bilge for any length of time while she was out of the water. The mosquitoes would surely find their way in and nest in the bilge if I had. It would make the work needed to be done even more uncomfortable. The refit was not pressing, so I delayed it longer. Every time I was set to start, I began feeling sick. I found it easier to stay in bed. I thought the work would take me a month, two at the most, and I would have her back in the water. The only hard deadline I had to meet was the March 10th sail with Bud Orpen, and that was months away.

Monday, 8/4/08—Sara Sheldon, my boss from California, came on island for the week. Generally we had several meetings planned in advance of her trips, but she would be short of time. My work was taxing enough and I was happy not to have the added distractions. We did set up a meeting on Thursday to discuss progress on the system upgrades, out-sourcing calling loads and hiring new Associate Managing Directors.

Wednesday, 8/6/08—I woke to find red spots in my underwear. I did not have time to stop and dwell on it, but I was praying the problem of urinating blood was not starting up again. Thursday morning, I produced a large amount of coagulated blood. I felt feverish and my forehead became clammy followed by cold chills, but I had a full day ahead of me, including a two-hour, one-on-one meeting with my boss.

On my drive into work my breathing became labored and I took some Nexium to calm my stomach. I concentrated on taking deep breaths. I was

214

already worried about the bleeding and the last thing I needed was a breathing attack. The morning was a nightmare as I tried to finish my reports. I was sweating profusely and feeling nauseous. Several times I was unable to fill my lungs with air. Pounding my chest with my closed fist seemed the only thing that helped. This would have been a shocking way to start the day, but I had been through this so many times, I knew I would survive. Besides, I had to present myself to my boss in less than an hour. I could not stop sweating and went to the restroom and splashed water on my face time and time again.

Our meeting tone was straight and to the point. We had long ago dispensed with niceties. Generally there was some tiptoeing around, tension-filled questions passed down from above. Somehow Sara always remembered broaching these subjects in meetings past. I would have no recollection of ever speaking about them. Inevitably it always ended the same—with me scrambling to put together new proposals or reports so she had ammunition to take back up the food chain. There never seemed to be a seamless passing of information or requests for work. It was always a guarded situation that only ended one way—with my back against the wall. The one-way flow usually associated with our meetings was absent on this day, and I felt all talking points had been covered and agreed upon. It was rather refreshing and as our time wound down to the two-hour mark I was feeling good about my group's progress. Our time behind closed doors had not been spent discussing previous blunders or missed missions that had somehow been lost in translation. It was by no means perfect, but we were making strides towards improving our communications.

Before I reached the door Sara stopped me and said, "By the way I have decided to hire a person that will be placed between me and you in the chain of command. She will be your boss and you will report directly to her and she will report to me." Knowing Sara had been spread too thin with all of her duties this made sense. I didn't have time to digest this news, but a strange, uneasy feeling settled over me before I'd made it back to my desk. Before the end of the day, I knew this hiring would not leave me in good standing. There was not going to be enough room on the payroll for me to continue at my current salary and pay a new manager to stand between Sara and me. I made the comment later in the day to Melissa that this was going to be my downfall at The March Group.

As the news of a new boss settled in, my breathing issues resumed and by midafternoon I had retired to the downstairs bathroom where I continued to urinate blood as I battled a bout of diarrhea. Emerging from the restroom I was sweating and clammy. I had to concentrate on deep breathing and calming my nerves.

The fact that my new boss was moving from the states to St. Croix, and would be stationed in the same office, was the one hurdle I struggled with the most. For my entire career at The March Group I'd been allowed to operate with minimal direct oversight. I had regular meetings and definitely answered to a higher power, but I did not have someone right in my backyard standing over me. This was going to be a change that I did not relish. It took several days before I came to terms with the new situation.

The bleeding and breathing issues continued through Friday and I was relieved the week had finally come to an end. Pat and I had plans to golf at the Buccaneer Resort golf course on Saturday morning. We generally golf there once or twice a year, but had not had a chance over the past two years. I had just started to drive a golf ball again and was eager to see what I could do with some of the longer holes on the course. I knew my physical limitations did not allow me to post a good score. However, I was getting better hitting from 100-to-120 yards into the hole. The problem had been reaching those distances off the tee.

I was viewing this golf outing as a gauge to determine how far along in the rehab process my shoulders had advanced. It had been over a year since I broke the head off my left shoulder in Tampa. Golf was one of the easiest forms of comparing pre-to-post surgery. In the weeks leading up to this day I had developed a complete new swing built around the limitations in the rotation of the shoulder. The abbreviated back swing shortened my drives and diminished my accuracy.

The Buccaneer plays short compared to most eighteen-hole courses and I was convinced I could still post a somewhat decent score. I'd been hitting the ball straight but was going to need to concentrate on accuracy instead of power. With that in mind we teed up at the first hole. I spent fifteen minutes stretching my shoulders and arms before stepping up to the tee box. My first swing was light and controlled. The ball flew about 140 yards fairly straight up the fairway. I was off to a good start. I had slight pain in my right shoulder every time I played, but that had become normal for me. I'd tested the shoulders several times, and knew I was not inflicting any more damage. The pain was going to be part of my golf game for the rest of my life. I'd come to grips with this issue, and had used it for motivation to continue my daily arm exercises.

By the seventh hole I was sitting two strokes over par and holding my own. I was determined to break one-hundred and any score lower than that would be icing on the cake. My concentration level seemed to increase with each hole. I'd escaped into the round of golf. My energy was up and I felt like I was accomplishing a new mark in my rehabilitation. Just being able to attempt to play this course was something I could not have entertained a few short months before.

I struggled with the longer par five holes and made up ground on the shorter ones. This was a complete one-hundred and eighty degree turn from my previous playing days. Pre-injury, long holes provided me a chance to post a low score if I hit the ball straight. Now the short holes had become my saving grace. The golf gods lined up in my favor this day and I was sinking putts left and right, shaving strokes off my final score.

By the end of the round I was tired. Even though we rode in a cart, I had little energy left as I stepped to the eighteenth tee box. The par-four hole is long and straight. I ran out of gas and posted a seven, but I'd played one of the better games in recent memory. Both Pat and I ended up with matching 88s. For me that was a great round. After lunch at the Yacht Club I needed to get home and ice my shoulders to keep the inflammation to a minimum.

We had driven by *Folly* on the way out of the Yacht Club and it pained me that I was not further along in the restoration process. I vowed to start the very next day. The first order of business would be the sanding of my teak cockpit. It was well past time to begin the painstakingly long process. I put myself on the work clock that was eventually ticking down to Bud Orpen's visit in early March.

I had stopped by the hardware store on several occasions and bought reams of different grit sandpaper. I'd talked at length with my landlord Tony about the products he used on teakwood. He had three boats in various stages of restoration, and showed me some teak he had recently varnished with a product called Sikens. I spent some time online and did some research about wood varnishing and boat painting. There were several choices to be made but I needed a UV protection for the teak in *Folly's* cockpit because of the direct sunlight that bathed her daily as she rode on her mooring.

7:30 a.m.—I arrived at the Yacht Club and spent three hours climbing around looking at the project for the first time in earnest. Before leaving I had lightly sanded my teakwood combings and bench seats. My shoulders were on fire from the previous day's round of golf and the sanding motion only added to the discomfort. I knew my shoulders wouldn't stand up to the rigors of sanding the entire ten-foot cockpit by hand. Recently at a yard sale I'd purchased an electric palm sander and a belt sander, and was convinced I would need to use them in this restoration project.

I measured all the teak pieces that needed replacing and planned to get the new ones installed before varnishing. That was a long way off. I still had to remove all the old caulking and get the surfaces smooth. It doesn't sound like much work but before the teak was even prepared to be varnished I would have over thirty hours of sanding on it. This was going to be a lengthy refit. I decided early on in the first day that I was going to dedicate my time to the refit and throw every ounce of extra energy I had into the project. It gave me a sense of control, lost long ago in my personal life.

I had witnessed several of Mother Nature's greatest performances, including sea life and storms, from the cockpit of this boat. I felt like I owed her something in return. My favorite times were taking her to the ocean and being heeled over in a churning sea. I loved the fight and I knew how admirably she would perform in strong winds. The challenge was great and *Folly* always answered the call. Most days, however, were spent with passengers on board in much calmer conditions. I always trimmed her for day sailing and comfort, and she always delivered the quality ride.

Over the years I'd taken good care of *Folly* and installed new systems and conducted regular maintenance. By the end of the initial shock of my second shoulder surgery, my body was so battered, my mind was in no place to continue regular upkeep. I was not even sure if I was going to be able to get back into sailing. *Folly* wasn't completely ignored, but this was by far the longest she'd ever been left in the salt water. I ran down and checked on her mooring lines each day, making sure she was safe. The few times I had tried to sail with friends in charge of her were difficult. On Christmas, when I had to give up the helm and be rushed in to shore, was a low point.

Despite the fact I'd not been able to sail as frequently as in the past, I knew I enjoyed being on the water more than doing almost anything else. The Caribbean is intoxicating and becoming a sailor had taught me much about nature, myself and my boat. I have been fortunate to be able to race in regattas on some of the finest racing boats ever produced. These experiences provided a great learning opportunity. You really have to practice and go through the dings, bumps and bangs to understand what is possible within each situation and how to approach it. In sailing as most situations in life your reactions are based on past experiences. Most people who step on a sailboat for the first time are fearful of the unknown. If the boat heels over to one side it scares the crap out of you. The motion is uncomfortable at first because you don't realize it's designed this way. I crossed all those hurdles years before. I really enjoyed being heeled over, sailing for speed. The rougher the water, the more I seemed to enjoy it. I missed the competition of the regattas and being in charge of my own boat for pleasure. Mostly I missed the sense of accomplishment sailing has added to my life.

Sunday, 8/10/08—I'd been sanding *Folly*'s teak since before 7:30 a.m., but decided to shut down due to the heat at noon. I lay on my bed the rest of the day and tried not to move out of the flowing air from my floor fan. The sweat was nonstop. Between urinating blood, and being sore from playing eighteen holes of golf, I felt sick to my stomach, but I did enjoy the feeling of accomplishment for the few hours of work that morning.

I had started the refit project and felt in control for the first time in a long while, but most days the illness was relentless and the heat was not helping the situation. I had to rest for hours at a time. I felt as if I had to save up enough energy over the weekends to go to work on Monday morning. By midweek I was dragging, and by the end of the week I was barely getting by. The more I lay on my bed and thought about the situation the more the anxiety would fill my head. I could not stop it. My stomach would begin to rumble and diarrhea would soon follow. By this time I was convinced that the bleeding I was experiencing was connected to the stress I was under. I needed to accomplish this refit to gain confidence that I could still give maximum effort and see results without breaking down.

My condition had spiraled out of control so quickly there was little time to plan. My only game plan was to push through the pain and the stress. It was not working. The one question I could not wrap my head around was what if this is it? What if the rest of my life is spent feeling this miserable? It scared me. I could not afford to let these thoughts linger and take root, and before I took a sleeping pill that night I went to the restroom and proceeded to fill the bowl with bright red blood.

Just before the pill kicked in, a dull pounding headache formed over my left eye. I woke up early Monday morning and the headache was still there. Whether I was willing to admit it or not anxiety and stress were taking their toll. I did not completely understand the symptoms because I had never experienced this level of stress.

Dr. Wiesblat was the first to really try and discuss anxiety with me. He believed it was playing a large part in my numerous ailments. I was too busy denying it and disagreeing with what he was saying to benefit from his expert opinion. He brought it up on more than one occasion and the reality of these conversations was difficult to accept. In my view, if this doctor was correct, it meant I was out of control—weak. As with everything, I tried to take it all in stride, pushing it aside, concentrating on what I was good at and had a history of being successful with.

Work had been my salvation. I poured all of my limited energy into it. My position at The March Group continued to grow in scope, and the tasks grew in numbers greater than one person could control. We had passed this point long ago. The company's solution was to provide an additional supervisor rather than allowing me to take charge of the situation. I would have to forfeit some control over processes I'd implemented and administered in the past. I hated the idea. It was a difficult time to keep my emotions and professional demeanor in check. If I'd had the foresight to listen to Dr. Weisblat, and taken a hard look at my situation, the mounting stress and anxiety playing a part in my overall health would have been evident.

Monday, 8/11/08—I entered into the sixth straight day of urinating blood. I continued to have diarrhea, but I worked even harder at my job and dreaded the looming arrival of my new boss.

Tuesday, 8/13/08—The limited energy I had Monday morning was already spent. I struggled to finish out the remainder of the day. Throughout the week, I resorted to taking short breaks, putting my head down on my desk, and closing my eyes for ten to fifteen minutes. It was the only way I could remain at work and continue to function. I averaged three to four hours of sleep each night. It had become such a problem that even when I took an Ambien, the pill did not always overcome the stress. I would lie awake until the early morning hours and feel like the walking dead the next day.

Wednesday, 8/14/08—In the morning I noticed the bleeding was starting to taper off. I was never so thankful for something to come to an end. It was impossible to ignore and although I felt better after having the problem thoroughly checked out, I was sure there was something more sinister behind its recurrences. I'd stopped taking Nexium because I felt I was eliminating it before it had a chance to do its work. Not taking Nexium caused acid to be pushed from my upset stomach into my esophagus leaving me with breathing issues. The rollercoaster ride continued.

Sunday, 8/17/08—My stomach issues and headaches seemed to grow over the weekend. The clock on the TV box read 5:30 a.m. Monday morning. I had concentrated on being in bed by 9:30 p.m. the previous night in hopes of a long, sound sleep. I tried to calm down, using deep breathing and relaxation techniques, but the constant tossing and turning made it impossible to shut down. I sat up and started to read. After forty or fifty pages about Stalin, I was ready to give it another try. It was well after midnight, but my mind refused to be turned off. As with most nights, it started running through multiple thoughts on different subjects at the same time. One thought right after the other—with no pattern. Once the floodgates opened, I was relegated to passenger duty as control was snatched away.

It was around this time that I began experiencing large muscle contractions in my arms and legs. My bicep would contract so hard my arm would jump one or two inches. The same thing took place in my hamstrings. The muscles would contract uncontrollably for long periods of time, release, and then contract again. It became unnerving when the contractions started happening to the muscles running up and down the sides of my neck.

Thursday, 8/21/08—I was a wreck in need of sleep and salvation. The tingling started in my face and quickly spread to both hands. I was not in control of my nervous system and it was scary and unbelievable that this condition continued to affect me so severely. I was sure a stroke was imminent. I called Pam and she helped calm me down, but I was agitated, nervous and scared out of my mind. And I only had patience to absorb Pam's encouraging words for so long. Keeping my temper from invading the conversation was my ultimate goal but that did not always happen. I would get agitated with the line of questions or too many back to back suggestions. This beautiful woman was my lifeline and I was lashing out at her. I would get off the phone and within twenty minutes have an uncontrollable need to call her back and thank her for her help. We were on the phone for the third time when we finally said good bye just before 1:00

a.m. She always said she understood and was there for me whenever I needed her. I always wondered, if we lived together, how run down I would have made her during this period of my life. She would not have been able to sleep. I moved positions in bed several times a minute, popped straight up when the breathing became too hard, and then paced the floor for hours rubbing my muscles—trying to control the contractions.

I needed to take back some semblance of control after making it to work the following morning with less than two hours of sleep. I could not allow my life to continue in this manner. I set up a face-to-face meeting in Cleveland with Dr. Weisblat. I had to schedule it after my new boss' arrival on island. I bought my plane ticket for Friday, 9/12/08.

My doctor's appointment was scheduled for 9/15/08. I would work from Cleveland the following week. I requested a full physical and blood work. I needed answers and was prepared to take any tests needed to get to the bottom of what was happening. Having these plans in place seemed to ease my mind. I still had daily tingling in my face and hands and sleep continued to be elusive but the diarrhea and breathing issues started to diminish. I was happy knowing help was coming in the form of a doctor's visit. This speaks volumes as to how far I'd come and how bad my situation really was. I spoke to Dr. Politz and kept him in the loop. He again asked me to explore the anxiety issue and tried to reassure me that my situation would eventually get better. Again the message I was receiving was hang in there and avoid making the situation worse by stressing over it. Easier said than done.

Even with the doctor's care looming, I still needed to persevere for three weeks. I vowed to turn the TV off before 9:00 p.m. and read. This,and taking Ambien, helped me get a solid five to six hours of sleep each night. My plan was to continue my restoration of *Folly* on the weekends. Hopefully I would then tire myself out and fall asleep, easier.

Saturday I worked on *Folly* from 7:30 a.m. until noon. Progress was slow. I continued to prepare the teak for the first coat of varnish. Sunday, 8/24/08 was a repeat performance. I started the work at 7:30 a.m. to avoid the heat of the day. The majority of what I was doing was sanding and removing old caulking. I spent countless hours upside down under my teak benches, bent over sideways or curled up on the floor boards. To work on the teak combings I stood in the bottom of the bilge three-feet below the floorboards. While I was down there I removed rusted screws and plotted the new cross beam. It was difficult staying focused on one job when there were so many to do.

I had several smaller areas that needed to be reinforced with West System Epoxy. There were all kinds of paint that needed to be stripped and replaced. The surface area included the entire cockpit and decks, the side walls, inside the cabin and the bottom of the boat. None of that could get underway until I had all of the teak and the wood work preparation completed. Working on the boat seemed to release energy within me and I fell asleep easily on Saturday night. After working close to four hours on Sunday I was hoping for the same outcome, butsleep eluded me. I took an Ambien after 9:30 p.m. and was still awake after midnight, my mind racing from subject to subject. There was no shutting it down.

The following workweek was filled with the tension from loss of sleep and the need to function efficiently. Wednesday was the same. Thursday and Friday were spent in a continuous fight to stave off exhaustion. As with the past several weeks, I was never so happy to see the end of the workday come on Friday. This was a special occasion because Monday was the Labor Day holiday. A three-day weekend was exactly what I needed. I planned to work on *Folly* every day.

I stuck to the schedule of 7:30 a.m. to noon to avoid the heat of the day. I made several trips into the hardware store to buy supplies, including a large tarp to provide a shaded area over the cockpit. I also needed various new tools including scrapers, stripped screw and nut removal drill bits etc. The work progressed, though it was difficult to measure. I was in the stripping and tearing down mode but I knew I was taking care of the work in the correct fashion. I'd read painting manuals and product reports for weeks in my spare time. Most of the information was new to me. I'd never worked with teak or the varnish on such a large scale. The learning curve was steep. I tried following the detailed instructions, but working outside in the heat of summer is not what the manufacturers suggested. I pushed on and found with each passing day things looked better and better. I actually had completed one coat of varnish on half of the cockpit by the end of the long weekend. Not where I'd hoped to be, but I had a new understanding of the amount of work the project would take. I slept soundly Monday night.

Tuesday, 9/2/08—It was a mad dash of catching up and clearing tasks off my desk in hopes of finding time later in the week to prepare for inspection. I was anticipating an invasive look into all facets of my work. Other people had been so displeased with the impending arrival of our new boss that they chose to look for other employment. The feelings ran deep that the hire should have come from within the organization.

The number of mergers and acquisition had been declining throughout 2008. The news was not good out of Wall Street. Banks were struggling under the weight of bad debt. Access to bank loans was impaired due to the bank's sizable exposure to mortgage-backed securities. The ominous news also affected the demand of potential buyers.

The Private Equity Groups I dealt with on a daily basis were still flush with investor cash, but their normal course of action was to borrow money and add on acquisitions. As the spigot for loans was slowly turned off, deals sat on the shelf waiting to be completed. In the final months of the year, TMG found itself falling short of annual sales goals. Around the office speculation about job security was rampant.

Friday, 9/5/08—the workday mercifully came to a close. Before I was able to run out the door, Kiril asked me to help move his desk from one office to another. My new boss was moving in to his office. It was a cross between simultaneous grunting, cursing and sweating as we shoved the huge wooden desk across the old, coral brick floors. Before we finished, an lightheaded feeling overtook me as if I was going to pass out. We finished and I immediately headed for the front door and the stairs that led to the courtyard below. Everyone was meeting for drinks after work, but I needed to get to my car and make it to the safety of home. I was barely able to navigate the five-block walk to my car, staggering to the halfway point before sitting on a park bench in front of the fort. I put my head in my hands and closed my eyes. It was fifteen to twenty minutes later before I felt I could make the remaining walk to my car. The drive home was spent leaning against the door for support. When I reached my house I quickly got undressed and flopped into bed. My head was spinning.

I was able to get five solid hours of sleep and early Saturday morning felt good enough to continue work on *Folly*. I chalked the strange feeling from the previous afternoon up to exhaustion.

I was at the Yacht Club before 8:00 a.m. I was able to put in three strong hours of varnishing before the fumes took their toll. I called it a day and raced home for a quick shower and the comfort of bed. I would not move from my bed except for restroom and food breaks. This is what my life had become. My level of fitness had fallen to an alarming state. My one saving grace was the doctor's visits and tests I had coming up the following week. I was not about to throw in the towel. At times I would tell myself, "You can make it." I held daily meetings within my own head arguing the need for more effort and reinforcing the need to hang on and fight.

Monday, 9/8/08—The weekend seemed to fly by and then it was back to the grind. I had meetings with the new boss scheduled on Wednesday. I needed to have all other work completed before then. I would be asked to produce new reports, documents and future plans that would inevitably increase my workload. I was not looking forward to opening my entire operation up to a newcomer. I was proud of the accomplishments during the course of building this side of our business. At the same time, I understood the work was not finished and explaining this to someone who had not been involved with the inner workings would be difficult if for no other reason than the sharp learning curve needed to reach familiarity with the company's operations.

Midmorning on Monday Sara Sheldon and my new boss, Deborah Walker, took the vertical climb up the twenty-two stairs, turned right and presented themselves at my office door. I was on the phone when they arrived and they took up chairs right next to my desk. The whole time I was finishing my phone call I felt as if I was being sized up. When I finished I stood and shook hands with Deborah. I would be lying if I said it was not awkward. Sara broke the ice by giving me what sounded like a rehearsed compliment. She quickly excused herself and left the two of us alone.

Deborah explained that her role was going to be big-picture oriented and that she needed to understand exactly what it was that I did. I spent the next half-hour running down the list of my responsibilities. It was a long list that touched on marketing, list generation, client meetings, buyer identification and relationship building. With a somewhat empathetically pained face she asked how I stayed on top of it all. I said I'd been asking to hire assistants for over a year and it had not been approved because of budget concerns. I knew times were tough, but proceeded to explain my belief that if I was to continue with this many responsibilities I needed skilled assistants to take over some of my menial tasks so I could concentrate on the big picture. In retrospect this was probably not the best tactic for the first meeting with my new boss. Even as the words tumbled out of my mouth, I could see the conflict between her agenda and mine.

For weeks I'd wondered what this lady would be like and how we would ultimately interact. She was reassuring in that first conversation. She was open to suggestions. I knew I was no further along in my quest to get new assistants, but she did listen and vowed to help in any way she could. We set our times to meet and said our goodbys.

Back home, Monday night quickly turned into early Tuesday morning as sleep eluded me. My arms and legs continued to tingle and go numb. The Ambien I took only made the situation worse by clouding my head, making me more restless. I finally talked myself into a temporary sense of calmness and fell asleep sometime between 2:00 and 6:00 a.m.

Not drinking coffee or caffinated sodas left me with little choice. I loaded up with fruit hoping to get a sugar rush that would carry me to the lunch hour. My healthy alternative failed miserably. The day dragged on and I was left thinking it would never end. I had several phone calls to make and three marketing meetings on my schedule. I was exhausted by the time I got home. After ingesting the Ambien, I was out cold by 10:00 p.m.

Wednesday, 9/10/08—My meetings with Deborah went well. She seemed attentive to what I was saying and took notes. I found her to be engaging and intelligent. She had worked with The March Group in the past and demonstrated a partial understanding of our present goals and objectives. My impression of her was one of trustworthiness and someone who was going to help the company.

Thursday, 9/11/08—I was busy making last minute arrangements before leaving for Cleveland, Friday morning. This was a working trip for me but I still had to have contingency plans in place for the time in the air. Inevitably questions and issues would arise that needed my attention. I gave my team last minute instructions and prepared to finish up my final reports for the week. The day before, Deborah had asked me for several group specific reports to be delivered when I returned from Cleveland. I worked hard and by the end of the day I had what she requested loaded onto an e-mail with several attachments. As soon as I hit the send button I was out the door with my laptop, headed home to pack.

Friday, 9/12/08—The flight out of San Juan was delayed thirty minutes. There was a good chance I was going to miss the connecting flight out of JFK. My original arrival time in Cleveland was 7:10 p.m. I rushed to the departure gate as soon as the doors opened. The connecting flight had not left because there was no crew. They had been delayed coming out of Pittsburgh. I jumped on my laptop and answered fifteen e-mails. I made four work-related phone calls and got a sandwich from a vendor in the lobby. The crew arrived three hours later and we finally got ready to board. As the regional flight descended through the clouds, my mind was able to shift gears and focus on the joy of being reunited with Pam. We touched down a few minutes after 11:00 p.m.

In her usual, positive manner Pam explained the delay had been no trouble. She didn't mind picking me up at the late hour, though I knew she had a busy day, and had to wind her way back through traffic to come pick me up. All seemed right in the world as we embraced.

The weekend was spent relaxing watching movies and eating fresh fruits and vegetables. On St. Croix, good fresh produce is almost unheard of. There are a few local farmers, but ninety percent of what you find on store shelves has spent several days in the cargo hold of ship or has been tossed around in the belly of an airliner. Fruits that are not already deteriorated and vegetables spoiled or half-covered in mold, are few and far between. The summer months, when the cargo container schedule is cut back due to hurricane season, is when the store shelves are next to bare. You do your grocery shopping on the Monday following a cargo ship's arrival. Even then, the quality of the products is poor and the variety offered would shock the average American. I feast on all the fresh fruits and vegetables I can get my hands on whenever I reach the states. Pam had a refrigerator full of cleaned and prepared vegetables in individual plastic bags so I could make salads to my heart's content.

On Sunday, we went to a movie with Pam's sister. We made plans to play cards later that week. I had a list of books I wanted to purchase and CDs from the local music store. I was in a good place and felt relaxed and content. This made the ensuing breathing issues all the more surprising and disappointing. I sat straight up in the early morning hours unable to fill my lungs with air. I had gone to sleep without the aid of a pill. Hours passed and my body was unable to regulate itself. As I paced Pam's floors, I tried to remain calm. It was becoming increasingly more difficult with each new episode.

Monday, 9/15/08—I worked through the morning hours, still experiencing some breathing issues. My appointment with Dr. Weisblat was scheduled at 11:15 a.m. The logistics of getting me back and forth was maddening, but Pam insisted she come along.

I had asked for a full physical and Dr. Weisblat put me through the paces including an EKG, shoulder mobility measurements and complete blood work. My blood pressure was 145/82. This was better than in March but still too high. My weight had ballooned to 267 pounds. This was especially disheartening. I'd worked so hard to control my weight. I'd always been on the heavy side, but this was by far the heaviest I'd ever been. The inactivity and the constant struggle staving off one affliction after another had taken its toll. I'd been experiencing major discomfort in my right hip and had pulled my right calf muscle, which had kept me away from strenuous aerobic exercise for months.

When it came to the breathing issues Dr. Weisblat drilled into the subjects of stress, anxiety and depression. Reluctant to face my weakness I waited for my turn to discredit his theory. According to the doctor I presented the classic symptoms: a severe lack of energy, difficulty breathing, and time pressures from both personal and professional activities. I said I was handling the work stress and I didn't think that was an issue. He went on to explain that stress can manifest itself over the course of the day and by the time you come home, the symptoms start to appear. Most of my nervous-system attacks, breathing issues and stomach problems came after the workday had finished. I conceded that point. I'd been reluctant to take any Xanax during the workday, though Dr. Weisblat had urged me to, thinking Xanax would keep me more relaxed throughout the day, and increase my chances of a good night's sleep.

It was obvious from my lack of sleep that the Ambien was not working out, so Dr. Weisblat prescribed a new pill named Klonopin. It had the added benefit of controlling anxiety and was a stronger sleeping aid. I ran through my usual concerns about adding a new drug to my pill regimen. He assured me there were no side effects if taken properly.

A lot of information was being tossed my direction, and I felt uncomfortable in the hot seat as Dr. Weisblat continued to address my concerns. He believed my body was reacting to stress, manifesting itself into pain in my jaw and the swelling in a gland just below the jawline. My breathing difficulty had become pronounced and was an issue both day and night. The EKG showed no problems in the heart muscle. Relief flowed through me as if I'd just dodged a bullet. Dr. Weisblat insisted stress and anxiety led to acid rising from my stomach which exacerbated the breathing issues.

He went on to explain that once I started having breathing issues, panic would set in, adding to the symptoms. "Panic is a normal reaction when you are unable to take a full breath of air. Xanax should help alleviate that." Unable to accept reality, I cut the doctor off mid-sentence and insisted I did not panic. "Look, I simply try my best to calm my systems down so I can breathe. There's no panicking." I was not sure if I was trying to convince him or me, but I believed I'd made my point.

I said the tingling and uncontrolled muscle spasms in my legs, fingers and face were brought on by unregulated calcium levels in the blood. The symptoms, according to Dr. Weisblat, were enhanced by stress and anxiety. He was unwilling to give up his point. We would be able to confirm just how much they affected the symptoms with future blood tests.

The new prescriptions included Klonopin 1 mg tablets for sleep and anxiety, Xanax .25 mg tablets to be taken as needed during the day for anxiety. The blood work included a Lipid Profile Panel (hyperlipidemia Instructions: Blood/Serum), ALT (Llanine Lminotransferase) (Hyperlipidemia; Blood/Serum), Tsh (Thyroid Stim Hormone) (Hyperlipidemia Parathyroid Hormone, including calcium and ionized calcium) (Primary Hyperparathyroidism; Instructions: Blood/Serum), Ck (Creatine Kinase) (Myalgia and Myositis; Instructions: Blood/ Serum). The last test on the list was to check and see if the drug Lipitor had side effects that had manifested into soreness in my hip and calf muscles keeping me from working out.

The wellness clinic staff included a dietician. Dr. Weisblat voiced his concern over my weight gain and urged me to have a consultation with her. I was exasperated with all the information by this point but went ahead and set an appointment for Wednesday morning at 8:30 a.m. This gave me time to have my blood drawn at the laboratory down the hall before returning to his office. The ease of getting tests performed and the speed in receiving results was in direct contrast to how the system worked in the Virgin Islands. All test results going forward would be gathered by Dr. Weisblat and he would contact me with the numbers and discuss progress and future steps in the recovery process. I walked out of his office knowing my heart was okay and feeling thankful that the process was less convoluted and daunting than it had been in the past.

After fasting from 8:00 p.m. the previous night, I sat motionless in the chair and donated the necessary three tubes of blood. A short walk down the hall I found myself scribbling my name on the sign-in sheet. The date was Wednesday, 9/17/08. Thoughts of the previous twenty-three months battling illness filled my head as I anxiously tried to push them aside and think of other topics while waiting for my name to be called. I was not looking forward to an entire hour scheduled with a dietician, but I needed to show the doctors I was willing to try anything.

"Mr. Krehbiel." She began by asking me a series of questions about my eating habits. I explained I ate fairly healthy but always seemed to remain on the heavy side. She had me run through a list of what I ate over the course of a week. At the end she had come to the conclusion that part of my weight issues were from my diminished activity level over the previous twenty-three months and an even larger part of it was my weakness for ice cream and peanut butter. She thought that these cravings could be caused by my body's need for more calcium. It was not uncommon for me to eat an entire half gallon of ice cream in one sitting. I was buying three to five half gallons a week. She brought out molded models of ice cream and peanut butter and showed me the same molded amounts of fat they would produce in the body. Her demonstration made me disgusted with my eating habits. We discussed how to limit my portions and the need to stay away from trans fats. I had high levels of bad cholesterol and needed to get my diet under control. What I'd thought was going to be a long, boring hour actually turned into an informative look into what I would become if I did not change my ways. If I continued gaining weight I would end up with heart disease or diabetes. It was a shocking wake up call.

I had one final test on Thursday at 4:00 p.m. Dr. Weisblat, in conjunction with Dr. Politz, had prescribed a full body bone density scan at Spectrum Imaging in Cleveland. After my usual pre-test interrogation of the people who ran the operation, I was assured this was not going to be invasive. I had to undress and a density machine was passed over me for less than ten minutes. I was in and out in under an hour.

Bones act as calcium storage units for your body. My parathyroid had been abnormally pumping large amounts of hormone into the blood stream, causing calcium to be pulled from storage at an alarming rate. The best guess by the most renowned professionals in the Endocrinology field was this had been going on undetected for years. The resulting loss of calcium in the bones caused them to become paper thin, running the risk of cracks and fractures. In addition my nervous system was paying a heavy toll. What would be the next bone to break? I had to think about every movement, including walking up and down 200-year-old stairs and sidewalks every day. My sailing routine was limited to the basics and I sat in a guarded state for most of the trips I took out on the water. One mistake and I could be rehabbing again.

The ferry ride was over in a half-hour as we docked in Put In Bay. The water was calm and Pam and I were excited to be catching the island after the major summer rush was over. A short getaway was just what we needed to decompress, and my head was still swirling with medical issues as I searched for a release valve.

We quickly settled in and found Main Street, a few blocks from our lakefront hotel. We took a golf-cart ride around the island and looked at all the beautiful homes built at the turn of the century. We toured a vineyard with a cave on the grounds. The weather was fantastic and we enjoyed exploring.

As Sunday rolled around, I knew my time with Pam was coming to an end. I was eager to get the test results back, but I was not looking forward to returning to St. Croix on Monday morning and getting back into the exhausting workload.

Monday, 9/22/08—My flight took off for Chicago at 6:30 a.m. I'd spent an hour the night before answering e-mails, and compiling a list of calls in order of importance. During time between flights in San Juan and some work at home in St. Croix, and I was almost caught up.

Tuesday, 9/23/08—I received an e-mail from Dr. Weisblat explaining my CK blood test was abnormally high and could be the cause of the calf and hip muscle pain I'd been experiencing. Creatine Kinase (CK) is the formal name of the test and a high count can indicate damage has occurred in some muscles, including the heart. I needed to stop taking the Lipitor. He also advised me to avoid strenuous activities until my Creatine Kinase levels were in the normal range. I had asked Dr. Weisblat about this prior to the blood test. In reading the side effects for Lipitor, it cautioned the persons taking the drug to monitor any muscle cramps or strains because it could be a sign of a serious side effect.

I was pleased with the communication available through Dr. Weisblat's service. He took the time to explain the potential for good and bad results in each new medication he prescribed. He wanted to hear all my concerns. As in the case of Lipitor, Dr. Weisblat listened to my issues and tested for possible problems. I felt a sense of accomplishment and that my treatment would improve.

By consulting with the dietician I was trying to correct my weight gain. She stressed the need for breakfast and to eat before each workout. I added a daily breakfast that included plain yogurt and fruit. I cut out cheese, ice cream and peanut butter. I was also cleared to engage in low-impact exercise.

After work, I went to the Yacht Club and pumped a full bilge of rainwater out of *Folly*. My mind was racing with test results and work-related issues as my right hip and lower back muscles began to spasm. It was 10:00 p.m. There was no chance of sleep. With some trepidation I reluctantly took my first Klonopin. Within a half-hour of taking Klonopin I felt my shoulders relax and I started to get drowsy. Minutes later I was out cold. Seven hours later I woke up feeling rested and relaxed.

I'd not heard from Dr. Politz concerning the new test results. I called Friday morning, 9/26/08. He had received the blood test and bone-density scan results from Dr. Weisblat. Dr. Politz understood from the numbers why I was feeling so poorly. My calcium levels were at 7.2ml, well below the normal range, and my ionized calcium level was low—explaining, in part, why I constantly felt sick. My parathyroid hormone level was barely in the normal range. All these numbers needed to improve before I would see positive results. Dr. Politz explained that I needed to increase my calcium intake from ten pills per day back up to fourteen. He wanted me to increase my vitamin D intake from two pills a day to four. He did not agree with Dr. Weisblat that the amount of Nexium I was taking had a negative effect on my calcium levels. He requested all previous bone-density scans be sent to him for comparison with the most recent results. I expressed my concern over my hips. I felt I needed to be guarded in every action I took to protect them from breaking. I viewed the revelation of thinning hip bones as a ticking time bomb. This was mentally challenging for me. He reassured me that we would find a solution that would elevate my calcium levels to the normal range. He reiterated that bones can rejuvenate their supply of calcium and that in the future I might see benefits from, again, taking a drug like Fosamax. First, we needed to get the calcium regulated. I left the conversation feeling confused and a little disappointed that Dr. Politz's pep talk had missed its mark.

As the workweek came to an end, I was still feeling discomfort in my right hip. I'd stopped the Lipitor and eased up on any heavy cardio workouts on the elliptical machine. The pain was dull and constant. I was concerned it was a bone fracture. Over time I came to the conclusion it was likely muscle related. Nevertheless it was uncomfortable and never let up.

On Saturday, I walked nine holes of golf at the Reef Course. The pain in my hip increased after the round was finished, but I still needed to get some work done on *Folly* so I limped down to the Yacht Club. I spent two hours working on her teak before relenting to the swarms of mosquitoes. Sunday morning was no different. I vowed to wear a long-sleeve shirt and full-length pants even in the extreme heat.

I completed the second coat of varnish on the starboard half of the sanded teak cockpit. My goal was three coats on each side. The hours of work kept adding up. I'd purchased a large tarp and at the end of each session covered the cockpit. The one good thing about working on *Folly* in the summer heat was instant weight loss. I lost twenty pounds within the first six weeks. The downside was uncontrollable spasms near the bicep muscle in my right arm, lasting for hours, contracting several times per second causing a jumping sensation. Over time, the spasms spread from my arm to the right side of my neck. I concentrated on keeping them under control by rubbing the area and applying pressure regularly.

Monday, 9/29/08—I had a morning meeting scheduled with Deborah. She was scheduled to go to our Florida office the week of October 12th. Because I'd traveled to Florida, frequently, and knew the entire staff at Coral Springs, I was asked to go along and introduce her. It was beastly hot, and I jumped at the chance to spend time in an air-conditioned hotel room. We made our plans and I went to work booking my ticket and rental car. This was going to be a good opportunity for us to get to know one another. Sara was going to meet us in Florida on Thursday. We had a working dinner planned for later that night.

Knowing the Florida trip would delay results on the boat project, I ran down to the Yacht Club after work to get some varnishing done in the fading sunlight. It was pitch dark by 7:00 p.m. I'd not reached the halfway point on the first task on the list. I did the math and figured I would need close to 200 more hours to finish.

My arm continued to spasm uncontrollably, especially at night and when I was typing at work. My right hip was sore and I had tingling in my face and the back of my head. These were conditions I was growing accustomed to living with. I mentally had to keep myself grounded and not let the combination of symptoms cascade into a full blown attack. The semantics used in conversations between brain and body at this time still left the word panic out of the equation: "Stay calm. Breathe. This is going to be a good day! You can fight through this. Forget about how sick you feel and get your ass out of bed and do some work on the damn boat!"

I continued taking Klonopin which allowed me to fall asleep every night. This was a major improvement.

Friday, 10/3/08—I communicated with Dr. Politz via e-mail. I'd sent him several questions earlier in the week. He had received my previous bone-density scans but they had few usable numbers. The laboratories would need to give detailed numbers in five specific areas. The numbers he received were in condensed form. I was going to have to contact the labs in St. Croix and Cleveland and request the original, non-condensed version be sent to him. The information he received showed that my bones were not regenerating. The calcium, in his estimation, was not getting to the blood stream where it could travel to the bone structure for storage. There could be several conditions causing the issue, including molecular or receptor defect in the stomach. The receptors allow the calcium absorption to take place. He talked about hypophosphotaemia—low levels of phosphates in the circulating blood. Rickets, a vitamin D deficiency—a long shot since I was taking 4000 units of Vitamin D daily. He did explain that patients with Rickets can be prescribed upwards of 50,000 Vitamin D units daily.

I was not willing to accept the symptoms of the illness and pain. "What can I do to better manage this disease?"

Dr. Politz was frank. He wanted me to have Dr. Weisblat arrange a visit with a top Endocrinologist. The receptors in my stomach needed checked. He was willing to take the time to go over my entire case with the new Endocrinologist before my first visit. He also wanted me to have more blood work done to check Vitamin D 25 along with calcium levels.

During the course of our conversation I brought up the fact that I thought he was a top professional in the Endocrinology field. Dr. Politz explained that my case was unusual and that it needed the attention of a practicing Endocrinologist who specialized in severe cases. He was a trained surgeon and I needed to see a specialist. One of my questions had to do with liquid calcium. I had received bags of it intravenously in the emergency room. We discussed the possibility that synthetic parathyroid hormone might be a potential future treatment option. Synthetic parathyroid hormone was rather new to the market and only used to treat severe cases of osteoporosis in elderly women. He felt I was on the right track and might get some benefit from taking it. The liquid calcium was something he would also look into on my behalf. As far as he was aware, the only place it was being applied was at Bariatric Clinics after obese patients had stomach surgery. He thought it could be a sure-fire way to increase calcium absorption if I was able to figure out the proper dosage. It was a long shot because he didn't think it had ever been used for this purpose.

Although it was a step in the right direction, talking to Dr. Politz did little to alleviate my fear of breaking a hip or other bones. I called Dr. Weisblat and spoke with him about my concerns and the need to get a top-notch Endocrinologist on my team. Dr. Weisblat agreed and said he would look into it and get back to me within the week.

By the end of the long workday I was wiped out. Instead of heading to the boat as planned, I opted for rest. My arm and neck spasms continued. I would need Klonopin to help me sleep. I reluctantly popped the pill in my mouth and drank a full glass of water. A drowsy sensation came over me a half-hour later and I drifted off to sleep. In my life I've only had a handful of dreams, and I'm rarely able to remember more than one or two details. This night was filled with vivid, action-packed dreams. I fought valiantly against thugs, had sex with strange women and came under attack by monsters. Each dream felt real. The dreams continued for the next several nights. Whether it was the drug or just another bizarre consequence of this illness was a mystery.

Saturday and Sunday were spent working three hours per day on *Folly*. Unlike my health situation the rehabilitation of my boat gave me an opportunity to control the outcome, including the quality of the work and the timeframe for completion. The deeper I got into the project, the more time I could tell it would take to finish.

After resting all afternoon and evening on Sunday, I entered the workweek with some renewed energy. Knowing this feeling would be short lived, I barreled through process enhancements involving the Business

Development Group, read over marketing material related to upcoming client Business Strategy Meetings and attended three conference calls. By the end of the workday on Tuesday, 10/7/08, I'd come down off my high and found myself in total exhaustion. I spent an hour and half after work preparing the second half of *Folly's* cockpit for varnish. Having finished three coats of the starboard side, I switched my attention to the port side. I was saving the floorboards for last.

Wednesday came and went with the same low energy. Later that night Pam asked several questions about my conversation with Dr. Politz. She had learned it was best to leave a little time between her questioning and the actual event because I needed time to process the information, but Pam wanted to keep track of the medical information. She was eager to help, and understood the frustration I was feeling, and the pressure I was under to accomplish all the doctors wanted in an appropriate timeframe. I reached a point fairly quickly in the conversation when I'd had enough. I didn't want to discuss it any longer. I always felt bad when my frustration would come out in the form of anger towards the one person who was with me every step of the way. I loved Pam and didn't like the way I reacted. We came to the conclusion that I would let her know when I was fed up talking about health issues, and we would work through it at a later time.

Thursday, 10/9/08—I woke up and found traces of blood in my urine. My mind raced as I closed my eyes and tried to concentrate for half an hour on keeping calm. I did not want this to turn into a full-blown nervous-system attack. After gathering myself together, I headed off to work, listening to my favorite Rolling Stones CD. It seemed to take me out of the moment for a few minutes.

As the early workday progressed, preparations for the trip to Coral Springs was top priority. I contacted my counterparts in the Business Development Department, setting up times to meet with Terry Dibert, Senior VP of Operations and Sales Support, and George Markis VP of Sales. I also made plans to introduce Deborah to the Human Resources and office management staff.

Part of my job was being the link between the front end of the business and the back end. Along with my counterparts, we worked to overcome the perceived communication flaws our owners saw as a weakness in our competition. We had forged strong working relationships and willingly passed information between the separate business groups. This process had evolved into several shared projects. One in particular was a system for the front-end telephone group to be able to send me business owners they had contacted that were not interested in selling their company but had an interest in buying a business for growth purposes. It started out small but had blossomed into a 100-lead-a-month project. I contacted each one of these leads, and had the power to approve them or deny them for inclusion in the growing database. Keeping track of these buyers, and making sure they were informed of any clients that met their acquisition criteria turned into a daunting task. I had asked for a new hire to take over the calling aspect and the building of the database. Because of budget constraints I was left working this process day in and day out on my own.

One of the first things Deborah asked of me was to break down the exact amount of time I spent with all the different aspects of my job over the course of a week. When I finished the time budget I was reluctant to send her the results. There was no question I was overloaded, which she would see, and she could easily start to shift responsibilities.

The March Group had made it clear with Deborah's hiring that I'd advanced as far as possible. Nevertheless, I vowed to form a good working relationship with her. I found Deborah intelligent and in our few meetings she expressed a sincere desire to see the company succeed. The changes being discussed in high-level meetings included new ways of using databases and innovation to improve labor intensive processes. I knew tracking my time would affect me, but the lingering question was by how much.

The March Group scrambled to distance ourselves from the banking industry. All of our logos were changed, eliminating our once proud proclamation, "The March Group, A Private Investment Banking Company." They now read "The March Group, A Private Mergers and Acquisitions Firm." It was simple economics and we had changed our whole identity because of the perception in the marketplace and the court of public opinion. Things had changed quickly and I could see this new business landscape would soon be affecting my job.

As the weekend approached, stinging pain accompanied each episode of blood in my urine, adding to my darkening mood. I continued to work on my boat, but my nervous system reacted negatively to the varnish fumes—even after I started wearing a heavy-duty air filter mask. Wearing the mask in the heat caused a rash to form in a ring around my face. If I chose not to wear the mask, the fumes made me sick, causing tingling in my head and numbness in my arms and legs.

The temperature continued to climb. August and September were hot and October no better. Sunday night, 10/12/08. As I prepared for the following travel day I watched the weather channel. The tropical update showed a small depression off the coast of Venezuela. Forming off the coast of Africa and traveling west across the Atlantic ocean before slamming into the warmer waters of the Caribbean, the tropical depression had slipped south of St. Croix down to the coast of South America—400 miles away. There was no real threat of a tropical storm forming from the depression while I was gone. As usual before a trip, I asked Pat to get any rainwater out of *Folly* if we got showers while I was gone. I mentioned the depression, now located near Venezuela. We both thought it was nothing to worry about. Storms on St. Croix generally come from the east.

Monday, 10/13/08—Deborah and I flew to Florida but were seated at opposite ends of the plane. We were also on opposite sides of a growing economic issue within our own company. I had been working at The March Group for four years and was well paid. Deborah was new to the company, but she'd worked with The March Group in the past. Cost cutting changes were taking place all around us. Most commissions were now based on the number of companies sold. I was still being paid based on the number of signed confidentiality agreements produced each month. How long would this continue?

We met at the baggage carousel at Miami International Airport. The Fort Lauderdale flight I preferred to take had been canceled by American earlier in the year due to slow sales. The only option to get to Coral Springs was the flight into Miami, leaving a thirty-five mile drive north to our office. We gathered our luggage and took the shuttle to the rental compound. It was a nice drive to Coral Springs, and Deborah and I had a pleasant conversation. We found a sense of mutual respect for one another. To my surprise, I genuinely enjoyed her company. Like me, she was an avid reader. I knew where the Barnes and Nobles was located near our office. We agreed to go after work one evening. The week ahead was going to be long, but I was feeling much better about my travel partner.

After checking into the room, I immediately turned on my laptop and got to work. An hour into e-mails, I had a strange feeling I needed to check the weather. What was just a blob off the coast of Venezuela had formed into a much larger depression. Forecasts hinted that it was going to strengthen into a tropical storm overnight. I was more interested in what was coming from the east. I scanned the radar from Africa heading west. There was nothing that looked like it was going to affect the Northern Leeward Islands. The depression off Venezuela had little chance of moving straight north and affecting St. Croix. There was a warning to keep an eye out in the Northern Leeward Islands, but that was a common occurrence when any depression or storm was within three-to-four hundred miles of our island. I took a Klonopin and slept great.

We arrived at the office at 7:30 a.m. on Tuesday morning. Throughout the day, I took Deborah around and introduced her. We had meetings with Terry and George, and I spoke at a Business Development Managers meeting. I gave the group a pep talk about the Buyer-Lead Program and discussed the success we had working those leads. I answered questions, ending on a high note with the year-to-date top commission earners in the BDM ranks.

Everyone left with a bit more understanding of what and why this was so important. All of this was done under the watchful eye of Deborah. I was still going strong in a meeting with one of my Associate Managing

Directors when 5:00 p.m. hit. I still had another two hours of work left. I went down to the office and started responding to numerous e-mails. I also took the time to check the weather forecast. The tropical low had turned into a depression and briefly reached tropical storm strength before breaking apart. It had moved north and was closer, by 100 miles, to St. Croix. I was glad it had started to break apart, but at dinner I commented on what a strange development this storm system was. Deborah and her husband had lived on St. Croix in the past and experienced hurricanes. We both felt the depression had no chance of developing that quickly and the current path to the Northwest was not going to hold.

Later that night I logged on to the laptop and checked the weather, almost as an afterthought, and was shocked to see what was taking place. The tropical disturbance had strengthened into a tropical storm. Omar was predicted to feed off the warm waters of the southern Caribbean and race northwest as it strengthened into a hurricane. By October 15th, Omar began to quickly intensify. Later that afternoon, an eye developed and the storm began to accelerate to the northeast. I spoke to my landlords, Donna and Tony. I also called Pat. Everyone was prepared and bracing for a mild storm, but throughout the night Omar shifted its track more to the northeast and was heading directly for St. Croix.

After a late dinner with Deborah and Sara, I raced back to my hotel room to watch the Weather Channel. Their coverage of Omar consisted of a reporter standing on a beach in Puerto Rico, sixty-five miles to the north of St. Croix. I watched all night as waves lapped up on the moon-lit sands. According to the Weather Channel, nothing was happening. The satellite images of the Caribbean on my computer told another story. Omar was a small, highly concentrated storm. It reached its peak intensity with winds of 135 mph with a barometric pressure of 958 mbar early in the morning of October 16th. Omar skirted the southern edge of St. Croix, sparing the refinery from a direct hit, and roared ashore over the eastern end of the island later that morning. The counter-clock-wise rotation caused the most damage on the northeastern facing of the island. Cotton Valley was the hardest hit. Downtown Christiansted sustained major damage along the boardwalk.

As daylight broke, Deborah and I headed to the office. It was difficult to focus on work. We kept each other informed of any updates as Thursday's mad scramble to check on everyone back home rolled on. I was able to reach Donna and Tony, Pat and Kathie, and Kiril at our office in Christiansted. The power had been knocked out island-wide. The phone lines remained functional in some spots and there were even some pockets of cell service. Several poles had been snapped off and lay blocking the roads,making travel difficult. No one had been able to venture out because of the downed power lines, but as far as they knew, everyone had made it through the storm safely. That was the most important news. Pat called me later in the afternoon on Kathie's cell phone and gave me an upsetting update. He had been able to drive over and around eight power poles downed in the mile and half between his house and the Yacht Club. Several boats were lost to the storm. Most sustained damage. *Folly* was in a row of boats out of the water and most of them had been tipped over on top of one another. *Folly* was full of water but sitting upright on her trailer.

My landlords called me and said that the dogs were okay, but we lost most of the fruit trees in the yard and an entire row of privacy trees behind the guest house were snapped off like twigs. The more I heard, the better I felt. Nobody was injured and nobody had sustained any structural damage to their homes. Deborah had heard from her husband, and their situation was much the same. Their new home on the North Shore was operating on generator power. The road leading up to their house was blocked by debris including a power pole, but everything else seemed okay. We were scheduled on the only nonstop flight to the island the next morning, and would be arriving on St. Croix one day after a category-three hurricane. It was going to be tough times without electricity, and with the increase in humidity and lack of moving air, the foreseeable future looked grim.

Throughout Thursday, there were several meetings scheduled and everyone in the Florida office, having been through numerous storms of their own, continually asked for news from St. Croix. The March Group did not have a backup generator. We were able to get communication lines open with our colleagues via cell phones.

With each bit of news we received, it was apparent that the office was going to be off line until at least Monday. We spent most of the afternoon into early evening working off a list of computer-related projects to keep everyone in St. Croix caught up before leaving Florida. Having that much work to do helped the time pass. Before I knew it, night had turned into morning and Deborah and I were at the airport in Miami passing through the TSA lines.

I needed to find a quiet, comfortable place in the departure terminal to run the private equity conference call. To be honest my heart was not in it, but my guest was talkative and gave me long, flowing answers to my questions. Despite the background noise, we burned through the half-hour with ease. Once it was finished, my thoughts quickly turned to home.

Deborah and I shared one last lunch in air-conditioning before boarding the plane. We knew this would be the last time we would have that luxury for some time. We talked about the storms she had lived through during her previous time on island. We both understood exactly what we would be heading back to.

As we boarded the plane it was apparent that the other passengers did not understand that St. Croix had been hit by a hurricane the day before. Omar did not devastate a highly-populated area, so it did not receive much press in the states.

As the plane roared away from the gate, the quiet Indian lady seated next to me bowed her head and closed her eyes. I was sure she softly spoke some sort of prayer, but I didn't understand it. Watching her, I felt a sense of relief knowing some higher power was looking out for us all. The moment struck me as pure and heartfelt. As the jet revved up and hurtled down the runway I glanced over at my flying mate and smiled. I received a look of sheer terror in return. As we climbed through the clouds, I broke the silence and asked if she lived on island. I knew the answer before she offered it, but felt I needed to speak with this lady. She was visiting her sister who had moved to St. Croix a year earlier. Digging her nails into the armrests, she explained that this was the fifth flight of her life. The last one she had been on was ten years earlier. As we talked about flying and travel, the terror slowly left her eyes and she loosened her grip on the fabric-covered armrest. She was looking forward to seeing the Caribbean for the first time. I asked her where her sister lived and she told me on the east end. She found it odd that she had not been able to reach her on her house phone for the past day and a half. She was worried that her sister might not remember what time to be at the airport to pick her up. In the middle of a plane loaded with people, talking about what they were going to be doing on their vacations, I leaned over to the stranger seated next to me and explained that Hurricane Omar had hit the island the day before.

"This is your Captain. Welcome aboard American Flight 1593. Our destination today is sunny St. Croix!" A loud cheer went up from the vacationers as my travel partner digested the new information. I shook my head and closed my eyes.

This was the weekend of the popular Buck-to-Buck Island swim. I was able to gather from their conversations that the three rows of passengers directly behind me were all college swim-team members. I overheard them discussing strategy for the race. I was pretty sure the swim would be canceled, but I did not want to intervene and wreck their enthusiasm. I had already put the fear of god into the lady sitting next to me and that was enough for one day. I had enough to contemplate, and did not feel the need to inform everyone else what was waiting for them when we landed.

As the plane descended over the west end of St. Croix, the ground cover was lush and green. It had been much less so when we left on Monday. As the pilot pushed the nose down in a big sweeping turn, the view down island had changed dramatically. All the demolished shells of buildings left abandoned in past storms like Hugo, Wrong Way Lenny and Maryland were visible. The vegetation that had covered them for years had been blown away. As the wheels touched down, another cheer went up from the party group which had been drinking most of the flight.

Stepping off the plane, a wave of heat and humidity jolted my senses, making the walk down the stairs onto the tarmac highly uncomfortable. I immediately broke out into a sweat as I hurried to the covered walkway, through the doors and out into the parking lot. There were few taxis at the stand, and the place seemed empty. Passing the open-air baggage claim carousel I hesitantly turned the southern corner of the building thinking my car would be gone. The rental companies had moved all of their vehicles out of the storm's path and the rest of the airport parking lot resembled a ghost town. Looking like she had been power-washed, my car was one of five or six others in a usually full lot.

I had left my car parked next to a line of rental vehicles. Because they were moved out of harm's way, my car had not banged into anything when it was jumping around in the wind. It had moved a full foot and half to the right and sat somewhat sideways. I was relieved to find all the glass intact and the tires inflated.

I met Deborah and her husband standing over the conveyer belt, willing it to life. It would take over a half-hour before the luggage started to flow. Deborah's husband works for a contractor at the refinery and he explained that the entire operation had shut down. Shutting down the refinery was a huge deal and had only happened a few times in past storms. The road they lived on was still blocked by downed power poles and they would be forced to drive through Kasha bushes and Tan Tan to make it home. He had heard from co-workers that Cotton Valley was hit much harder than the North Shore where they lived. We could hear the distant hum of generators and the faint smell of diesel fumes lingering in the air.

When a storm comes close to the island it sucks in heat and humidity. The winds also get sucked into the convection and leave with the storm as it passes. The lack of electricity compounds the debilitating heat and over-whelming humidity. After all the rain and wind are gone, there's a steep increase in mosquitoes and Jack Spaniards—whose natural homes in the tall grass have been destroyed. Debris on the roads makes it difficult to get around, and driving any distance is a risk because of the potential for flat tires and damage from other drivers who, under ordinary circumstances, show little regard for other vehicles. The island quickly turns into a twenty-six mile long obstacle course filled with hot, angry people boiling in their own sweat. Thank god it was a fast moving storm!

Minutes down the only road leading away from the airport I found myself stuck in a long line of cars at the first of four, non-working street lights. No one seemed to know whose turn it was to go as cars started and stopped in utter confusion. So far, the only evidence of the strong winds were a few Tan Tan trees and Kasha bushes snapped off, laying on their side. All the homes and buildings visible from the road looked intact. As I reached the end of the double highway, I ran into a major traffic jam at the four-way intersection leading past the Sunny Isle shopping center. People were trying to pass through the intersection at the same time from all directions. There were three or four cars off to the side of the road, obviously damaged in accidents. With the South Shore road blocked by fallen power poles, my only option was to wait out the long line and continue straight ahead. As I waited, watching the complete ineptitude of island drivers, a group of five young Rastafarians rode right through the middle of the traffic jam bareback on ponies. They passed within inches of the line of vehicles. Chickens were darting in and out of the stalled traffic, feasting on the abundant selection of bugs that accompany the passing of any storm. The horses reared back at the sight of the chickens moving around their feet, almost tossing their riders into the already confused mix.

Trucks filled with children, family members, and five-gallon jerry cans for gas and water, were lined up as far as the eye could see. The traffic lights rocked back and forth lifelessly in the light air, oblivious to the circus below.

As I crept along the roads west of Christiansted, I continued to search for any signs of damage. It was light. As I approached downtown Christiansted the view changed. A 200-year-old, twelve-foot-high, brick wall had collapsed across the sidewalk and spilled into the street. Light posts lay across the road. The side streets leading to the harbor were littered with debris, including satellite dishes, signs and garbage cans. It was eerily quiet. Only a few people were mingling about.

As I drove down King Street, the views towards the harbor revealed several boats stacked up on the boardwalk. I could see several more bobbing in the water, de-masted with rigging dangling over their sides. As I came to the last turn by Fort Christiansvaern, numerous vessels had been slammed into the break wall, creating a large, floating debris field that rolled with the calm surf of the ocean. The park in front of the fort looked like a war zone. Trees were uprooted and benches had been ripped from the concrete sidewalks. Trash, boat parts, street lights and exposed power lines littered the ground. I set aside my urge to stop and investigate, and chose to continue on towards home. As I passed Company Street, where The March Group offices were located, I slowed as I saw the damage to the steeple building—constructed in 1753. Red tiles from its roof littered the sidewalk and street below. Further up the hill, older stone buildings were still standing and looked in good shape.

What little traffic there was on the roads after the Sunny Isle intersection moved at an extremely slow pace. Normally a twenty minute drive, had taken over an hour to reach Gallows Bay from the airport. Everyone was taking it easy, trying to avoid the myriad of potholes and debris strewn across the roads. I was almost past Schooner Bay before remembering I needed to stop. The parking lot was filled to capacity. I was forced to pull off into the grass field to the east. As I stepped out of my car the distinctive hum of a large generator blasted my ears. Drinking water was the big draw. The storm had taken most people by complete surprise and they didn't have time to prepare. I bought the last five remaining gallon jugs of water on the shelf. I also picked up energy bars, nuts and carrots. With no power for the foreseeable future, nothing perishable would last. The conversation taking place up and down the aisles in Schooner Bay Market was centered on how bad the east end was hit and when WAPA was going to get power restored. Everyone was hot and there was no mistaking the shocked look on their faces. They had rode out another storm, shuttered up inside their homes praying for the wind to stop. When your wish is finally granted and the damage is surveyed, there is an urgent focus on the issues at hand—the need for water and food.

The boating community was the hardest hit. With little time to react to the storm, boats had been left in the water in hopes that the original weather forecasts which predicted Omar would remain a small tropical depression, were going to hold true.

Heading east after leaving Schooner Bay Market, I came across the first of many telephone and power poles that had been snapped off like a cheap board in a karate exhibition. The storm's power was evident as I had to drive off the road and around downed power lines from this point all the way to my home. Trees lay across the road in several spots completely void of leaves or small branches. Along with the leaves, the tall grass that stood just days before in the open fields of the east end was gone—blown out to sea. All the homes seemed to be intact with roofs and decking still visible in the fading grey haze of October 17, 2008.

It was nearing five o'clock when I finally reached Cotton Valley. The drive down the one-lane dirt road was blocked by several fallen trees. The dirt and rock road had eroded into one big rut. My landlord had cut through some bush and trees blocking the driveway entrance. The broken-off trunks and branches scraped against the side of my car as I squeezed through the tiny opening in the pile of debris. Surveying the yard, all the fruit trees had been snapped in half or uprooted. There were all kinds of corrugated roofing sections scattered in the trees and the bush behind my guest house. I was immediately attacked by a massive ball of mosquitoes as I opened the car door. The Jack Spaniards were also out in force. They buzzed around my head as I dashed for my door.

I made a quick check of the inside of the guest house in the fading light. While changing my clothes I noticed the constant hum of the diesel generators powering the homes throughout Cotton Valley. With no breeze, the air was thick with diesel exhaust fumes. Tony had a generator for the main house but the guest house had none. Our compound was not contributing to the loud environment around us because Tony and Donna only ran their generator for brief moments throughout the day.

I stopped by Pat and Kathie's house as I drove back into the valley after a failed attempt to make it to the Yacht Club. Too many trees and power poles blocked the roadway. The hills looked bare and stripped of most vegetation as goats roamed free on the side of the road. I could see shells of homes lost in hurricanes long ago that had not been visible to me in the previous seven years of living in this neighborhood. Nature has a strange way of clearing the bush and tall grass, revealing a completely different landscape. Pat was in the front yard making piles of downed plants and tree limbs. He was visibly worn out and had not slept in close to twenty-four hours. The picture he painted of the Yacht Club was not pretty. He offered to take me there the next morning in his 4x4 truck.

After squeezing my car down the debris-lined road and scraping more paint off the doors, I stepped out into the hot, humid air. Again I was attacked by a swarm of hungry mosquitoes. Bats dove on the flying bugs as the last light of day turned to darkness. The air was motionless. Not even a wisp of wind could be found. I quickly shut the front door behind me and lit as many candles as possible to avoid using up the batteries on the numerous, strategically placed flashlights. Life without electricity is something one gets used to living on island. You go through your set routines and hope for the best. To the veterans of stronger storms such as Hugo, who had lived for months on concrete slabs where their homes once stood, Omar would soon be forgotten. Although the aftermath of Omar meant living in adirty, humid, bug infested environment with no electricity for days to come.

There had been a quarter-inch of dust and dirt deposited by the storm inside my tightly, buttoned-down guest house. The hurricane shutters and wooden window slats breathe with the high winds. My first order of business was removing the mess. All-in-all, everything was void of standing water, a sign of Omar's short duration. The humidity made every surface damp—including all the bedding and furniture. I dug out some new sheets

251

and pillow cases from plastic bins and went through my power-outage routine. I lined the top of my bed with beach towels because I didn't want to sweat directly on the sheets. The temperature, after the sun went down, was still in the mid eighties. If the heat and humidity did not keep you up the constant roar of generators powering homes throughout Cotton Valley would. Standing over the last of the dirt and dust piles, I was dripping sweat faster than I could sweep. It made a pasty adobe mixture I promptly tracked all around the floor in my bare feet. Cleaning up was one step forward and two steps back. The rest would wait until morning when I could see without trying to move with a lit candle in my hand.

My last memory of the day was the struggle to read the exploits of a young brutal dictator named Stalin through the candle-smoke-filled-haze surrounding my bed. The mindless hours normally spent in front of the TV needed to be filled with other entertainment, otherwise I would be left facing the ultra-humid days head on—with few distractions.

October 18—The sun was just rising over the eastern hills as dew dripped from the wooden window panes. The piercing sound of the wild rooster crowing in the back lot forced me off the sweat-soaked beach towels. I'd dealt with wild roosters in the past and knew in the days ahead I would come to hate this bird, but for now he was earning his keep by feasting on the bugs swarming outside the house.

The first thought of the day was getting the pill routine going. I could not afford to fall off the wagon. If I varied the hours and intervals too much, I ran the risk of having a nervous-system attack. The last thing I needed was having to rush to the emergency room.

I scanned the available channels on the wind-up radio, searching for an English-speaking station offering time and weather updates. Winding the generator handle for more than a minute or two caused sweat to pour off my forehead, forming a puddle on the floor. I set out to perform all the chores I could not do in the dark, including cleaning and throwing out all bad produce from the refrigerator. I knew, a short time later, the heat would make it unbearable to stay inside.

252

The familiar sound of Bud's tail hitting the handrails on the front porch led me to open the front door. Bud and a handful of mosquitoes rushed in with a strong dose of morning heat. His shedding hair quickly covered the wooden kitchen floor where I'd placed a bowl of water for him to drink. One more mess to clean up. It was time to get dressed and spend some time in the air conditioning of my car.

After speaking briefly with Tony in the front yard, I was busy counting the new bug bites on my legs as I made my way to Pat's house. A thorough inspection of *Folly* waited. Between the entrance to Cotton Valley and the Yacht Club, a distance of one and a half miles, there were eight power poles, snapped off at the bottom, lying across the road. Numerous trees and large branches covered entire sections of the two-lane winding road. What vegetation was left on the hillsides was golden brown after being inundated with salt-water spray from the winds roaring in off the ocean surface. The ocean was calm with little to no surf breaking on the reef. Driving off the road up a hill and into a goat pasture avoided another downed power line.

Pat stated, "It is flatter than a platter of piss out there." He rode out Wrong Way Lenny at his brother-in-law's home and was sure Omar's winds were much stronger. His French doors leading to his great room bowed in and out several inches during the worst of it. Leaning against them with all his weight he hammered several of the largest nails he could find through the doors into the frame. The quick fix held, saving the living room from an onslaught of 125-mile-an-hour, saltwater inundated wind.

As we pulled into the Yacht Club yard, Omar's wrath was visible in all directions. Large palm trees lay across the parking lot next to damaged boats of all sizes. In the mad rush to pull as many boats out of the water in the hours leading up to the storm a forty-foot sailboat on a trailer was crammed into the space between *Folly* and the twenty-six-foot sailboat directly to the south. There were no more than a couple feet of separation between boat trailers, hulls, riggings, bumpers and lines. The owners of the forty-foot boat had not lashed it to the trailer properly. What transpired during the storm was a violent bouncing of the hull on the trailer when apparently enough space was created between the two where the winds funneled underneath and the boat was picked up and deposited on top of the twenty-six-foot boat to the south. The counter-clockwise rotation of Omar's winds had saved *Folly* from certain destruction.

My heart sank at the sight of the destroyed vessels. There was a forty-five-foot catamaran that just days before was a young couple's home. It had been flipped upside down and driven into the sandy beach. Two mono-hulls lay in a tangled heap in the bush directly behind it. Three racing catamarans hung precariously from treetops. The boats still floating in the mooring field had missing sections of paint and topsides where debris had slammed into them. Most had been de-masted by the high winds and their rigging dangled in the calm water. We could make out the dark shapes under the water of several sunken powerboats. Four or five masts broke the surface of the water at odd angles, the hulls attached to them lying on the sandy bottom.

Only a few people milled about in complete silence as there was little need for fast action. The damage had been done and the cleanup would take a Herculean effort over the course of the next several weeks. Cranes and heavy equipment would be needed to do the lifting and to haul away the discarded trash. These machines are in limited supply on a small island so their first duty is clearing roads of downed power poles, trees and debris. It would be days, if not weeks, before they would reach the Yacht Club.

After climbing onto *Folly*, and removing all the water trapped in her bilge, I surveyed the work I'd recently completed. Surprisingly enough, the tarp I'd covered her with when I left on my trip, had done its job. It was ripped and torn, but the teak in the cockpit still looked good. I had a few patches that needed touching up, but I could move forward with my work as soon as the roads were cleared.

The entire time spent outside of Pat's truck we had been under attack by mosquitoes. There were several pools of standing water and the west side of the boatyard was a virtual swamp. The water gut leading to the beach was blocked with debris, causing a large portion of ground just west of the clubhouse to become inundated with runoff water. The swamp became the breeding ground for thousands of mosquitoes.

After leaving the Yacht Club parking lot and climbing the hill to the east, the road was blocked by a herd of goats. The fence had holes blown in it during the storm, and faced with freedom, the confined occupants took the opportunity to roam the roadside, eating the newly sprouting green grass. A couple of long blasts of the truck horn forced the slow-moving animals to either side of the road, allowing us to pass.

Retracing our steps over and around the downed power lines, we made our way west. The road cleared considerably as we passed Gallows Bay. The King Cross Building, where Pat works, had held up well with no damage. Pat was sure his office would be working Monday with power being provided by the building's massive generator. We walked down King Street and turned to the north heading for the boardwalk. Debris lined the empty streets. It was getting close to noon and the heat index was over one-hundred degrees. It was overcast with no breeze and was stifling.

As the boardwalk, stretching from the fort west to the sea plane docks, came into view, we could see that downtown had taken a substantial hit. There were several sailboats piled up on the wooden pathway over the edge of the water. Their masts angled towards the front of the bars and restaurants, almost blocking the entrances. Large sections of the wood planking were missing, and the finger docks that are home to sport fishing and the dive and day-sail businesses on island were destroyed. Below the debris-covered surface of the water lay the remains of vessels sunk next to the cement pilings they were lashed to before the storm hit. Scanning the mooring field I could see what was left. Large numbers of sailboats had been de-masted and looked like complete wrecks bobbing in the water. Several more had been sunk. In the weeks to come a boat graveyard would be formed to the west of the temporary seaplane docks. The salvage crews would fill it with over forty wrecked hulls pulled from the bottom of Christiansted Harbor.

As we carefully made our way up the boardwalk, avoiding holes from missing boards that exposed calm waters below, I recognized a group of

255

tourists from my flight the previous day. As we walked by I heard one of them say, "So this is sunny St. Croix?"

The menu at the Christiansted Brew Pub was limited. Anything that could not last without refrigeration had been lost. Now that the generators were running, they could keep the few remaining vegetables they had, but no cargo ships would reach the island for several days to replenish what had perished. Fresh produce was as hard to come by in the coming weeks as finding gold bars on the seabed.

Faced with a long uncomfortable afternoon, we stayed downtown as long as possible before heading home. The number one wish on everyone's mind was for WAPA to come through and have the power back on as soon as possible. We knew from our trek to the Yacht Club that the east end was probably in for an extended period without power. I needed to get my water bottles filled and continue cleaning the floors and the walls before everything molded over. Two hours later, I found myself naked, broom in hand, with sweat pooling beneath me. As I swept up the quarter-inch of dirt that had infiltrated my house, my thoughts continued to come back to the same conclusion—we got lucky with this storm.

Tony was outside working on the generator for the main house most of the afternoon. The previous attempt at running it had resulted in a fire that had burnt the staircase leading up to their back patio. He had replaced the defective carburetor but was not sure that was the only problem. I threw on a pair of shorts and braved the swarms of mosquitos to join him. Tony told me they would most likely run the generator for short intervals to keep their products fresh in their freezer and refrigerator. I could take anything I wanted to save out of my freezer over to their house. Our conversation was more of a yelling match as we struggled to hear over dozens of generators running nonstop throughout Cotton Valley. They never shut off, and the drone of the motors continued to invade every moment. The first hours back home had seemed like days, and the days to come seemed like months as the struggle against the oppressive heat marched on.

As the day ground on, I searched for any puff of air to relieve my sweat-soaked skin. I had no way of bathing so I decided to drive down to the beach in front of the fire station and rinse off in the salt water. The AC in my car would provide a break from the heat that had built up over the course of the afternoon.

I'd been telling myself for some time that I lie around and watch the idiot box too much—a good five hours a day. Most of the time it is background noise, but since my first shoulder injury, TV provided all my entertainment on most days. Having no electricity forced me to break my bad habit. I'd always been a reader, and really enjoyed biography or history books. During the aftermath of this storm, I planned to increase my volume of reading.

Night comes early in the Caribbean. In October the sun is down by 6:30 p.m. I didn't like using candles because of the fire risk, and I had problems getting enough light from the flames for reading. They also created extra heat in an already stifling environment. I quickly switched to battery-powered lanterns.

Sunday, 10/19/08—Positive thinking goes out the window early in the morning when you wake to the hum of the generators and the pungent smell of diesel fumes. Before the sunlight broke over the eastern hills of St. Croix, the wild rooster was behind my house announcing his presence, at bull-horn volume, for an hour straight. Twenty-five pages into a book about Joseph Stalin and the murderess rampage he and his government unleashed over Russia at the start of the Twentieth Century and it was time to get out of bed and start moving.

I could tell the heat and lack of wind was starting to take its toll. I took extra calcium pills and tried to drink as much water as possible. Tingling sensations filled the back of my head and around my jaw. The daily grind at the Florida office was intense. It would leave me feeling run down by the time I returned to St. Croix. My nervous system always needed a few days before bouncing back, but the heat and uncomfortable nature of life after Omar did not allow for proper rejuvenation.

I didn't want to dwell on health issues, but with no electricity for TV or stereo, it was a lot easier to dwell on negative thoughts. The one plan of action was to contact Dr. Weisblat and find a new Endocrinologist who could help me balance out my system.

The late morning sun rose in the sky, the rays pierced the humidity-filled air. I prayed this would be the day electricity would come back on so the fans could get some air flowing inside my house.

Too hot to stay inside, I headed down to the Yacht Club with my tools, sand paper and varnish brushes. I wanted to continue working on my boat, and I was not the only one. I ran into a lot of fellow boat owners I knew. With no electricity, the art of conversation took over with stories of how each of their boats fared, from being damaged, de-masted, sunk or lost altogether. I was almost ashamed to mention that I'd been lucky and had sustained little to no damage.

I helped a few people by providing leverage as they tipped their boats back onto jack stands. The cleanup of the downed palm trees was underway and groups of people were working out plans to pull boats out of the bush or remove them from the tops of trees near the beach. The amount of activity was good to see and I was able to socialize with several friends. There is a strong fellowship that exists between people after a natural disaster. Everyone was pulling together to come to the aid of the next person. The people with the biggest problems had to figure out how to bring their boats up from the bottom, and received top priority. The salvage ship that would eventually come to St. Croix from Tortola, would pull boats off the bottom of Christiansted Harbor before making its way to the Yacht Club. In the meantime, several attempts were made with air bladders and water pumps to bring the sunken vessels up. Some attempts were successful and some failed, but the spirit and energy to help a fellow boater was evident in everyone's efforts.

It was the following weekend before the roads leading to the Yacht Club were clear enough to bring in a crane to lift boats off the beach and out of the bush. A bulldozer plowed a twenty-five foot wide swath through the Nium and Tan Tan trees to the edge of the water. The forty-five-foot catamaran that had been flipped on its roof and buried in the sand was the first extraction for the crane. The boats driven up in the bush behind the catamaran were next to be hoisted towards the sky and liberated. They would eventually be cleaned up and salvaged.

The crowd grew over the course of the day as the spectacle of the forty-ton crane was free entertainment. *Folly* was pulled forward so the massive machine could maneuver into the right position to extract the entangled mess a few feet to the south. Boards and jack stands had been used to proptwo boats up as they waited their turn for rescue. The forty-foot sailboat resting on top of *Folly's* neighbor was gingerly hoisted in the air. The popping noise of the metal shrouds separating from the two boats forced pained guttural sounds from the owners.

Monday, 10/20/09—Not having heard if the power was up in our office, I had to assume we would be working. Tony and Donna had agreed to run their generator at the main house every morning and allow me to shower before heading to work.

Freshly showered, I opened the office on Monday morning just before 7:30 a.m. I was happy to have a purpose and somewhere to go. As I unlocked the front doors, I could tell the power was still off. There was an old wood-burning stove with a chimney that rose through the roof on the wall facing the courtyard. Buckets had been lined up in the brick oven portion under the opening to the chimney. During the heavy rains the water poured into the office through the chimney and flooded the floor. I could see large puddles and quickly cleaned up the mess before anyone could slip on the slick tiles. As my colleagues rolled in, we sat in a circle in the conference room and listened to storm stories. A few people from mid-island, near the hospital, had power and the general sentiment was that downtown would have electricity restored soon. Just before 8:30 a.m. the lights flickered and then stayed on for good a few seconds later. A big cheer went up as we all headed to our offices. Our computer system was inoperable, and it would take us the better part of the day to get back online.

My nervous system was acting up, my face tingling all day. I pushed my condition aside and concentrated on the work at hand, but by the end of the day I was out of energy. Wanting to stay in the AC as long as possible, I performed as many marginal tasks, including filing and cleaning up. I didn't go home until long after the sun had gone down. It was pitch black by the time I reached my house. The sound of the generators , and the haze of diesel exhaust greeted me as I stepped out of my car. There was still no power on the east end of the island.

Heat from the burning October Caribbean sun had built up inside my house all day. I could not leave my front and back door open because the mosquitoes would invade even more than they already had. After removing my pants and work shirt, sweat-stained from walking from my car, I settled in for a long hot night. I continued to read about Joseph Stalin by flashlight. Although what this man and his followers did was reprehensible, I felt positive our system of government was different and we would never allow a dictator to rule in the same fashion.

I was hoping morning would come sooner rather than later. I still had nine hours until 6:00 a.m. when I could go to Tony and Donna's house and shower. Rumors spreading throughout Christiansted during the day had the power out for several more weeks on the east end. I was hoping the people spreading them did not know what they were talking about. I knew from past experiences that it is best to not listen to the gossip. When I talked to Tony and Donna the next morning, they had not seen any WAPA crews in Cotton Valley. That was all I needed to know. I was happy to have a job to go to where there was running water and AC. I was thankful that all the people I worked with were okay. Everything else was secondary. Having no electricity was an inconvenience that we would all survive.

Throughout the week, it was easy to spot the people whose power had been restored. They came into the office looking well rested and clean—with smiles on their faces. The inconvenience was growing into frustration for the rest of us.

Wednesday, 10/22/08—The wind had not picked up and the humidity hung in the air like a thick haze. It carried with it an eerie presence. On

260

the return drive from work I witnessed a massive convoy of WAPA trucks and SUVs heading west. I started counting as the third one passed me and I finished at fifteen. My excitement grew. According to Donna and Tony they had invaded the valley earlier in the day, working for hours, but the generators continued to hum, blending in our post-Omar environment. I quickly ducked inside to avoid getting swarmed by bugs.

I settled in for another long night of reading by lantern light when I heard the distinctive hum, and then the first flicker, of energy hit my ceiling fan. The blades moved a couple of inches and stopped. I knew there had been no wind coming in through the screens to cause the blades to turn. I questioned if the movement of the fan blades had even taken place because they stopped as soon as they started. Was this just wishful thinking? Ten minutes passed and nothing else happened. All of a sudden the fans roared to life and the lights turned on. I yelled across the yard to Tony and Donna. Their power had come back on as well. I checked my phone and it worked. I called Pat and Kathie and told them we had power. What a great feeling to deliver good news. It had been six long days. As soon as I got off the phone with Pat, as if playing some sort of a cruel joke, the house went dark and the fans wound down making a racket as they became unbalanced. The power was out for only ten minutes. The fans cranked up again. Over the next couple of days, the power would flicker on and off as the WAPA crews worked to restore all of the downed power lines on the east end of the island.

Friday, 10/24/08—I arrived early at work and was thankful the AC was already running. About 8:30 a.m. I received a call from Dr Politz. He'd received the bone density scan I'd faxed him. He compared each number to the 2007 scan. The previous lumbar spine measurement was -1.8. I'd gained density in the spine region reaching a number of .8, within the normal range of -1 to +1. My wrist number in the first scan was -2.8. In the second scan the same wrist spot had gained density to -2.4. This number is below normal, putting these bones in the osteoporosis category. However, it was moving in the right direction. My hip area in the first test showed -2.1. The bad news of this report was decreased density in this area. The number was -2.6. This fell in the severe osteoporosis range and was a real cause for concern. We discussed the possibility of going back on Fosamax. The hips were at risk and I needed to be careful to not overstress them. The feeling that my hips could break at any minute was gaining traction. I tried to downplay the severity of the issue.

Dr. Politz left the next move up to me. He understood that the last time I was on this type of medication it had presented side-effects that made me ill, and it seemed to affect my memory. He was still waiting on the latest blood test results which the St. Croix lab had presumably sent twice in the previous week. We shared a laugh as if to say, "what else is new." I explained about the storm and he promised to contact me as soon as he got the fax.

I passed several electrical crews near Cotton Valley on my way home. After running to the front door in an effort to avoid the swarms of bugs, I was thankful to find the electricity was still working. I checked the TV and cable was still out. I spent the night plugging away at the books I'd bought in Florida.

Saturday, 10/25/08—I focused my energy towards work on *Folly*. I loaded plastic carrying tubs full of tools, paints, sanders and varnish. I was relieved to find the power restored to the base of the light pole next to *Folly's* trailer. My first order of business was repairing the starboard side of the teak benching in the cockpit. Laying on my right side in between the rudder shaft and the teak bench posts, I was able to see where the supporting fiberglass had separated from the side mounts. It was not going to be easy, but I needed to apply epoxy resin upside down while holding it in place long enough for it to become tacky while keeping upward pressure on the entire section to fuse the two pieces back together. To make matters worse, I was under constant attack from the hoards of mosquitoes living in the bilge of my boat. The sweat pouring out of me made it nearly impossible to hold the tools in place to finish the job. I tried three times, wasting large amounts of West System Epoxy. One attempt failed when the upward support system—a stick off the ground—broke in half and the whole project crashed to the floor-boards, another because the resin was mixed too thin and the third because it was mixed too thick. I released a curse-word laden tirade and again found myself contorted back in the corner of the cockpit. Several choice words later I was hard at work trying, yet again, to fix the problem. Each time I had to contort my body under a bench and up and under the back seat that sat on top of a slanted floor. The mosquitoes found me an easy target, burrowed into the small space with no swatting capabilities. I was sure this would work, and on the fifth attempt the mixture of epoxy held. I carefully extracted myself out of the tight space, and sat on the opposite teak bench, drinking an entire bottle of water in one long gulp. The sweat was forming in puddles below me.

After a short break, I ran the long extension cord from the power pole under my neighbor's trailer and into the cockpit. I climbed back on the deck feeling a little light headed. I carefully maneuvered along the rail around the cabin back to where the work was taking place. Within minutes I was dizzy and feeling sick to my stomach. Feeling the need to get off the boat before I passed out, I left the tools where they lay and scrambled off the front of the bow. My feet safely back on ground I raced to my car and the cool-flowing AC. Feeling bad enough to question if I should drive, I waited a minute or two before leaving the parking lot. When I reach home I immediately jumped into the shower and ran cool water over my head. I was flat on my back in bed the rest of the day, continuing to feel dizzy. I couldn't lift my head off the pillows.

Sunday, 10/26/08—I headed back down to the Yacht Club to gather my tools. When I arrived, a slight wisp of wind was in the air. I was happy no one had taken my power cord or any of my tools that were in plain view from the day before. I checked the epoxy and it seemed to have held. I wanted to get another coat on for good measure. After that task was finished I tackled some light sanding and patchwork on the varnish coat which was coming along nicely, but the mosquitoes were thick and I was eaten alive. I lasted an hour and a half before the same dizzy sensation came over me.

I once again made a dash off the boat and into my car. I repeated the race home and the long shower when I arrived. Flat on my back the rest of the afternoon, I was able to get in many hours of reading.

Monday, 10/27/08—Back in the air conditioned office, the worn-out sensation I'd experienced over the weekend had diminished. As a further indicator things were moving in the right direction I was able to fall asleep that night without the aid of a pill. It rarely happened. I felt it was a good sign that my system was starting to balance out.

Tuesday, 10/28/08—Mid-morning I spoke to Dr. Politz who had received my latest blood test results. He explained that my magnesium and phosphate levels were normal. My vitamin D 25 test registered 51. According to Dr. Politz, patients having a vitamin D deficiency should have a level no less than 50. My calcium level was 8.8 and my PTH level was 11. Both of these numbers were normal, but at the lowest levels. The numbers reinforced hope.

Over the next few days it became evident that my energy level was tapering off. I was dragging myself around throughout the days and sleeping without the aid of a pill earlier and earlier each night. Even the simplest movements were labored. The joints in my body were incredibly stiff, and I became agitated, feeling a strong need to contain my anger and keep myself in check. Something was happening, but I didn't have the time or the energy to figure out what.

Nothing I'd felt from calcium fluctuations had made me feel this way and by Friday I was drained of all energy before the day had even started. The morning seemed suspended in time, and I struggled to make it to the lunch break. I walked the three blocks to Rumrunners in silence. My head felt very hot. Melissa went to the bar and spoke with one of her friends as we finished eating. Kiril and I had gotten into a discussion about managing databases. Kiril said something about my capabilities that I would normally let pass, but instead I exploded and called him a fucking asshole. He took offense and we were arguing when Melissa came back to the table. This was unlike either of us. Before getting back to the office, Kiril and I agreed to disagree. I didn't know where this outburst had come from, and it bothered me the rest of the afternoon. When it was time to leave, I got the same dizzy feeling I'd gotten on the boat the previous weekend. The four-block walk to my car felt like a marathon. I sat on a park bench in front of the fort resting before laboring over the last block to my car. Pain had infiltrated every joint in my body and my head throbbed as if I'd been kicked in the temple.

I drove home propped up against the driver-side door unable to hold myself up right. I collapsed onto my bed and was fast asleep within seconds. When I woke up around 9:30 p.m., I was sweating profusely and my skin had turned bright red. I could barely roll over. It took every ounce of strength to remove my work clothes. I collapsed back onto the bed, my head still pounding as sweat ran down my chest. My stomach felt like it was turning upside down. I wanted desperately to take a cool shower to lower my body temperature, but I passed out before I could move.

When I came to, my teeth were chattering. I was colder than I'd ever felt in my life. It was 3:30 a.m. I struggled to take the lid off a plastic tub containing extra bedding. I covered myself with all the thin blankets I could grab, then the light switched off and I was out again. The next morning the sheets, covers and pillows were dripping with sweat. I'd put on a tee shirt at some point throughout the night and I was actually able to wring it out over the sink. When I looked in the mirror my entire body was covered in a red rash, but my joints had stopped hurting and the headache gone.

After drinking large amounts of water and extra calcium pills, I experienced a wonderful euphoric sensation. I knew several people living in the Virgin Islands that had contracted Dengue Fever, a disease passed through the bite of an infected mosquito. I realized I'd probably been infected. I'd heard the nickname many times as people told of living through Bone-Crusher Disease. As I cleaned the bedding my energy increased. I assumed the illness had drained out of my system.

I also came to the conclusion that I had more energy than at any point in the past two years. It didn't bother me that the rash was still visible over ninety percent of my body. I started to feel almost too good, over energized.

It was a welcome feeling . The only thing I could think to do was to put that energy to work. I headed to the Yacht Club. I punched in the numbers to the key box on the electric gate and drove down to where *Folly* sat in the yard along the fence. The morning air was warm, but not overpowering, and with my new-found energy I planned to work at least three to four hours of work.

Less than an hour later, I had a ventilator mask on and was painting varnish on my teak combings when the life drained out of me in an instant. One second was all it took to knock me down as if a five-hundred pound weight was dropped from the sky. My head began to throb and my joints hurt like hell. I was on fire and sweating profusely. I removed the ventilator and lay down on the floorboards, unable to sit up. What if no one finds me? That thought alone made me pull myself up and find the strength to climb over the cockpit combings and crawl to the front of the boat. I half-rolled and half-leapt to the ground and limped to my car. I sat behind the wheel and fought to remain upright during the short ride home. It was a struggle to climb the four steps to my front door. I didn't shower or remove my dirty clothes and was lucky to land on the bed when I collapsed. The fire in my head returned and I sweat profusely for hours. My arms wouldn't move. I had no strength.

The noise felt like a cannon shot across my forehead as I woke to the phone ringing. It was dark. Kathie called, wondering why she and Pat hadn't heard from me. I explained my situation. Her son had experienced Dengue Fever the previous year. She had spoken with Dr. Bishop about the disease and knew all the symptoms. She explained that there's no cure. It has to run its course. If I got too dehydrated, I would be forced to go to the hospital. I crawled to the water cooler and drank as much water as I could hold. From that point on, I kept a full bottle next to the bed. I had no intention of going to the hospital over a mosquito bite.

The fever broke Sunday night as my joints began to wind down from the pain. After eating a large dinner and drinking several bottles of water, I took a long shower. Standing in front of the mirror I could see the bright red rash covering my entire body except for the palms of my hands.

Monday, 11/03/08—I opened the office at 7:30 a.m. The first thing I did was go online and read about Dengue Fever. The fact that the rash was the result of broken blood vessels near the surface scared me. I was thankful to have gotten off so lucky. It seemed I'd contracted one of the lesser strains of the disease.

By 8:30 a.m., my face was tingling, and my muscles in my upper arm were contracting nonstop. I waited for Kiril to get into his office, and went in to show him the rash. I explained that Dengue had definitely contributed to my outburst on Friday. I knew I'd felt bad before leaving for lunch, and I should have stayed at the office. It was my attempt at an apology. He was glad I was feeling better and accepted my overture.

Work continued at its fast pace, and I found myself drained, and left with little motivation. The rash made me look like a big red Popsicle. Death from Dengue Fever generally results from prolonged periods of internal bleeding and there were a few deaths reported on island in the aftermath of the storm. I was lucky. I felt a sense of accomplishment for cheating death, yet again. What a year!

The Boardwalk After the Storm.

New Dr., New Meds & Racing (Day 601 - 712)

Now that 2008 was coming to a merciful end, I focused on finishing the year strong at work. My other priority was the advancement of my restoration project on *Folly*. Bud Orpen's arrival loomed larger every day. He was battling advanced stages of cancer and the odds that he would be able to return to the island for more visits was slim. I wanted to make sure he got his sail in while he could. We had e-mailed each other several times and he had pinned me down to March 10th. At age eighty-seven, Bud was still the most organized and prepared person I knew. He had checked with me several times to make sure we were still on. I was feeling the pressure and knew I needed to get to work on *Folly* before something else went wrong with my health.

The start of November followed much the same pattern as the past nineteen months. Except for my arm exercises, not much else was getting done on the exercise front, and I was still struggling to lose weight. My pill regimen bounced around and generally I felt miserable. My face and lips contorted daily, sleep eluded me, and my head felt cloudy. There's no technical term to describe the feeling. I just felt off course. I remembered what normal felt like, but from the time of my parathyroid surgery I'd not experienced that feeling.

Working in a numbers-oriented business, it's surprising how hard it was for me to step back and look at the data involved with my illness. I didn't like hearing about the blood test results or discussing them with anyone more than once. I felt over-taxed managing the illness. It was all consuming. If I was not scheduling pills, I was filling prescriptions, or spending time tracking down doctors. Throw in the time arranging for and attending tests and rehab, a large portion of my free time was invested in my illness. It smothered me and distorted my ability to see the big picture. I felt as if all the care I was receiving was just enough to get me to the next day. Nothing was being done to eliminate the real threat that my hips or other bones in my body could break. In my mind, I was a sitting duck. I came to the belief that my present set of doctors could not help me reach a final cure. After months of internal debate, the decision to consult with Dr. Politz and Dr. Weisblat and ask their help in finding a specialist to take on my case became clear.

Dr. Politz agreed that I should seek out the help of an Endocrinologist. "Preferably one that does not concentrate on surgery." He explained that a new perspective from a practicing Endocrinologist could help shed some light on the troubles I was having with the regulation of my system after removal of the parathyroid gland. The conversation made me angry at first until I realized Dr. Politz was giving me some sound advice in that he was a parathyroid surgeon first and did not practice endocrinology daily. Having so much riding on this made each decision that much more difficult. I found it much easier to ignore and press on than face the issues at hand. Making matters even more difficult was the fact that a set of similar circumstances had cost me dearly in the past. I thought I'd made an informed decision to have the parathyroid surgery in the first place. Adding another new doctor was like passing a stone to me. I knew it would involve new tests and potentially new treatments. On the other hand, I had to get to the end of this. The health issues had dragged on long enough. I was in need of closure. After taking a couple of days mulling over my conversation with Dr. Politz, I called Dr. Weisblat.

The heat of summer finally started to break and the Christmas winds arrived stronger than ever. With the temperature change along came a new sense of purpose, a fresh start, and a desire to finish the work on *Folly*. I missed being out on the water enjoying my boat instead of working on it.

Saturday, 11/15/08—Pat and I took out a Yacht Club Rhodes 19 to get our sailing fix. The Rhodes is a much lighter boat than *Folly* and is susceptible to the power of water currents. I found that it pointed higher into the wind than *Folly* but would get sucked down in the bottom of the trough of a wave—stopping its forward momentum. The side-by-side comparison of the *Rhodes* and *Folly* reinforced why I was working so hard on my boat. We were out on the water over four hours, crisscrossing in front and behind Buck Island. I realized how much I had missed sailing the vibrant Caribbean waters.

Sunday, 11/16/08—Afraid of being bitten by mosquitoes, I purchased two cans of fog spray and two cans of deer repellent. Prior to contacting Bone-Crusher Disease I refused to use the cancer-causing bug spray. Now I gladly coated myself from head to toe. I fogged a twenty-five foot swath in the grassy area around my boat trailer before starting my work. The next several hours were spent in the cabin and I didn't get one bite. Progress was slow, but I was coming to the end of the teak varnish and had been working on sanding down the sidewalls and using epoxy to strengthen the lower chain plates. Few people would notice this job, but it was probably the most important of the entire restoration project. If the chain plates failed, the mast would crash to the deck, endangering everyone's safety. I took my time and worked on this area over the course of several days. Eventually I had reapplied epoxy to the chain plates and painted the area with two coats of metal primer and marine paint. I continued painting the remainder of the interior cabin and still had major work to do in the cockpit, including primer and paint on all the surfaces. Once that was taken care of, it was the deck that would get a new make-over and then the side walls and bottom. I realized I still had several weeks of work before she would be ready for sailing.

Early the following week, Dr. Weisblat called. He agreed with Dr. Politz that finding an Endocrinologist to oversee my case was essential. He would do some investigating on my behalf. I found the whole process unnerving. I would be facing new pills, prescriptions to fill, tests to take, results to track down, etc. The interaction of pills and how they affected my system had become a huge concern. In the past I had experienced adverse reactions to new medications and did not want to go through that again.

I had learned the hard way that doctors, although acting with good intentions, do not have all the answers. Proven treatments that work on a high percentage of patients are no guarantee for my situation. It had been a surgery to remove my parathyroid, the latest and greatest treatment idea on the face of the earth, that was supposed to be the one that was going to solve all my problems. Instead, it had landed me in the situation I was currently in. To say I treated new medical treatments or a new doctor with caution is an understatement. Even with this level of skepticism, I was seeking out new help for a reason. I needed this to end. The clock was ticking on how much longer I could continue to fight to keep my head above water. No one had been able to make it all stop. That's what I was hoping to find, and I was willing to try a new doctor to see this end.

11/28/08—Pam arrived on St. Croix. She found a somewhat confused and frantic human waiting to be rescued. I had really sunk to my lowest ebbs of skepticism. I was not sleeping for days at a time, and the constant battle being waged every day had long since taken its toll. I was losing what little grip I had on the situation. Wanting Pam to have a good time, I put on the best front I could. She immediately removed some of the doubt I had been feeling about life as we spent some time together. Not all in life was bad. I had come a long way, and Pam reminded me of that. She kept telling me I needed to give myself a break and be proud of my progress. Although I would hear her speak the words, it did little to stop my mind from continually racing in all directions. It was as if I was standing guard twenty-four hours a day, and my life depended on me getting the job done right every time. The length of the struggle had become the mental fight of my life—and it was draining me. I had begun questioning my capacity to overcome this challenge. I needed a break.

I continued to work while Pam was on island. We had the extended Thanksgiving holiday weekend, and then it was back to the office. Pam loved her time alone to explore the shops and spend relaxing days floating

271

in calm bays. We always took walks after I got off work and we ate well. Just having another person with me helped ease my mind. I found I slept better when Pam was with me—and I felt better about life, though I was still tired and my face continued to tingle and twitch.

Saturday, 12/6/08—As we walked out the door Pam re-assured me that working on *Folly* would be fun for her. I don't believe she knew what she was getting into. As we pulled into the parking lot she was impressed with how good *Folly* looked. Before she arrived on island I had prepped the decks which included epoxy repairs on the rubrail and lots of sanding. I had painted a coat of marine-grade primer, then two coats of paint. The teak really stood out from the bright white of the freshly painted deck and cockpit walls. It had been a huge undertaking and the most time consuming projects still lay ahead.

The sidewalls needed sanding for primer and two new coats of top paint. The first step was taking the forty-year-old hardened, sun-baked paint off without gouging the gel coat that lay below it. I had tried hand sanding sections with several different grains of sandpaper. Nothing seemed to work. It left me with two sore arms and the same amount of paint as when I started. My rotating hand sander and the powerful belt sander would be the tools of choice. Listening to Pam talk before we started I was questioning my sanity in bringing her in to help during this difficult prep work. The last thing I wanted to do was get upset over a mistake on *Folly*. After all, she was helping me out. I needed to remember that. My worries turned out to have no merit. Pam spent five hours, Saturday and Sunday, working every bit as hard as I was. Her lines were smooth and even, and she didn't gouge the gel coat once. We worked great as a team—each with a separate job. Pam used the palm sander and took the top layer of paint off and I evened the surfaces out with a litter-grain sandpaper on the belt sander. We were a filthy mess by the end of Sunday, 12/7/08.

We had spent over ten hours working on *Folly*. Pam had come down for vacation but willingly helped me with my project because it was important to me. She worked hard and did a great job. I wish she could have helped me the rest of the way. *Folly* still had a long way to go but I was starting to see the light at the end of the tunnel.

My morale had been boosted. It was if I'd been pulled out of hole in the ground. My tanks were filled again and I was ready to face the coming months. I was not happy to see Pam off at the airport the next day.

Tuesday, 12/09/08—Dr. Weisblat assured me that Dr. Jay Morrow was a top-of-the-line Endocrinologist. Dr. Morrow was booked with appointments for several months to come, but after Dr. Weisblat reiterated my urgent need for guidance, Dr. Morrow relented, creating time to see me on 12/22/08. I immediately agreed. That set into motion a laundry list of tasks, including notifying work, buying plane tickets, contacting Dr. Politz, who had agreed to speak with Dr. Morrow. It also meant getting all my medical records copied and moved to Dr. Morrow's office as soon as possible so he could actually look through them before I was in his office at the end of the month. These tasks would have been impossible before enlisting Dr. Weisblat. He had the majority of my records which made distribution much less painstaking.

Although I was concerned about new treatments, I was excited about the possibility of a cure. Pam was excited that I was coming to Cleveland for the Christmas holiday. Even though this was going to include a doctor's visit, and tests, Pam and I made plans to visit Mom. We decided to drive the seven-hour trip from Cleveland to Illinois, and my older brother Tim decided he would come up from Oklahoma. The plans fell together quickly and I was really looking forward to spending time with family and friends.

We were in the middle of the rush leading up to the end of the year, but my group and the projects I was in charge of seemed to be on track. I was feeling upbeat and in cruise mode. For all the bad news in the economy 2008 was a good year for my bonus and compensation. The structure was bound to change as 2009 approached. I was not happy with all of the potential changes that I was being briefed on as The March Group was looking for ways to streamline the bonus system. They wanted bonus payments more closely linked to closings rather than individual accomplishments.

The change would take the ability to make a bonus out of the hands of the individual and place it in the hands of the Managing Directors. Ultimately Managing Directors would be responsible for closing sales. As the new plans were formulated, I found myself on the side-lines during the decision processes.

12/18/08—An upset stomach followed by diarrhea kept me running down the stairs at work all afternoon. I raced home barely making it to the privacy of my own restroom. Why this kept happening was a mystery and the least of my worries. I was experiencing some severe tingling in my face. My lips and cheeks were contracting involuntarily. I worked on calming my nerves with deep breathing, closing my eyes and rocking back and forth on the corner of my bed. The right side of my face tightened up. Exhausted, I found myself laying down in the dark rubbing my jaw. It did not release and within a few minutes the onslaught of panicked feelings began invading my head. On the physical side, the worn-down ill feeling and diarrhea was overshadowed by stabbing sensations from the back of my head to my toes. The third battleground was severe cramping. What little energy I had left drained away fast leaving me feeling weak and unable to move.

I reached for the phone and called Pam. The conversation lasted over an hour and basically consisted of Pam speaking and me listening. She was confident that I could ride this out. It was comforting to hear her voice as I continued to rub my face with increasing intensity. At one point Pam reminded me that I needed to get better so I could make it to Cleveland. I had been so busy at work, I'd actually forgotten the trip was in two days.

The right side of my face continued to be a problem for the remainder of the night. I rubbed it for hours. My breathing became labored and I continued to suffer from diarrhea. There was no sleep. Pam was willing to spend the entire night on the phone with me if it would have made me feel better, but I was in a dark mood, and the positive approach Pam was taking only irritated me further. I needed to face this issue alone. We said our goodbys and Pam reminded me to call her any hour of the night if I needed her.

I found it too uncomfortable to lie down and remained sitting on the

274

corner of my bed unable to keep my head from drooping below my shoulders. My hands were cramping to the point I had to stop rubbing my face. Locked into a contorted mess, my face and lips quivered uncontrollably. My leg muscles started to contract as I continually tried to take in deep breaths. I was losing confidence with each passing moment that I was strong enough to ride this attack out. Was it time to give up? I knew that meant a trip to the ER. That thought, alone, kept me at home in the dark.

The experience gained from similar episodes indicated I had seven or eight more hours of nervous-system disorders ahead of me. If I was to have any chance of fending off the feelings of panic, anger and hopelessness I needed to concentrate. The stakes were high, and if I lost the battle I would find myself in the ER or worse. There would be many moments of doubt in the coming hours. I prayed to God I was not having a serious stroke—offering any kind of trade-off I could. I got up and started pacing. My head hurt as my body contracted and tingled uncontrollably. I crushed more calcium pills, taking an additional twenty-four throughout the night. The last fifteen weren't crushed due to the cramping in my hands. Swallowing them whole proved to be every bit as challenging. Before the night was over, my breathing would become so labored I struggled to inhale enough air to fill my lungs.

As the sun rose over the eastern hills I felt like I'd been through a heavyweight prize fight, pounding away at me for over eight hours. Dealing with non-alcohol-related-hangovers had become my specialty. It was vicious by nature and was a byproduct of billions of malfunctioning neurons unable to pass on their individual messages because of the calcium deficiency. My head was filled with pain. I'd had zero sleep and was running on fumes. Work was going to be tough, but I knew I was leaving the next morning and that left me no choice but to take care of all the usual preparations for time away from the office.

At the start of the day, I lined up each individual project, from left to right, on my desk. This took over an hour, but I knew, even in my haze, important matters were likely to be forgotten. I'd become an unwilling novice at perfecting work survival techniques the day after a nervous-system attack. I had little choice. The consequences would be more pronounced if I took additional days off. Knowing the grind it would take the following week to catch up forced me to persevere.

My low calcium hangover rules included extra checks and balances on all material sent out to be viewed by other parties. Early on I discovered a much higher rate of e-mail mistakes, forgetting to add attachments, not signing off on documents to my group, spelling errors. The prefrontal cortex of my brain was not operating at full capacity. Neurons did not pass on the normal messages from one to the other. Essentially, my brain was a misfiring sparkplug.

When I was finished, my head hurt and I found myself unable to pack for my trip. Walking around my small house, half in a trance, wasting time pulling drawers and cabinets open for no reason was more than I could take. I knew the basics I needed, gathered them up, and called it quits. I hoped to have a clearer head by morning so I could finish and leave for the airport at 5:00 a.m. My last thought of the day was one of hope. Maybe this Dr. Morrow knew what to do. I still held onto hope. I wanted to believe this would all be straightened out. That's why I was getting on a plane and flying over 2,000 miles to find out what Dr. Jay Morrow of the Diabetes & Endocrine Center of Cleveland, Inc. knew about the subject. Drowsiness caused by Klonopin was soon followed by a deep sleep.

The next morning my head still hurt, but my thought process had cleared enough to allow me to quickly pack. I spent more time preparing and planning my pill regimen than my clothes for the trip. Crushing calcium pills in the large mortar and pestle and pouring them into individual lip-balm jars is easier said than done. These would be stuffed into my pill pack which Kiril and other co-workers had aptly called a murse. I carried this black bag with me wherever I went. Besides the calcium. the pills included Xanax, Klonopin, Ambien, Nexium, Citrocal and Ativan. I was a walking pharmacy. I woke up on my own without an alarm clock as I have done every morning since I ran a paper route in the fifth grade. The time was

3:30 a.m. I finished stuffing the garment and pill bags to capacity. The indecision that had plagued this simple process the day before was gone.

Starlight, and the sounds of my distant neighbor's donkey, greeted me as I stepped out into the early morning air. It was beautiful—cool with a slight easterly breeze. I looked up, thinking how nice it would be to sail in this breeze. The moonlight was easy on my eyes, but halfway into my drive to the airport I needed to put on sunglasses as the bright orange orb rose in my rear view mirror. Bright light seemed to trigger a reaction. This struggle against bright light would continue for the next two or three days as my brain slowly returned to normal.

The first flight left at 6:15 a.m. By the time I reached San Juan, the temperature was eighty degrees and rising before I boarded the 10:00 a.m. flight to New York. When I walked off the plane at JFK, it was thirty-six degrees, grey and overcast. The electronic arrival and departure board was loaded with red numbers. Several flights were delayed or cancelled. I had more than three hours of layover time and I was hoping the weather would break before my flight was set to depart. People were moaning and groaning in all corners of the airport as I passed through the crowd. I took the extra time to read my book and people-watch. With each passing hour, my mood lightened. Once an episode was in the rearview mirror, the heavy symptoms usually did not come back for several days. I was pretty sure I would be all right for the remainder of my trip as long as I kept to the pill schedule.

Flight delays of twenty minutes, forty-five minutes and then an hour kept pushing my 5:30 p.m. departure time back. As I approached the counter and asked what was happening, I was greeted with cordial indifference. The counter person explained one stewardess was unable to get a timely flight into JFK from Pittsburgh. The departure board was starting to fill up with red cancellation notices for the majority of the regional flights. And worse, bad weather was moving in across the Midwest and Eastern U.S. Other than being grey, overcast and wet, it looked like perfect flying weather to me. I held out hope that my plane would eventually leave.

The airlines provided comical relief by delivering updated flight information through a distorted loudspeaker which struggled to top the ambient room noise. In the vast confusion following each announcement, people would come hustling in from far-off yogurt kiosks and newspaper stands increasing the population at the gate twofold. Profoundly determined to figure out if their plane was taking off, each individual struggled to decipher the latest communication. Adding to the confusion, insufficient seating caused many to stand and pace around bags of Christmas gifts and luggage. As the hours passed, the reaction after each garbled message reached a fever pitch. Another delay, another eruption of distaste from the crowd, complete with babies screaming, cursing in foreign languages and salesman pitching social commentaries on the declining state of today's travel. Head shaking and temple rubbing was common as the crowd slowly dispersed back to the far corners of the airport. The inclement weather finally moved out to sea and flights came pouring in. The weary, departing passengers added to the already overcrowded conditions. Soon whole sections of angry people were hoarded through crowded gangways as planes scrambled to pull away and taxi to the runway. The weather window was to be short-lived and only the chosen few would escape that night. JFK roared to life.

Remaining calm had been my mantra for the day. As time passed I was finding this task more difficult. It was looking more and more like I would be spending the night at the airport. At the moment I was cursing the gods, an olive branch was offered.

The electronic board filled with red cancellation notices, flickered. A flight for Washington D.C. appeared in all white letters. That was the flight originally scheduled to leave a half-hour earlier than my flight to Cleveland from the same gate. With all the confusion over the past several hours was it really possible this meant the Cleveland flight could still happen? After the Washington flight boarded, the electronic departure sign flickered one last time. Cleveland was a go! I called Pam to let her know she would need to drive out to the airport after all. The plane was loaded and we had pulled out and rolled onto the tarmac before the clock struck 10:15 p.m. Crammed against a window in a small regional airline seat, I looked out over the dark, cold landscape below as we lifted off the ground.

The wheels touched down in Cleveland as the clock struck midnight. The eighteen hours spent traveling proved to be more of an exercise in patience than miles traveled. I was three-quarters asleep as Pam pulled the car into her garage. Stumbling up the stairs I collapsed into her bed. Sleep came easy. There was no need for any pills or self-relaxation techniques— just one long exhale.

The following day was spent eating fresh-baked turkey and watching movies in bed. There was snow on the ground and little sunshine. It was the perfect setting for an entire day of decompressing. I thought of the following day's agenda, but cleared my head as best I could. My shoulders relaxed as the tension drained from my body.

Monday, 12/22/08—My appointment with Dr. Marrow was scheduled at 12:30 a.m. The medical building housing his practice is right up the road from Dr. Weisblat's office. There were seven or eight patients waiting to see the doctor when Pam and I arrived. I had several papers to fill out before taking my seat. It was a short wait. My name was called within ten minutes. Pam accompanied me back to the waiting room. I had a long list of specific talking points to cover with the newest member of the team. By the time the door swung open, I was bursting at the seams to get my story out in full. Recalling accurate details of the events that transpired over the past two years was a daunting task. Holding the doctor's attention that long was nearly impossible.

After the initial handshake, and customary blood pressure test, I seized the moment to take control of the proceedings. I was in rare form when Dr. Morrow stopped me mid-sentence and proclaimed that he was not interested in the breaking of any bones or my nervous-system disorder. His only concern was why this had happened and fixing it. The bulging folder in his right hand was my complete medical history. He was concerned with the pills I was taking and had me explain the complete laundry list.

At first, Dr. Morrow was puzzled by my parathyroid surgery. The records faxed to him from Dr. Weisblat and Dr. Politz did not include the pre-surgery blood tests, and the blood test numbers post-surgery did not warrant cutting out a functioning parathyroid. The records he was looking at were incomplete and did not show the PTH levels at the time of surgery. This was a bit disconcerting, but later this point was cleared up by Pam and her memory of the pre-surgery numbers. After reassuring me we could fix the underlying issues, he ordered a twenty-four-hour urine test believing the calcium was passing through my system and the low levels of PTH in the body was causing the kidneys to under-perform their correct function of maintaining the calcium for absorption into the bloodstream. This would explain the body pulling calcium from the reserves in the bones, leaving them in a weakened state. Dr. Morrow did not see the full-body scan numbers that showed the present bone density levels. He needed these tests to help make a determination of proper treatment. There was more work to be done tracking down medical records.

Addressing the hip issue was one of my major concerns. Dr. Morrow did not think my hips would break from low impact exercises. I could walk and work out on an elliptical machine. He wanted me to avoid high impact exercise, like running, until we got a good understanding of my osteoporosis.

Dr. Morrow would contact me the following week after the urine test came back. At that time he would be able to determine if the amount of calcium I was eliminating would require an additional medication. I was less than pleased hearing that. I hated pills and was already living the daily nightmare of keeping track of how many and when to take them. There was nothing normal about how my system had reacted to new medications in the past, and the severity of the parathyroid disease seemed to amplify the negative reaction to all new drugs. My mind was racing as I struggled to remain calm.

The visit ended before I could get a quarter of my thoughts communicated. I felt a need to tell the whole story, and Dr. Morrow was only interested in looking forward to controlling the issues at hand. Past history with broken bones, peeing blood, not being able to breathe and experiencing nervous-system failures were not his issues to deal with and therefore not his issues to listen to. It took some getting used to, but I came to see his point. Dr. Morrow assured me that my case was one of the rarest he had seen, but the problems could be controlled. I thought the word controlled was a lot different than the word cured. His focus would be on calcium absorption and parathyroid function. Before dismissing us from his waiting room, Dr. Morrow promised to see it through to the end.

I was not so trusting of the new guy. My best guess was this was not going to fix all that ailed me. According to Dr. Morrow, in some rare cases, there had been parathyroid glands that did not come back on line after one or more had been removed. He suspected this was the case with me. He went on to explain that if this was the case, a patient usually runs into large problems because there's no real way to force the glands back to life. Regulation needs to happen through other techniques.

My only questions were would I ever be normal, and when? These questions never got answered. It was always a wait-and-see response. In each case I'd stormed out of the gates believing hard work at rehabilitation would produce normal mobility. That never happened. I believed I would some day be able to regulate the calcium and PTH and feel normal again. I had to give up those ideas and settle for making things better, never reaching the dimming memories of normalcy. It was a tough pill to swallow.

Tuesday, 12/23/08—For the next twenty-four hours I collected my urine in a large plastic jug—by far the easiest test I'd undertaken to this point. The only instruction was to keep it cool. The temperature was in the teens and there was snow on the ground. I kept the jug on the steps in the garage.

The holiday scramble was put on hold to fit in my doctor's appointments. At 11:30, there was an appointment with Dr. Weisblat. The first order of business was a discussion about the meeting with Dr. Morrow. Agreeing with Dr. Morrow, Dr. Weisblat felt my hip pain was muscular in nature and was not related to the thinning bone density. He was pleased to see I'd listened to the nutritionist and lost twenty-six pounds since our last visit in September. I was cleared to resume normal exercise, which included

281

elliptical training and swimming. I should still avoid heavy, weight-bearing leg routines until another bone density scan could be performed in early 2010. Bone density scans are spread out over the course of at least a year so the doctors can compare numbers and get a good idea of the density trend and how well treatment is working. Dr. Weisblat ordered a blood draw that included the normal calcium and PTH numbers and a cholesterol check. I would need to fast after my last meal until the test the next morning. I had to bring back my jug of urine to Dr. Morrow's lab the next morning, too.Once these final errands were run, I would be free of the medical grind and only have to wait for results. The hard part was over.

Pam continued working to make up for lost time through the end of the week. She gladly rolled along with the crazy pace, keeping notes and making sure my best interests were being cared for. The doctor-patient relationship is not an easy one because everything has to be questioned. Doctors rarely want to explain every detail. If I did not remember to cover all the bases, Pam reminded me, or jumped in herself to ask specific questions. I never would have been able to capture all they were telling me without her help.

Wednesday, 12/24/08—Feeling like two sprinters coming to the finish line, we pushed ahead. Pam had parties to prepare for and the house had to be cleaned, but she never complained. I tried my best to help, which mostly meant staying out of the way. She was a body in constant motion. It was amazing to watch. I shoveled snow from the driveway and front porch to contribute. Several inches would come down over the next three days and this would not be my last workout of the week.

Pam was working hard to prepare the house for a Christmas day family party. Her older brother, JR, was visiting from Iowa with his wife. Also scheduled to attend were her brother Jackie, and sister Robin. I'd been dreading Christmas. The thought of it just seemed to annoy me, but not Pam. She goes all out for the holidays and even with such a negative outlook I soon got swept up in the spirit. By the end of the day her house was completely decorated. Somehow she found time to bake a turkey, several batches of cookies and desserts. Christmas music played in the background

282

nonstop. I shoveled snow for the second time that day, listening to a Bing Crosby holiday song I could hear through the living-room window. The holiday spirit was back just in time.

12/25/08—The guests arrived around 2:00. After the tall stack of gifts was handed out, and everyone ate way too much food, we sat around the big table playing card games until late into the evening. I actually didn't think about work or health-related issues the entire day. My nervous system stayed in check and everything went as planned. It was a great day all the way around!

Friday, 12/26/08—We had stayed up late the night before, cleaning, but Pam went off to work and I signed back on the laptop set up in her living room. Re-energized, I worked through the morning hours.

The next morning we had plans to drive to Illinois. I just hoped all the health issues would hold off for the second half of our holiday vacation. The afternoon workday was long, and I had few interruptions. Most people were on vacation, so I concentrated on finishing presentations, projects and reports. I was happy when Pam finally made it home in the early evening. The snow had continued to fall most of the day and I'd shoveled the porch and walk ways two or three times, trying to stay on top of it. I wanted them clean when she arrived.

Saturday, 12/27/08—It was 9:30 a.m. before we'd finished cleaning the house and renting a car. We packed for the seven-and-a-half-hour drive to Mother's house. CDs had been strategically placed in the car. Each driver was able to play what they wanted to listen to while they drove. I started off, and did not turn the wheel over until we were two hours away from our final destination. It was sunny and the roads were clear of snow and ice— we had hit the weather window jack pot. Our drive was a blast, a chance for the two of us to enjoy time alone before the family gatherings in Illinois.

Mom had planned a large party for Sunday so the Reed side of the family could all come and celebrate a late Christmas with Tim, Tami, Pam and me. It was a lot of fun seeing all of my step-brothers and sisters. We played a lot of games, including cards, and several rounds of Catch Phrase. The food spread was incredible and there was little left to do but eat too much and catch up with some great people. The very same holidays I had been dreading turned out to be the best part of my entire year. I was tired when it was all said and done, but I'd survived without any major setbacks. My breathing issues remained in check and it felt great being around family again.

Pam had another family gathering at her house for New Year's Day, so after a little over two days, we packed up and headed back to Cleveland. Pam's brothers and sister, and aunts and uncle would be attending the sit-down meal—the third holiday feast since I'd arrived. That's why Pam and I had kept up a workout routine throughout the holiday. We'd taken a five-mile walk in the cold weather around the campus where both my mother and father had taught, worked out to Debbie Severs DVDs, and walked the cold streets two miles every morning.

Friday, 1/2/08—Dr. Morrow called to report results of the urine and blood test. He started off by saying that before my parathyroid surgery in July of 2007 my PTH Hormone level was 123 (12-65 is normal)—hyper-parathyroidism. Now my level was 6.2 which is well below normal. In his professional opinion, there was good reason why I felt so poorly. The result of my earlier numbers was secondary hyperparathyroidism—where one or more parathyroids are overactive, usually the result of overcompensating for something else that is not functioning in the body. This affliction draws calcium out of reserves kept in the bones. After removal of my parathyroid gland in Tampa, both my PTH and Calcium numbers remained low. I was now battling hypoparathyroidism.

In medicine (endocrinology), hypoparathyroidism is decreased function of the parathyroid glands, leading to decreased levels of parathyroid hormone (PTH). The consequence, hypocalcemia, is a serious medical condition.

Signs and symptoms
- Tingling lips, fingers, and toes
- Muscle cramps
- Pain in the face, legs, and feet
- Abdominal pain

- Dry hair
- Brittle nails
- Dry, scaly skin
- Cataracts
- Weakened tooth enamel (in children)
- Muscle spasms called tetany (can lead to spasms of the larynx, causing breathing difficulties)
- Convulsions (seizures)
- Tetanic contractions

In the event of a life-threatening attack of low calcium levels or tetany (prolonged muscle contractions), calcium is administered by intravenous (IV) infusion. Precautions are taken to prevent seizures or larynx spasms. The heart is monitored for abnormal rhythms until the person is stable. When the life-threatening attack has been controlled, treatment continues with medicine taken by mouth as often as four times a day.

http://en.wikipedia.org/wiki/Hypoparathyroidism

A human's usual calcium output in urine is between 50 mg and 300 mg per day. The test results showed I was expelling 754 mg per day. These are numbers Dr. Morrow was not used to seeing. He stressed the need to address this as soon as possible. His recommendation was taking a diuretic named Hydrochlorathiazide (HCTZ).

The purpose for taking the diuretic is to help the kidneys perform the task of holding back calcium which is later absorbed into the bloodstream and used in normal nervous-system and brain functions. This was the only way Dr. Morrow knew to stop eliminating so much calcium in the urine without proper functioning parathyroid glands. I asked when he thought my parathyroid glands would start to function normally again. Dr. Morrow did not believe they would ever regain normal function. It had been over a year and half since the surgery to remove the rogue parathyroid and there had only been limited periods of time when the parathyroid hormone numbers were secreting PTH—at the lowest end of the normal range. The majority of the time they were lacking any functionality at all. I again expressed my concern over adding new medication into my system. Dr.

Morrow explained that HCTZ has been used as a diuretic for several years with few reported side-effects. This did little to ease my mind.

The doctor understood my concern, but felt there was little chance of adverse side-effects. I was to take a .25 mg HCTZ pill once a day. He wanted a blood test to be performed one week after starting the new drug. The blood test would be used to monitor the calcium and PTH levels so we could adjust how many calcium pills I was taking. I hung up the phone feeling I was headed in the right direction, but I was left with concerns about the new medication.

Saturday, 1/3/09—I was on the 6:15 a.m. flight out of Cleveland headed for Chicago. The flight left on time and I made the connecting flight to Miami without any issues. From Miami, I had the direct flight to St. Croix and I arrived at 4:00 p.m. After touching down and gathering my luggage I stopped by the pharmacy on the way through town and dropped off the prescription for the HCTZ. I would pick them up on Monday morning and start my new regimen.

Sunday, 1/4/09—I played nine holes of golf at the Reef Golf Course with Pat and then had lunch at the Yacht Club. Afterwards, I climbed onto *Folly* and mentally went over the list of work still left to be finished before I'd be able to put her back in the water. I planned on starting the work in earnest the following weekend. The final push prior to Bud Orpen's March visit was on.

Monday, 1/5/09—I was the first customer in line after the doors to the pharmacy opened. I read instructions that came with the bottle of HCTZ. I decided I would take the pill with my calcium dosage at lunch every day. I worked through the morning and hesitated for a moment before sucking the tiny pink pill down with a large drink of water just before noon. Half expecting a complete meltdown, I closely monitored how I felt the remainder of the day.

Later that evening, my left knee began to ache. It felt like a vessel under the kneecap was being hammered. By Tuesday morning I could hardly bend my knee. I limped around at work. I didn't think it was related to the HCTZ because of Dr. Morrow's reassurances. Wednesday the knee cleared up, but the pain came back on Thursday. The pain was on and off again through Friday. I attributed it to a mild strain of some sort.

Saturday, 1/10/09—I'd been driving around for weeks with cans of primer and paint for the topsides and bottom of *Folly* on the back floorboards of my car. I didn't want the added work of lugging them in and out of the house before finishing the work on the boat. Three hours after starting to sand the old bottom paint, I started feeling really run down. My arms and shoulders were burning from the rigors of sanding saltwater and sun-hardened paint. I'd been wearing cheap facial masks that covered my mouth and nose. They were soaked in sweat and covered in blue, bottom paint dust before I'd finished. I was filthy. After cleaning up at home I laid down, pretty sure I felt sick but too tired to really care.

Sunday, 1/11/09—I was having a hard time finding the motivation to get out of bed. I had to set aside how tired I felt and get going. I forced myself to drive to the Yacht Club. I was paying a heavy price with a throbbing pain in both knees. Sanding for any length of time caused my shoulders and joints to burn. Although the repaired shoulders do not possess the same mobility they once had, I was sure something else was happening. If I'd caught a flu bug, I thought working outside in the heat would help me sweat it out. I pushed on through another three and a half-hour work session. The progress was becoming more visible with each passing day. The decks were finished, topsides primed and painted and I'd just added a new water line complete with two coats of bright red marine paint. Preparing the bottom for primer and paint was the second to last item on my to-do list. I came home filled with the sense of accomplishment. I was drained and fell asleep late in the afternoon.

The next seven days were spent becoming increasingly ill. I could hardly stand at times and found the simplest motor skills eluded me. Holding a glass or turning a doorknob became a battle of mind over matter.

Monday, 1/12/09—My eighth day of taking HCTZ. I woke, unable to pick my head off the pillow. I felt as if I could sleep all day. I dragged myself out of bed and into work. I had trouble breathing walking up the stairs to the office. I was winded by the time I reached the second level. I felt dizzy and lightheaded all morning. I was not sure what was happening. After lunch, I found the energy to drive to the lab at Sunny Isle and had my blood drawn to test calcium and PTH levels as requested by Dr. Morrow.

8:00 a.m. Tuesday, 1/13/09—Totally exhausted, I rested my head on the desk, recovering from the climb up the stairs to my office. Fifteen minutes passed and there was no change. My eyelids felt like they weighed hundreds of pounds. I was unable to move. Noon came and it was time for my daily HCTZ pill. I reluctantly popped it in my mouth and drank some water before putting my head down to rest again. I had to leave work. I took my laptop and worked from bed the remainder of the day.

Wednesday, 1/14/09—I was having troubles breathing and felt dizzy. My stomach ached and I was incredibly weak. I left a message for Dr. Morrow. He returned my call later that day. He had received my blood work numbers by fax from the laboratory on St. Croix. He said there was a good reason I was feeling so poorly. Ionized calcium is freely flowing in the bloodstream—not attached to proteins. My ionized calcium levels were high. My PTH was very low. He went on to explain that the HCTZ had done its job too well. I wasn't sure I would live to see another day but according to the doctor this was an improvement. His instructions were to immediately stop taking the diuretic. I had no problem with that, but he then went on to say I would start back up the following Monday after reducing my calcium intake from fourteen pills a day to three. I was also to reduce the number of Calcitriol from four to one per day. Calcitriol helps the body absorb calcium and was amplifying the symptoms I was feeling.

I was less than pleased with the outcome of this new medication, but I was too sick to fly into a rage. I had no choice but to believe we were on the right track. I wanted to find an outlet for my frustrations but blowing off steam at the doctor who was trying to help me was not the best tactic. I kept my total disdain bottled up inside.

Thursday, 1/15/09—I'd bounced back just enough to think I could make it through a full day at the office. I lasted three hours. I was dizzy and felt like I was going to pass out. I spent the rest of the day in bed.

Friday, 1/16/09—Feeling poorly, I dragged myself to work, determined to make it through the entire day. I was two days clear of my last HCTZ pill. There was just enough energy in the tank to make it through to 5:00 p.m. My head started to clear and my motor functions returned. The internal cloud was lifting.

Saturday, 1/18/09—I spent the entire day in bed. I wanted to continue work on *Folly* but there was no fight left in me. In the wake of the calcium imbalance I was left struggling mentally with depression, anxiety and anger. The dark mood swings of this day were complete in their mission. My memory loss had reached new heights. I tried in vain to run through the names of my aunts and uncles, Mother's maiden name—nothing came easy. Phone conversations with Pam that afternoon were filled with negative talk. She felt I was to sick too be left alone.

Sunday, 1/18/09—I had enough energy to walk outside in the yard for a half-hour. The sunlight felt great on my skin. I was faced with starting the next round of HCTZ the following morning. I had to convince myself it was the right thing to do. I ran the scenario over and over in my head. I was determined to call the whole thing off, but what were my alternatives? I had no choice but to trust Dr. Morrow's expert opinion. He felt we were headed down the right track. He assured me we would find the right balance. Better days were just around the corner. I had to stay the course. It was like talking a five-year-old into eating broccoli.

Monday, 1/19/09—The time came to take the tiny pink pill that had knocked me down for an entire week. I fought the temptation to toss the entire bottle down the drain. Anxiety caused my shoulders to rise toward my neck as I popped it in my mouth and swallowed. I felt sick most of the day at work but completed a full eight hours. Sleep did not come easy as I fought off the desire to replay the nightmare journey I'd been on for the past two years in my head. I took a Klonopin at 10:30 p.m.

Tuesday, 1/20/09—The single benefit of the new pill regimen was the reduced numbers of calcium pills. It felt like an extra free hour had been added to my schedule. I also did not have to keep track of the extra pills and when I had taken them. I could carry all the day's supply in my pants pocket eliminating—the need for my murse. My energy level started to bounce back and the calcium hangover seemed to be lifting. I still had headaches most of the day, but these turned out to be the last remains of a sinus infection that had also brought with it a dry cough. It had started at the same time I took the first round of HCTZ and gone unnoticed. After work I experienced symptoms that told me I had low calcium in the blood. I had tingling in my lips and spasms in my left shoulder and right quadriceps muscles. I just wanted my system to make up its mind—one week too much calcium—the next week too little. Frustrated I took a Klonopin to help me sleep.

Wednesday, 1/21/09—Although I was feeling somewhat better, my energy level was not up to par. What little gains were being made on the health front were negated by increased workloads. The March Group was examining all procedures looking for any fat that could be trimmed. The process became a laborious, detail-oriented investigation of every function we performed. The bull's eye was squarely on my group's back. I was answering questions and being probed every day by the review board. Several reports and flash assignments came from these meetings. They never seemed to end as the inquisition probed deeper into every aspect I managed. The whole troublesome process was a direct reaction from the board of investors as the company did not reach our intended sales targets in a faltering economy. I'd heard from other managers, who'd already gone under the microscope, about impending changes to the bonus-laden pay system. The changes were made to better reflect company-wide goals of increased closings. I had no say in the process. The final verdict on my group would flow downstream soon enough.

Thursday, 1/22/09—For a diuretic drug Dr. Marrow proclaimed had few known side effects, it was becoming increasingly evident that HCTZ was going to be difficult for my system to handle. I started experiencing a painful, throbbing sensation in both knees soon after taking the new drug for the second time. I didn't know the pain was related to the pill but started to suspect it.

The symptoms progressed to my left forearm which felt strained, then weak. By mid-day I had a pain on my belt line that felt as if I was being poked with a sharp piece of metal over and over again. It escalated to a stabbing sensation in my right knee and spread to both feet by mid-after-noon. By the end of the day it felt like both knees were being bludgeoned with an ice pick. I knew that it had to be related to HCTZ. I called and left a message for Dr. Weisblat. When he called me back the following morning it was the first I heard that HCTZ raised uric acid levels in the blood. He would confer with Dr. Morrow and get back to me with a game plan to off-set what he believed to be the onset of Gout. My father had suffered from gout, and all sorts of bells and warning lights went off in my head. After immediately researching gout on line, and finding it was not heart related, I was relieved, pissed off, frustrated and thankful—all at the same time. I took a Xanax to calm down.

> Gout can present itself in a number of ways, although the most usual is a recurrent attack of acute inflammatory arthritis (a red, tender, hot, swollen joint).[2] The metatarsal-phalangeal joint at the base of the big toe is affected most often, accounting for half of cases.[3] Other joints such as the heels, knees, wrists and fingers may also be affected.[3] Joint pain usually begins over 2–4 hours during the night.[3] The reason for onset at night is due to the lower body temperature during this time.[1] Other symptoms that may occur along with the joint pain include fatigue and a high fever.[3][1]
>
> Gout can occur when serum uric acid levels are as low as 6 mg/dL (~357µmol/L), but an individual can have serum values as high as 9.6 mg/dL (~565µmol/L) and not have gout.[10]
>
> http://en.wikipedia.org/wiki/Gout

Friday, 1/23/09—Pam arrived on island mid-day and took a cab into Christiansted from the airport as I had several meetings and was unable to pick her up. I was excited to see her but wished I felt better. The pains in my knees made me hobble around like an old man, but I was determined to put on the best face possible for the short time she was going to be on island.

I really didn't want to spend our time together working on the boat, but Pam knew how important it was for me to finish the re-fit. It was by far the biggest long-term project I'd ever undertaken other than school or work.

In the morning Pam was hunched over, scrapping and sanding bottom paint—the last area to restore. I'd chosen a new product named Micron 66. There was a lot more involved in this painting process. We worked our asses off for five hours Saturday and three on Sunday. *Folly*'s bottom was ready for the first coat of primer paint.

Having Pam visit really lifted my spirits. I was reaching a breaking point where I had to see some better results soon or I was going to throw in the towel. Pam seemed to put it all in perspective and injected some of the fun and joy back into life. She understood this project was the one thing I had control over, and that it was an important goal to reach. I still had to finish up the primer and two coats of bottom paint, and Pat agreed to step in for the final stretch. At this point I needed all the help I could get.

Monday, 1/26/09—Pam's short mercy trip came to an end. She flew out in the afternoon after accomplishing her mission to uplift my spirits. I felt like my batteries had been recharged. Back at the office, I was still working on piles of reports and making several calls to business owners who were looking to purchase companies. Each month I was receiving over one-hundred and twenty leads from the BDM Group in Florida. I continued to press my superiors for a new hire.

Late in the day, one of my three Associate Managing Directors informed me she was leaving the company. She wanted to stay on the team for one more month. It gave me little time to hire and train a replacement. I pulled out the file of people I'd interviewed in the past. It was already going to be a long month, and now it included a trip to the Florida office.

Tuesday, 1/27/09—I started the day by having blood drawn at the laboratory in Sunny Isle. My routine was to rush right back to work. On this day, I took my time. Work had become increasingly complicated. I was still learning a lot about individual businesses, but the days were so packed with menial duties the enjoyment, for the most part, had vanished. My request for another person had been turned down, greatly limiting the time I could devote to customers and potential buyers. The management team was pressing me for the exact opposite. They had brought in Deborah Walker and she was going to take over the big-picture responsibilities. I was going to be left dealing with more phone work and reporting responsibilities. I was not happy with this new direction, but was thankful I had a job.

From the end of 2007 through the collapse of Bear Sterns in mid-March 2008, thousands of jobs were lost within the financial sector. The aftershocks of the recession reverberated throughout the entire system. In a ten-day span after Labor Day, Fannie Mae, Freddie Mac, Lehman Brothers and AIG were on the brink of failure. Credit Markets were frozen, stopping most deals involving mergers and acquisitions. Needless to say, I understood why The March Group needed change. My personal vision of growth within the company did not match the need for operational efficiency. Brief greetings and short meetings were about all the face time I had with the powers to be. All company-specific information flowed downstream without the possibility of input.

I continued taking only three calcium pills per day, and I was feeling okay, but in the back of my mind I knew this was a huge change, and suspected that it would eventually throw off the calcium balance in my blood.

Saturday and Sunday were spent completing *Folly's* restoration. I worked on filling recesses in the hull with epoxy. I'd already sanded the starboard side of the bottom smooth, allowing Pat to apply the thick primer paint. I continued to sand down the port side. After finishing the primer coat we had lunch at the bar allowing enough time for the paint to dry in the sun. It looked fantastic when we returned. The primer was gun-metal grey and really stood out. I almost didn't want to cover it with the first coat of blue bottom paint. After allowing the paint to dry, we would apply the final coat the next morning. The weather cooperated, and Pat and I arrived at the Yacht Club with the rising sun. We finished off the final coat of paint in three hours. She looked like a brand new boat!

Tuesday, 2/3/09—Dr. Morrow called to discuss the 1/27/09 blood test results. The overall calcium number was 8.8ml—in the normal range, ionized calcium was 5.1ml—again, normal. This was a good sign that my calcium levels had reached a balance for the first time in months. He went on to describe the game plan going forward. If I was in a situation where I was going to be sweating more than normal, I needed to increase my calcium intake. In the meantime the number should remain at three to four calcium pills per day. The HCTZ was helping my kidneys retain calcium long enough to be absorbed into the blood stream. Unfortunately the scope of the negative side effects was growing. I continued to feel joint pain. My knees and feet were especially vulnerable. Dr. Morrow and I discussed the increase of uric acid caused by taking HCTZ. He wanted me to tough it out for one more blood test and in a month he wanted another twenty-four hour urine test.

I felt good that we were making strides, but I did not like the pain in my knees. I was walking with a noticeable limp and continued the need to ice down my knees every morning before work and several times at night before going to sleep. It was a temporary fix that gave me short periods of relief, but my options were limited and staying the course and continuing the HCTZ seemed to be the logical path to take. Once again I was putting my life in the hands of a doctor in whom I found it difficult to trust.

To his credit, Dr. Morrow had taken the time to explain why this was important. The treatments beyond HCTZ were limited. We needed to build up some data with regular blood draws and see if the HCTZ regulated the up and down nature of the calcium levels in the blood. More than anything, I wanted the feelings of being sick all the time to go away. My coping strategies had been taxed beyond their capabilities. I was no longer willing to accept the torment of this illness. The only way to deal with it, according to Dr. Morrow, was to manage it. The parathyroid glands were not going to function properly. Dr. Morrow believed we would eventually reach a balance within my nervous-system aided by a combination of lowered doses of calcium pills and HCTZ.

I finished up the week strong at work. I'd been proving my worth through many new reports and question sessions with upper management. It seemed the inquisition moved on, focusing on other areas of the business. I was thankful to be out of the spotlight, hoping it was not just the calm before the storm. I'd had three straight days of high energy and I took full advantage of them, getting several goals accomplished in preparation for the upcoming end-of-year push. During my lunch hour I drove to Sunny Isle and had my blood drawn at the laboratory.

Over the weekend I finished some small touch-up jobs in the cockpit and cabin of *Folly*. She had new paint or varnish on every surface. The project had come close to breaking me. I'd used up every last ounce of energy to finish it. I felt a great sense of accomplishment as I called Brian's Marine to find out when he could put her back in the water. He thought he would be down the following Saturday putting in some power boats but needed to get back to me with a time.

Gout only added to my difficulties sleeping. To top it off, the Klonopin continued to deliver bizarre dreams. Averaging four or fewer hours of sleep a night left me with little energy. Contributing to the sleep deprivation was muscle spasms in my neck and arms. I was unable to get comfortable at any time in the horizontal position. Thinking this was a side effect of the reduced calcium intake, I increased the number of pills from three to five.

Monday, 2/09/09—I woke up at 4:30 a.m. with twitching in my neck, followed by a flood of anxiety. It intensified as I started my day. It was hard to think about anything else. I was also struggling with numbness and tingling sensations in my left leg. I had joint pain in my right foot and generally felt horrible. The yo-yo effect was in full swing. I had just finished off the previous week feeling much better, and now I found myself anxious and ill. I took two extra calcium pills in hopes of stopping the muscle spasms and tingling before going to work. The precaution had little effect as the symptoms continued to increase throughout the day.

Adding to the stress were the changes being proposed at work. I was informed of a new payment plan for the Associate Managing Directors. After looking the changes over I had several questions and did not agree with how it was structured. I asked to have a meeting with Sara Sheldon. My request was denied. I was basically told this was how it was going to be. My concerns stretched across several areas, but the main issue was that the proposal took my group's bonuses away for the number of signed confidentiality agreements they produced each month. It based all incentives on closed deals. Closings were few and far between, and out of the AMD's direct realm of influence.

The whole company was moving in this direction. I understood that it was a smart way for the Senior Management Team to save money and put the emphasis on closing deals, but my concern was the eventual downturn in productivity. Basically, I had to be the sacrificial lamb and explain the changes to my team. After much trepidation I arranged for a conference call later in the day. I was told to also cover the new plan in more depth on a visit to the Florida office the following week. I put on the most positive spin possible, and after breaking the news to my team I was left with the understanding that my jobs pay structure would soon come under the new policy as well. What other changes were in store for me and the position I held was not clear. The only thing that was clear, they were coming soon.

Tuesday, 2/10/09—I woke up from a three-hour sleep with my left knee throbbing. It seemed the calming feelings I'd experienced after first taking the HCTZ had worn off. Tingling and muscle spasms continued throughout the day in my face, neck and arms. My knees and feet were sore from the higher uric acid levels in my blood. Making matters worse, my busy schedule included individual phone meetings with each member of my group and a growing list of leads to contact from the Buyer Data Base project.

As the end of the day neared, I booked my travel arrangements for Monday to Coral Springs. I was thankful to be getting out of the office for a week, but I would be facing difficult meetings with my team as we implemented changes I had no say in. I needed to convince them that the new pay structure would afford them higher earnings potential if they continued to perform at an elevated level. It was a sinking feeling. My authority as the builder of this team had been usurped in full. I also had to hire and train a new member of the group. It was going to be a busy visit.

Adding to the level of frustration, I received news late in the day that the lady who was leaving the company at the start of November had potentially been using company leads at a second job with a local Florida business broker. This was a serious offense and I needed to take care of it quickly. After speaking with HR it was decided that the accusations, accurate or not, warranted immediate termination with pay. I did not leave the office until after 7:30.

Reaching home later than usual, I was behind in my pill schedule and my face was tingling. I was forced to go into lock-down mode out of fear the symptoms would intensify. I turned the lights and fans off and sat in the dark, concentrating on deep breathing. The shooting pains in my knees continued throughout the night. Early evening turned into late night followed by the sun rising over the eastern hills. Still no sleep!

Wednesday, 2/11/09—The tingling had diminished somewhat by morning, and despite being completely worn down, I was feeling better than the previous day. I had a lot to wrap up at work. I carefully crafted my speech for the team and the responses I was sure to face as I held individual meetings with each member.

I felt growing pressure and stress with only two and a half days left in the workweek to prepare. I knew I would be putting in some weekend hours before my flight on Monday morning.

Saturday, 2/14/09—*Folly* was scheduled to go into the water at 10:00 a.m. Enlisting Pat's help, the mooring was rebuilt in the early morning hours before Brian was supposed to arrive. Pat dove down several times with pliers, shackles and tie wire. I stayed in the launch lowering the new chain and handing down tools as necessary. Soon Pat had the new chain attached to the large sand screws that secured the heavy chain to the ocean floor. Several dives later, the work was finally over. With the new mooring ball floating on the surface, we attached lines that would keep *Folly* in place. I was confident she would be secure in the water while I was away on my trip.

My hopes of avoiding any scrapes, dings or dents while refloating *Folly* were soon dashed. Standing on the beach watching as the truck backed my boat down the incline leading to the sand, I saw the trailer hitch bounce a few inches in the air off the metal ball on the bumper. Brian's son was standing on the front of the trailer giving direction to his father. In an instant the trailer broke free. *Folly*, the trailer and Brian's teenage son gained momentum down the sandy incline. As *Folly's* 3,500 pounds rolled by me with increasing speed, I looked on in disgust. She hit the water with great force. The only thing stopping the axles on the trailer from digging into the soft sand and flipping the boat over on her back was the weight of Brian's son on the front of the trailer. For some reason he did not jump off. After seeing there had been no injury involved, I swam out and checked the trailer and boat. Surprisingly enough there did not seem to be too much damage. It took three of us to straighten out the trailer, now sitting in four feet of water so Brian could back the extension up to it. We connected the trailer hitch and *Folly* was pushed the extra fifteen feet where she finally floated. We towed her over to the mooring ball. She was back in the water for the first time in nine long months. This was an occasion to celebrate. I'd spent more time and money than I could have imagined on this re-fit. With a lot of help from others, this long project was finally over. Throughout the day I received several comments on how good *Folly* looked riding soundly on her new mooring.

Sunday, 2/15/09—My left knee was so sore when I woke up I could not put weight on it. I had an old axe handle in my guest house that I used as a cane. I was hoping to sail, but the Christmas winds had arrived early and the seas were rough. I drove down to the Yacht Club at 7:30 a.m. Sitting at the end of the dock, I watched *Folly* bob in the water as the currents pulled her new lines tight. She looked like the best-kept boat in the mooring area.

Thoughts of our annual regatta, scheduled for the next weekend, filled my head. I was hoping to race. Injuries had kept me sidelined the previous three years, but I was not sure if I could participate. It would be a last minute decision. The game plan was for Pat and Andy, to find a quality race boat to crew on. When I returned on Friday, I would meet up with them at the kick-off party. My knee was bothering me so much I had to lean against light posts that line the docks edge to make it back to the club house. I stayed home the rest of the day, working through my plans for the following week in Florida.

Monday, 2/16/09—It had been such a fast-paced couple of months I actually enjoyed having a day of travel to unwind. My knee continued to throb at times, but other than a noticeable limp I was able to walk unassisted. I checked online and found that drinking beer and eating spinach were the two worst things you could do while suffering from gout. When I visited Florida I usually ate as many fresh fruits and vegetables as possible—including spinach. I knew I would have to avoid that and alcohol if I was going to survive the week with any hopes of returning to race in the regatta.

Tuesday, 2/17/09—The day started with three interviews of potential replacements for the AMD I'd terminated. I made my decision and offered the position to a lady who was already a March Group employee. She was working on the buy side of the business. There were several challenges ahead for her but she offered the quickest replacement option available. Training needed to begin that day. The day was long over before everything was in place. In between fixing problems, I had one-on-one meetings with the remaining two members of my team and addressed the new bonus payout for the lead generation program with the fifty-six BDMs in a scheduled half-hour meeting. The change in the pay structure was met with muted anger or indifference. There were valid points brought up about the ability to earn the same amount of money under the new plan. The changeover was going to happen whether they bought in or not, but I needed them to see the wisdom behind it and continue their high level of performance.

It was well after 7:00 p.m. when I finally left the office and went back to the hotel. I noticed my cell phone message light blinking. Dr. Morrow had called me with the blood test results. My serum calcium number was 8.4, just below normal. My PTH was still well below normal. Dr. Morrow did not believe that my PTH would ever bounce back and that we needed to proceed under that assumption. We would have to continue to work to find the correct balance between calcium and HCTZ. He did not want me to alter the once daily HCTZ pill or the Calcitriol dose. I was to add an additional two calcium pills each day for a total of five. If I experienced tingling in my face or muscle cramping or contractions I was to up the dose of calcium as necessary. He wanted me to have another twenty-four hour urine test as soon as possible. By 10:00 p.m. I was nowhere near falling asleep, so I took a Klonopin. The last time I remember checking the hotel room clock it read 12:30 p.m.

Wednesday, 2/18/09—I reached the office at 7:00 a.m., still cloudy in the head from the sleeping pill. I sent several e-mail replies that had been left waiting from the day before. Training started at 8:00 a.m. for my new hire. The day was going to have few breaks. I upped my calcium, knowing I had to stave off any adverse side-effects. I ended up taking ten pills over the course of the day. I still ended up feeling worn down and vulnerable because of facial tingling and muscle spasms in my neck and upper arm. I made it through the day, but was feeling pain in my left knee and ankle from the gout. I left the office after 7:00 p.m. thankful the day was over.

Thursday, 2/19/09—It had been a short turnaround. I felt like I'd not left the office when I arrived back at the front door promptly at 7:00 a.m. I immediately ran through the previous day's e-mails and left several voice mails. Training again started at 8:00 a.m. sharp. I had two more days of information to cover with my new hire and one day to do it in. It seemed as if she was catching on, but I was not optimistic she was going to be ready to start on the phones Monday morning. If all went well, the last part of the day would be spent making live calls.

Over the course of the morning session we ran through scripts and procedures. It was a crash course and I worried that she was being overloaded. During the day, I had two, hour-long meetings I had to attend. I would leave Terry a long list of information to cover and scripts to practice while I was gone. The day went by quickly. We got word from our new out-sourced IT department about what type of modem was needed for Terry to work from home. She would have to purchase the modem in Florida, because we no longer provided them, in part to save money. I was wearing down by 5:00 and started feeling tingling in my face and upper body. I still had over two hours of work before I could head back to the comfort of my hotel room. I had no more energy and finally gave up at 7:30 p.m.

I took extra calcium and made sure to take my other pills. The tingling in my face and the muscle spasms in my neck and arms continued throughout the night but it was more of a distraction than anything. I never felt like it was going to get out of control. I was walking a fine line, but I was getting a lot accomplished. I was proving I could manage this illness under the most stressful situations.

Terry was on her own going forward. I would be in contact with her the following day at airport stops on the way home. She was going to have to have her computer, modem and VOP phone system set up without anyone coming to her house to physically help with the installation. This would turn out to be a stumbling block, but I'd done all in my powers to make her a success. We had a phone consultation set up over the weekend with the new IT department. Training was over.

Friday, 2/20/09—After a short night's sleep, I was on the road to Miami by 4:30 a.m. Because I booked the flight with such short notice, the one direct flight to St. Croix was already full. I had to fly to San Juan and have a three-hour layover before flying the last sixty-five miles home. I was still half asleep as I returned the rental car and boarded the plane. I would arrive with just enough time to set up my computer in San Juan and conduct the weekly private-equity conference call scheduled for 10:30 a.m. It was always difficult trying to interview a guest over a cell phone from a crowded airport terminal. On this day my guest happened to be traveling, and he was calling in from an airport terminal as well. It became difficult to determine if my guest had finished his statements. I ended up accidentally cutting him off several times before he'd finished his train of thought. The entire call was a distorted mess. There were several questions from The

March Group participants at the end of the call, which I had to cut off in keeping with the strict timeline set by our owner, who did not want forty to fifty of his employees off line for long periods of time, but controlling the number of questions from our BDM group at the end of the calls had proven to be an increasingly difficult task.

I was finally coming to the end of a long marathon. I still had several hours of work to do, but the worst had passed, until I received a frantic call and spent a complete hour on the phone with Terry before boarding my afternoon flight for St. Croix. She had a hundred questions after making calls for a few hours on her own. I had to cut her off as I boarded my flight. When I finally landed, I skipped going to the office and headed straight home. I needed an hour to unwind before attending the 2009 St. Croix Yacht Club CORT Series Regatta Kickoff Party. I hadn't spoken to Pat, so I was not sure if he had found a boat for us to race on. If we did not get on a boat I was not going to be too upset. I was tired and I knew it would be straining my system to the point of an attack to race after spending a week of nonstop work-related stress and traveling. As soon as I walked in the door the phone rang. Pat thanked me for lending him *Folly* for the day. Andy had really enjoyed his first sail in months after being remanded to the indoor comforts of his home during the upstate New York winter. Over the course of the day, they met up with the captain of a seventy-foot Santa Cruz that was looking for crew to help race in the regatta. We were going racing!

My mood quickly changed as I forgot about how tired I felt. It was going to be tough conditions with heavy wind expected all weekend. I love these conditions and was thankful that we would be racing on a larger boat which would provide more comfort. Andy was going to be the captain's main tactician in the cockpit and Pat would run foredeck. The boat had a self-tacking jib connected to a traveler forward of the mast. I would be Pat's backup and run the preventer and down hull. These devices are used to force the boom to one side and pull it tight to keep the main sail form flatter while racing. I did not throw caution to the wind. I spent several minutes thinking of my game plan to maintain calcium balance over the weekend.

I was feeling some slight tingling in my face, so my first precaution was to take it easy at the kickoff party.

The Cruzan Rum sponsored party is one of the largest gatherings on island each year. Free rum drinks are given away next to the food lines under a large tent. The band plays until midnight and the drinks are generally still flowing well into the morning hours. I knew I needed to keep a low profile and avoid alcohol all together. I arrived just after 6:00 p.m. with questions filling the back of my mind. Was I going to be able to pull this off without suffering consequences? It definitely would be the most challenging test to date. Was I strong enough to go out and race for two days straight? My shoulders were going to end up being very sore. That was a given. I was more concerned about my nervous system. I did not want to have a medical emergency and cause the boat to have to lose time while I was extracted off of it in the middle of a race. I put these worst case scenarios out of my mind and kept pumping my head with positive thoughts.

There were recent signs that I would be able to emerge on the other side of the weekend unscathed. My system seemed to be more balanced in recent blood tests and my energy level was on the increase. I'd also just returned from a tough work trip without any major problems. I had to talk myself into it, but I was building up confidence and looking forward to the challenge of racing for the first time in three years as I walked across the grass lawn facing the clubhouse. As the night progressed and I met Captain Steve Schmidt, my confidence grew. I listened as he told of his harrowing solo sail up from Venezuela on his seventy-foot Santa Cruz named *Hotel California Too*. It had taken almost three days battling six-to-ten foot waves in twenty-five to thirty knot winds. If Captain Steve could make that trip by himself, I could go out on the water for a weekend and give 110% effort.

Boats were still arriving in the mooring field late into the evening. It was fun to stand on the end of the dock and watch them slide into a slip or drop anchor. The number of masts bobbing up and down more than doubled the numbers of member boats. There were boats from the U.S. Mainland, St. Martin, Puerto Rico, The British Virgin Islands, St. Thomas and one from Europe. In all, we had forty-nine participants. Eight boats would be competing in the main and jib class including *Hotel California Too*.

I'd never raced on a boat of this size and was excited to be given the opportunity. My conversations with Captain Steve had gone well as I was reassured we would be racing with an experienced captain. Retired from Silicon Valley, Steve sails around the Caribbean and races mostly with pickup crews. He had been doing this for several years and seemed knowledgeable. What I liked most was his constant preaching for safety on board. It was similar to my beliefs when I sail *Folly*. That made me feel comfortable with my choice to participate in the racing.

With the addition of a strong crew like Pat and Andy, we had a good shot at winning our division—if not top honors. The forecast was for twenty-five to thirty knot winds all weekend. It was going to be rough out on the water. Steve wanted twenty people to use as ballast in the heavy winds and large seas. I called Kristin and Mickey from work and they both agreed to race for the first time in their lives. The excitement grew as the party kicked into full swing.

Rum drinks flowed and the band was playing as the crowd gathered under the tent. I made my rounds and caught up with friends who sail over from neighboring islands for the regatta. Everyone was talking about the rough conditions we would be facing the next two days. The energy is always off the charts the night before the racing kicks off.

Around 9:30 p.m. Captain Steve called a crew meeting. I was already past my allotted checkout time but needed to attend. We went around and introduced ourselves as Captain Steve gave out the assignments. Most of the crew would be rail meat, moving from side to side and hanging out as far as possible when we were heeled over. Steve spoke softly with confidence as he explained how we would be sailing for maximum speed. I liked his style.

With a pickup crew of twenty people, Captain Steve's mantra becomes even more important. Not everyone had sailing, let alone racing, experience. Kristin had sailed with me on *Folly* a few times and Mickey had only sailed once or twice. This was going to be a much tougher experience. They would have to move from side to side on a rolling, pitching deck of a boat racing for speed not comfort. Sailboat racing is one of the best arenas to let your competitive nature come out. Pat, Andy and I all wanted to win. We knew this was the right combination of weather conditions and boat design to do it. Not knowing other members of the crew made it difficult to gauge what they expected out of the experience.

We were given instructions to be at the boat no later than 8:00 a.m. Racing started at 10:00 a.m. sharp. I slipped away from the party at 10:00 p.m. I was already exhausted. I'd driven the thirty miles to Miami, flown 1,200 miles home on two separate flights, continued to put in a full day of work and just left a rocking regatta kickoff party. I focused on preparing for the physical sailing conditions we were going to be facing over the next two days. It was past time to get home and shut it down.

Saturday, 2/21/09—5:00 a.m. and the excitement was growing. I was up early preparing my backpack for the day of racing. I was ready to go out and test where I'd advanced to in my recovery. As I loaded the ice trays in the ice packs, necessary for later that evening, I smiled. I can do this! In my backpack I'd loaded all the pills I needed. I added Ibuprofen to ward off some of the shoulder pain I knew was inevitable.

My shoulders would be pushed to their threshold of mobility. Pulling sheets out of blocks on a pitching, rolling deck requires strength. I believed I was ready to take on the physical challenge—but was not 100% sure. The area of most concern was my endocrine system and whether all this activity would throw it out of what little synch it had recently found. Could my system handle the added stress? I planned to add at least six additional calcium pills daily in hopes of keeping my levels in check. The workload on the boat would cause me to sweat more than usual and I needed to replace the lost calcium. At the time I believed I was making the necessary adjustments. I'd raced several times in the past and always came out of the experience exhausted and beat up. I was aware of the consequences if something went wrong, but I truly believed I could do this. I calmed myself

305

down in the early morning by watching the sun come up from my back porch. I took several deep breaths and told myself that I was strong enough and prepared enough.

When I arrived at the Yacht Club at 7:00 a.m., it was already full of activity. The trash crew was there bagging up hundreds of empty bottles and cups from the party the night before. Several race crew members milled about at the continental breakfast in the club's bar area. The launch service was running and people were racing back and forth to their boats ferrying sails, crew and equipment. The main topic of discussion was the strong early morning winds. They were blowing over twenty knots already and were forecasted to pick up to thirty knots before 10:00 a.m. I saw the look in several boat owners' eyes that morning. Should we go ahead and race? I think everyone gathered at this regatta asked themselves that question. The forecast called for steady winds between twenty-five and thirty knots and seas at five to eight feet. It was going to be rough racing for sure. These are the types of conditions that will test the safety of the crew and the strength of the boat's equipment. Equipment failure in these conditionsamplifies the chances of someone being seriously injured. No one wanted to see that happen, so all captains were running over their safety precautions with crew and making sure they would strictly be adhered to, but the odds were still in Mother Nature's favor.

Before jumping on a launch and heading out to *Hotel California Too* I grabbed some breakfast and held several conversations with crew members from my club. The parathyroid effects potassium levels in the blood as well as calcium, so I ate two bananas at breakfast and stuffed two more in my backpack along with a couple of oranges. After double checking the contents of my backpack, I was ready for the adventure to begin.

The water inside Teague Bay was churned up and made it rough for the all-volunteer launch driver crews to hit their marks. As I stepped into the yellow banana-shaped launch owned by a local dive shop, I noticed it had three or four inches of water in the bottom. There were ten other sailors sitting against the inflatable walls shaking their heads. The drivers looked worn out from a morning spent trying to maneuver the odd-shaped inflatable in rough seas. Out in the protected mooring area boats were being tossed around and the launch driver was struggling to keep control as we approached the starboard side of each boat. As someone stepped off, the rest of us wished them luck. As the launch approached, it hit each boat on the sidewall with a resounding thud. The driver apologized to more than one angry boat owner.

Powerful swells were rolling into the bay out of the north-northeast. If it was this rocky in shore behind the reef, the unprotected race-course was going to be really rough. I took a leap of faith off the launch when it got within three feet of *Hotel California Too's* reverse transom. I scrambled up the stairs and found Captain Steve holding court in the cockpit. He had an undeniable calm smile on his face. As if I was a mind reader, I could tell he understood the conditions were as favorable for his boat as they could be. At seventy feet, *Hotel California Too* is only competitive if there are sufficient winds to move her considerable weight around a shorter six-mile course. She was designed to be a long distance ocean racer. There would be one downtown race that covered twelve miles, but the rest of the individual races would be on the shorter course where we would have to give time to every boat in our class. For this reason it was smart of Steve to only race in the main and jib class. Complicating things by flying a spinnaker sail several times each race with a new crew could only lead to slower times.

One by one, every crew member made it aboard and Steve had us all busy readying the boat to leave the mooring area. This was no easy task in the rough waters. He went through each section of the boat asking about crew member's experience. He then calmly explained the procedures and important systems onboard. Each boat has its own personality and only Captain Steve really understood the characteristics of this one. There was no way for a pick-up crew to know all there is to know about a boat of this size with one short, shake-down cruise and an hour discussion. That's why Pat, Andy, Ed Beacher and I were assigned specific tasks on the boat. Each of us had considerable sailing experience. Pat and Andy's resumes are long and impressive. They had been racing for over forty years, including an Olympic trial in the seventies. At least Captain Steve had an experienced core of crew members.

After a half-hour preparing the boat to leave the mooring area, the crew gathered around the cockpit. Safety was stressed as the number one goal for everyone on board. No one was to do anything unless an order came from Captain Steve or Andy. The Captain's speech and mannerisms were calming and demanded respect. "Safety is the number one priority! If we go out and have fun and everyone returns unharmed it is a good day." He did not put any final expectations on us. However the confident smile on his face further reinforced my belief that he knew how well we could do in this weather. We all had our assignments. Everyone on board had the job of being human ballast. You have to ride the high side rail while heeled over so the Captain can get maximum speed out of the boat. When the boat tacks and the high side becomes the low side, you have to scramble up a heaving deck and get into position on the new high side rail.

Healing is a natural motion of a mono-hull sailboat. They are designed to plow through the water in this fashion. It takes some getting used to, especially for people that have not sailed before. As the weather increased overnight, I had grown more concerned about inviting Kristin and Mickey to race, but they assured me they were up for the challenge. After the initial shock wore off I was sure they would be fine.

Andy, as the head tactician, was positioned in the cockpit with Ed Beacher, a couple young winch grinders and Captain Steve. Everyone else in the twenty-person crew was on the rail. Pat and I were farthest towards the bow of the boat. Steve went through his final instructions. No one else was to climb into the cockpit while we were racing and communication was to come from him or Andy. Each time he gave the crew instructions his experience racing with pick-up crews came through. Everyone onboard knew, within minutes, that this was a professional sailor who had run through this speech and gone over the policies many times in the past. I have raced with some really good drivers and with some I wish I'd not wasted my time and energy on. Captain Steve's calm demeanor and soft-spoken speech patterns carried instant respect. It galvanized the twenty-person team into a unified crew. We had a chance to really place high up on the leader board—maybe even take top honors. The competitive juices were starting to flow. I'd never raced on an overall winning boat. It would be nice to add that to the resume.

Steve's dinghy was tied off with the anchor lines at the bow of the boat. We pulled the crewmember up out of the dinghy and over the bow stanchions before backing off the mooring under power. The ocean was angry. The waves outside the reef looked huge from the elevated deck. The temperature was eighty-two degrees. The twenty-five knot wind made it seem much cooler. Later in the day, as we took waves over the bow, the salt spray felt cold. I knew extra calcium would be necessary to offset sweating throughout the day's exertions.

Riding out to the course moments before a serious day of racing is like a starting pitcher getting mentally prepared before a big game. You're in beautiful surroundings, tossing well wishes to other crews as you motor past. At the same time you're thinking of how the day will turn out. It's up to the Captain to race to the boats strengths and try and eliminate its weak-nesses. These factors change with the wind. I forgot all about my illness for the next few hours and got down to some serious competition.

After gliding through the cut with little room to spare on either side, we turned towards the wind and raised the large main sail. The mast that held it was easily five times bigger round than *Folly's*. It stood over sev-enty-two feet in the air. With this much sail, in these wind conditions, we were assured of a spirited ride.

After tacking back and forth and watching two classes of boats launch off the starting line in front of us, we entered our first countdown sequence. Everyone had a pretty good idea of what was going to happen when the horn blew. The committee boat, and buoy placed about 300 yards directly across from it, formed the imaginary start line. Each racing class had their own colored flag which flew off of the Committee boat's outriggers and determined the starting sequence. As the one-minute flag for the main and jib class rose to the top of the outrigger, a nervous excitement came over the crew. The deck fell silent waiting in anticipation of hearing the horn.

We broke upwind off the stern of the committee boat just as the noise of the starting horn cracked through the howling wind on deck. Captain Steve heeled her over on her ear as we shot off towards the easternmost point of Buck Island. We had eight boats of varying sizes in our class. Each one of them was jockeying for the exact same position on the exact same line as we were. Captain Steve had maneuvered us into the best possible position. We were mere feet away from two fifty-foot boats and five forty-foot boats, each heading for the same point off in the distance. Clearing the other boats gear with our mast by a few feet was exciting. Pat and I yelled, "Clear!" after passing each one. Everyone was screaming out loud at the same time for different reasons. Those of us who knew what was going on were happy for a great start. The rest of the crew was yelling out of shear terror, trying not to fall off the boat that was by now racing completely on her side.

Right away I was impressed with the *Santa Cruz 70* and its abilities to sail into the wind. The first race of the day was around the windward mark, leeward mark, windward mark, leeward mark, around the final buoy and back across the finish line. Eating up huge chunks of rolling sea at a time, we bolted out ahead of the pack. We knew we should be the first boat across the finish line for every race. At seventy-feet in length, *Hotel California Too* surpassed the next longest boat in the class by fifteen feet. That gave us a large speed advantage over the rest of the boats. Each boat has a scoring handicap, which meant we would be giving up lots of adjusted time at the scorer's table at the end of the day. The race committee uses these adjusted times to score the race and determine a winner for each class.

Immediately there was lots of talking. Steve yelled out for everyone to be quiet. He was barely audible from the cockpit. The wind was howling. He wanted all communications to come across clearly to Pat and myself up front. The first order was for everyone to hang over the guardrails as much as possible. For safety reasons he did not want anyone standing that did not have a specific job. He was going to race for speed all the way. That meant we would be on our ear and it was not going to be comfortable. It was going to be a long battle all day and the Captain knew enough about what he was doing to take immediate control. I liked the start and was growing more confident in our capabilities as a crew.

The first tack was just off the coral reef as we approached the eastern end of Buck Island. Steve made a great call and ordered the tack early knowing he pointed into the wind better than most boats in our class. The early tack gave us a clear distance advantage as we left the rest of the boats far behind. The spinnaker class of boats that had left five minutes before our start time were rounding the first mark and popping their chutes. It is a difficult maneuver in large seas with this much wind. From what I could see, several chutes were left flapping in the wind. Filling the big sails with air and keeping their shape on the downwind leg of the race was going to be a big chore all day. I was glad Steve had made the decision to just race in main and jib saving us from the same difficulties. As we approached the first course marker, a huge orange plastic pyramid filled with air floating on top of the eight foot rolling seas, I glanced back at the now fading pack of boats behind us. Shaving the marker within a couple of feet *Hotel California Too* was off to an impressive start. We were gaining on the spinnaker class ahead of us. The downwind leg of the race is always the best. The boat is relatively flat and the wind is at your back as you surf up and down the waves.

Steve drove a fantastic race. We hit all our marks and no one got hurt. During each tack, the jib sail was moved from one side of the boat to the other. The high side, where the human ballast is hanging over the rail, also needs to change at the same time. Each tack twenty people, including Pat and I, had to scramble across the deck. You had to time it right as the boat was pitching and rolling during the sail change. If you got caught in the middle, you risked tumbling off the boat into the water. The angle of the deck was steep—about forty degrees. It was during these tacks that I had to switch the preventor from side to side and tighten or loosen the down haul. The amount of pressure on the down haul made releasing the 5/8 inch sheet very difficult. I had to kick the rope out of the snap blocks and hold on for dear life as the force of the full main sail on the boom pulled my surgically repaired shoulders forward with a jolt. The stretching of my arms out of their comfort zone caused instant pain, but I felt it was a good opportunity to loosen up some of the scar tissue. Doing this on a flat deck would be difficult enough let alone on one pitching nearly forty-degrees and rolling up and down in eight-foot seas. Somewhere during the delicate balance between what seemed like leaping off a cliff one second and scaling a sheer rock face the next, I'd split the skin below my right knee leaving a trail of blood on the white deck. The surface of the deck was covered with metal fixtures that held down sheets, clamps and screws that were just waiting to tear into you. There is a true old sailing adage that you are not racing if you are not bleeding.

Mickey and Kristin had long since stopped looking at me like "what in the hell did you get me involved in." They were getting into the competition just like the rest of us. Everyone aboard, by this time, was completely aware this boat was an ass kicker and we were in good standing on the scoreboard by the end of the first race. If the current wind and sea conditions held up all day it was going to be a matter of how much time we beat every boat that would determine our overall standing in the regatta. After rolling up the jib sail and tacking under the mainsail alone, we watched as the next closest boats in our class raced across the finish line in a tight group.

The first day's action consisted of four races. Each start was good for *Hotel California Too*, but none matched the perfect maneuvering for position we had pulled off on the very first race. We crossed the finish line by a large margin over the next closest boat in our class in each of the following three races. The crew was beat up but feeling lucky to have been racing on such a large boat. The rest of the classes looked to have had a tough day of racing. During lunch, I was sitting in the cockpit listening to someone tell a tall tale when crackling chatter boomed out the speakers, breaking radio silence. A couple of boats had sustained catastrophic parts failure and had to retire from racing. One had broken its mast off and the other snapped its boom.

Boats were losing equipment left and right in the rough conditions.

By the end of the first race, the saltwater spray was caked on each of us like a second skin. I knew I was physically working hard, and the fact that I didn't have sweat rolling off of me did not mean I was not losing fluids. I remained conscientious about drinking large quantities of water and taking my calcium pills. It is difficult to find time between races to run back across the deck and go down below where my backpack was stored and get bottled water, pop the powdered calcium down and get back in time to hear the next set of instructions. I found the whole scenario to be a nuisance, but however much I did not like taking the pills, I also knew what the alternative was. We were scheduled to be on the water from 7:30 a.m. until 4:00 p.m. If I'd waited to take the HCTZ or the Calcitriol, and especially the calcium, my nervous system would have immediately flared up with signs of tingling and muscle twitching.

The racing that took place in the second half of the day was fantastic. Our Captain really knew how to drive his boat for speed. That meant little comfort for the crew as he pushed the boat to the limit each and every race. The downwind legs gave the crew a short break because the boat leveled out as we absolutely flew up and down and through the large seas. We carried boat speeds over nine knots most of the day.

By the end of the racing I was feeling sore in the shoulders and had scabs forming on top of scabs that had been ripped off several times throughout the day. The most afflicted area was the lower legs. There was no way to avoid being eaten up by the deck. I had given maximum physical effort, and other than being a little sore, I felt great. I thought I'd kept my calcium level in check. I'd felt only minimal tingling in my lips and along my cheekbone.

After we buttoned up the boat and it was safely back on the mooring, we sat around and waited for the launch boats to pick us up. Captain Steve made Margaritas down in the galley, which tasted fantastic, and removed some of the saltwater taste from the pallet. The winds continued to howl and the seas remained six-to-eight feet. The calmer afternoon conditions, expected at this time of year, did not occur as Captain Steve polled the crew over the constant howl of the wind and asked who would be back the next day. Although they had fun, Mickey and Kristin decided that they wanted to stay home on Sunday and heal their bruised legs and sore butts. I thought it was cool they'd given it a shot. The next morning they would be replaced with two guys who each weighed close to 250 pounds. We needed the extra weight. The forecast for the next morning was for even stiffer winds with gusts over thirty-knots the entire day.

Stepping off a seventy-foot racing machine onto a fifteen-foot launch in six-foot rolling seas is a tough task. Some people over thought the process and took a tumble, ending up rolling around on the water-soaked nonskid floor of the club's launch. I waited until after the second round of margaritas was poured and we had made our plans for the next morning. As I left, I congratulated the Captain on his driving. He thanked me for the day's effort.

It would take over two hours before the race results were posted. I knew I'd pushed it all day and was not planning to stick around for the party taking place in the clubhouse later that evening. I made my rounds, talking to some of the sailors from other boats to see how their day had gone. As I suspected, most crews in the smaller boats looked like they were exhausted. The stories they told were of parts breaking and minor injuries to crew members.

Everyone going out the next day would need to remain sharp as tomorrow's conditions would test even the most seasoned crews. After one full day of racing, five boats had been forced to retire. The first horns at the starting line the following morning would seem like the opening bell of a heavy-weight title fight. Mother Nature vs. boat and crew.

I needed to ice down my shoulders, take some anti-inflammatory pills and call it an early night, so I left before the results were posted. After taking a shower I noticed the impressive bruising on my hips and upper legs. I spent the next hour with ice bags attached to every body part as I stretched out on my bed. The thoughts of how beautiful the ocean was, and the tight racing at the starts, the motion of the boat and the sounds it made as we passed other boats in the field, proved difficult to remove from my head as I tried in vain to shut it down for the night.

Sunday, 2/22/09—Just getting my legs to swing out over the edge of the bed was a chore. I took a short shower and crushed up my day's supply of calcium pills. Every part of my body was sore and my actions were labored. I'd sailed enough to know that adding another day of racing on top of it was only going to cause the pain to extend its stay, but I was not willing to miss the opportunity to compete. I was eager to get to the Yacht Club and see what the first day's results were.

I arrived just after 7:00 a.m. The results were posted inside the front door on a large white board. We had taken two firsts and two seconds in the four races the previous day. Depending on the weather conditions and the courses raced, we had a good shot at winning our class. The twelve-mile race downtown and back to the starting line was where we could really open up a large lead. I was looking forward to this race because the first leg is downwind and after rounding a buoy in Gallows Bay, you can choose to hug the coastline or reach out towards Buck Island. The scenery along the way is incredible and you can really relax and enjoy the sail. Full of anticipation for the racing on the last day of the regatta, I ate a hearty breakfast before heading out to the boat.

The seas had picked up and the wind was howling. It seemed that everything that was easy the day before, was now difficult. The club was down to two launches. The yellow inflatable tub from the day before sat at the end of the dock, half-submerged, waiting to be rescued. We had our first bit of trouble getting Steve's dinghy to start. Two crew members were left to row the anchor in rough seas. Pulling the two crew members onto the stern of the boat almost cost us our first casualty. A guy slipped and just missed hitting his head on a stainless-steel stanchion. Although we had lost one crew by the numbers from the previous day, and stood at nineteen, we had gained weight and it would be needed to offset the winds that were picking up as we tossed off the mooring ball that held us in place. We were one of the last boats to leave as we waited for a crew member who was picking up sandwiches for lunch. It turned out to be a costly delay.

It was going to be a rough racecourse and Captain Steve continued to preach safety and did not like how some of the early morning day's work had gone. He wanted better concentration from the whole crew. Gathered around the cockpit, as we motored out the cut in the reef, Captain Steve again covered the ground rules of no standing up or talking during the races. He cautioned us on our movements about the boat under sail and thanked us for our hard work the previous day.

We watched as three classes of boats ran through the starting sequence and banged and beat their way upwind across the starting line and down the course. We calmly stayed a half-mile back off the action, crisscrossing north to south under main sail alone. We were moving closer to the committee boat, directly into the wind, when Captain Steve called for us to open the reacher sail. Pat went all the way forward and I followed closely. Pat pulled on the reacher sheet and it would not unfurl from the drum attached to the bow of the boat. There was no fixing the mechanism. We were within our five-minute start countdown sequence and we had to perform a huge sail change. Captain Steve turned her into the wind as ten of us lined the bow of the boat in rolling and pitching seas, removing the sail which stretched almost the entire length of the deck to the cockpit. It was lowered down a forward hatch into the cabin all the way back to the stairs leading up into the cockpit. A smaller sail was pulled up through the same hatch and slotted on. The crew worked together like a well-oiled machine. The horn went off just as we popped the sail and raced for the line. A full minute had past before we crossed the start line staring at the sterns of the other boats in our class.

During the first leg of the race, Captain Steve pushed for speed as we caught up to and passed over half the field. After rounding the mark perfectly, we passed the remaining boats in our class midway through the second leg. Up ahead we had clear vision of the spinnaker class rounding the mark trying to pop their chutes. Several ripped their sails, dragging pieces in the water, forcing crew into a mad scramble, all the while losing valuable time. Even with the malfunction of the reacher sail furling system, we crossed the finish line first by a couple of minutes ahead of the closest boat in our class. The seas grew and there were a few monster waves over ten-foot tall that washed across the deck. It was exciting to be out in the big water with the heavy winds. I loved every minute of it. You are forced to concentrate on every move you make. You have to put aside your pain and ignore the fact that you have blood streaming down your legs from fresh wounds. Holding on for dear life, your main concern was not taking a header off the boat. Two boats lost crew members overboard the first day. Valuable time was lost going back and plucking them out of the angry water. We were praying that did not happen to anyone on *Hotel California Too*.

The race committee sent out an announcement over the radios that the second race was downtown and back. An audible cheer went up from all the boats. Everyone needed a break and the long downwind leg to town would give crews a chance to have a flat deck for an extended period of time, eat and drink some much needed food and water, and tend to any cuts and scrapes.

After the start flags were raised and the horns blew, Captain Steve had driven another textbook start. We had close-in racing with other boats for the first two or three hundred yards. Our mast sticking out further than all the rest forced us to be careful not to get tangled in the rigging of the boats we were passing. The sailing was fantastic as we hurtled downwind towards Gallows Bay, the boats in our class trailing further and further behind, as we made up ground on the spinnaker class ahead.

Kite boarders raced off the coast and came alongside, performing amazing aerial stunts. They moved with such speed and agility. It was fun to watch for a few moments as we ate in silence. It was going to be a long sail after rounding the mark and heading back to the finish line between Buck Island and the reef.

After rounding the mark in Gallows Bay, we raced passed Hotel on the Key. The fort's cannons pointed directly at us. It was time to get back to work and race it home against the wind. Captain Steve made few, if any, mistakes driving the boat and we glided across the finish line well ahead of the other boats in our class.

The race committee delivered an announcement over the radio that we would only have one more race. It was going to be a longer course race that consisted of six legs. By this time, everyone was ready to get off the boats and start the closing ceremonies and the party at the bar. We hung back under main sail for over an hour, waiting to get our flag sequence started. All the boats in our class were up on the starting line, jockeying for position, each trying to be in the perfect position to tack just off the wind across the starting line when the horn sounded. It truly was a game of cat and mouse. The most knowledgeable boat captains usually came out on top. We had been very good on our starts the entire regatta—except for the one equipment failure which had cost us time.

Captain Steve maneuvered us between other boats in preparation to tack at just the right moment. We were first across the line as we picked up speed and cleared the other boats in our class safely. Leaving them in our wake everything seemed like it was going our way. We approached the southeast corner of Buck Island and tacked just feet before running into the coral reef. A few moments later everyone was in place on the high side, feet dangling over the edge. Pat and I were the only two who sat facing the deck because of our crew responsibilities. Our legs hung over the raised cabin top and lay across the 5/8-inch jib sheet. The power in the jib sail on this boat was amazing. The sheets were run through a self-tailing traveler forward of the mast. The wind had picked up above thirty knots and there was a constant whirling noise in our ears. Over the roar of the wind, I heard a short ping followed by a popping sound. The jib sheet, with all its power, ripped down the deck underneath Pat and my legs throwing them up in the air, knocking the Teva sandals off my feet. The block holding the jib-sail tension on the self-tracking traveler had failed. All the power of the sail was now bearing down on the base of the mast. The calves of both my legs felt like they had taken a hammer blow, but there was no time to worry about injuries. Ed Beacher,

318

who was in the cockpit, went below and found a spare block. We stayed our course as Ed came forward on the low side inches from the water, at speeds over nine knots, and lashed the block to the end of the traveler. We had to de-power the jib sail by turning into the wind while running a temporary sheet before rerouting the original through the new block.

For a complicated turn of events, the fix was made to look fairly simple. Ed Beacher had saved the day, but it had cost us time as we were forced to stay on our present tack much further than we would have. As we rounded the marker in good form, I could see we were not alone. Other boats that were struggling with equipment and sail issues. We could only hope that we got it fixed in time. Captain Steve pushed hard for the finish line as Pat and I rubbed our wounded calf muscles.

It was around 3:30 p.m. when all the boats got back to the mooring area. The other crews looked haggard. Everyone's story seemed to be a similar tale of ripping sails, breaking equipment or losing a crew member overboard. When a crew member goes overboard it basically ends any chance to finish at the top of their class. There were a couple of moments when the tack was made, and I was mid-deck, where I had to dive for a handhold on the rail and pull myself up before tumbling off. That would have ruined the race forcing the boat to stop dead in its tracks and double back to pick me up. It also would have wrecked the great sense of accomplishment I was feeling.

Everyone was waiting for the race committee to post the final results as the party raged on in the bar area. A couple hundred sailors stood around telling stories and congratulating each other for finishing one of the toughest regattas in recent memory. Just after 5:00 p.m. a Captain's meeting was called. A few minutes later the closing ceremonies got underway in the food tent on the front lawn. It was after 5:30 p.m. when the first winners were called to the stage. When it came time for main and jib class announcement word had been passed down that our final results for the second day of racing included a first, a second and a fourth-place finish. I was not sure how that would play out in the results. It was going to be close. As the Commodore announced the first-place winner our name was not called. With the adjusted times, we had barely lost out on overall honors. When Captain Steve was called to the stage for second place. He called the entire crew up and thanked us. He gave a classy speech and said this had been the best pick-up crew he'd ever raced with. A loud applause from the other sailors in the tent erupted.

We watched as the winning boat got the Captain's weight in rum. The Captain actually sits on a large wooden scale that was used in the 1700s to measure the weight of rum kegs. Cases of rum are added until the captain and his take are evenly balanced.

The Yacht Club had put on a great show. Even though the number of boats was lower than we wanted, the event was a huge success. Captain Steve talked to Pat and me about racing in the remaining CORT (Caribbean Ocean Racing Tournament) Series. These races were held every other week on different islands culminating in the Heineken Regatta on St. Thomas. I would have loved to race in all of them, but I needed to get back to work the next morning and did not see any chance of taking time off with all that was happening on the job front. It was a great offer, but I had to pass. In the back of my mind I knew that I was not strong enough to tackle any more regattas for the immediate future.

After taking a shower and patching my wounds, I dropped down on what seemed to be a bed made of ice. It was going to be challenging in the morning after all the muscles tightened up over night. I had stuck to the pill regimen throughout the weekend. I felt some tingling in my lips and some muscle spasms in my shoulder and neck, but I felt if I could shut it down and close my eyes and relax I'd be fine. I had survived a great regatta. In my mind I'd passed a huge test. I was finally starting to bounce back—or so I thought.

BACK TO THE EMERGENCY ROOM (DAY 713 – 723)

Monday, 2/23/09—Work was carried out at such a fast pace and high volume I barely had a chance to share the stories of racing in the regatta with anyone. From 7:30 until noon I was buried in paperwork. I tried getting contacting my new hire. She didn't answer her work, home or cell phone. I left messages expecting to receive a call back. None came. I left a second round of messages. A quick check of the systems and I could tell she was not on line or using her VOIP phone. I did not hear back from her as the afternoon progressed. I was certain my messages had been received and I was becoming worried. I spoke to Deborah and explained the situation. She asked that I keep her informed. By the end of the day, I still had not received word from Terry. Deborah was watching how I handled the situation. There was nothing I could do except call my counterparts in Florida and see if they knew what was going on. George Markis told me he would look into it. If she was unable to work from home, he would make room for her in the office. Space was at a premium, but he would take care of it, if needed. He reported that he had not been able to reach her.

As I left the office, I felt the familiar headache that accompanies my calcium imbalances. It was not severe, but was still uncomfortable. My face started tingling and the back, left side of my neck began to spasm in ten-minute intervals. I was distracted the entire drive home. When I finally got inside I noticed the message light flashing on my voice mail. A racing boat from St. Thomas named *Atlantic Rader* had hit *Folly* on her mooring ball in the high winds and rough seas the previous day. Although I gave the guy credit for calling and leaving a message with his phone number, I was pissed. *Folly* had been in the water for just over a week. I had spent nine months remaking every inch of that boat. Now some guy hits her inflicting god only knows what kind of damage. From his description, he was not sure of the damage because the jolt had knocked him off his feet and when he was able to stand up, his boat was in the trough of a wave and he was unable to do any inspection. Without changing my clothes, I raced down to the Yacht Club. According to the owner of *Atlantic Raider* he had hit *Folly* on the port stern section. From the end of the dock I could only see about half the way down the port side of my boat. The damage was out of sight. There was a large catamaran tied up to the dock. It had at least a twenty-foot beam. A couple stepped off the catamaran as I approached. I introduced myself and they said their names were Jeff and Kelly. I explained my situation and they graciously allowed me to walk across the back of their boat to get a better angle, hoping to be able to catch a glimpse of the damage.

The sunlight was fading and *Folly* was over 100 yards away. I could not see anything. I thanked the couple for their help and they wished me luck. I planned to kayak out and inspect the damage in better light the following afternoon. Little did I know that I was less than six hours away from another chance encounter with the man I'd just met.

As I returned home, unsure of how much damage *Folly* had sustained, the pain in my head was growing. My face began tingling with more intensity and the muscle spasms continued nonstop in my neck and the backs of my legs. My first instinct was to take extra calcium. A short time later, the anxious feelings started to permeate my mind and before I knew what was going on, I was forced into shutdown mode. After turning off all the lights and fans, I tried lying down with my eyes closed and could not comfortably stay horizontal. My breathing became labored, and within thirty minutes the tingling intensified into ice-pick stabbing sensations. I called Pam around 8:00 p.m. She tried her best to calm me down as I started losing my grip on the situation. I got off the phone abruptly, telling her I needed to relax. The symptoms continued to intensify and ten minutes later I hit the redial button. I was shaking in pain as the muscles around my mouth locked down, making it difficult to speak clearly. Pam kept telling me over and over again that I could make it through this. I tried every technique I knew to relax, but the monster kept growing. This had intensified quicker than any previous attack. I took ten extra calcium pills. Nothing seemed to help. Holding the phone to my ear, curled up in a ball on my bed, all my muscles from head to toe were either jumping out of control or clamped down tight as I struggled to get enough air past the growing tightness in my throat. Just after 9:00 p.m. Pam leapt into action, keeping me on the main line, while calling Donna and Tony on her cell phone.

I hobbled out of my house under my own power. My head was foggy and my body was suffering muscle convulsions. My hands were balled up in fists and I was unable to open the door to Tony's truck. I required assistance climbing into the seat. Through the entire ride I leaned forward with my eyes closed and my head down towards my knees. Tony talked the entire time. The half-hour drive to the emergency room felt like it took days to complete. I desperately tried to talk myself out of having a seizure or stroke. By the time we reached the hospital, I was experiencing a full-blown attack of my nervous system. The feeling was dangerously close to the one I'd had right before passing out in Tampa. I was getting scared that I would not make it to safety of the ER room before bouncing off the floor and breaking a hip in the process. My breathing became even more labored, which added to the difficulty speaking. My facial muscles had locked up, leaving my mouth in a permanent whistling position. The stabbing sensation spread from the back of my head to the bottom of my feet.

The local Crucian lady at the nurse's station proceeded to finish her cell-phone call before acknowledging that Tony and I were standing at her window. She was in no hurry to get the process started. I knew, with each passing second, the risk that I would pass out was growing. Standing up was a huge gamble. To protect my bone structure, I needed to be lying down so I did not fall. Finally the door opened. I started to explain what was happening, and as if this lady was judge and jury, she kept interrupting me and questioning my story. I finally told her I was getting close to passing out and needed to be in a bed. She told me there was no bed in the emergency room. I explained exactly what was happening and what needed to be done to take care of this. I asked her to check the records from July 4th of the previous year. By this time I was rocking back and forth, leaning forward as far as possible with my eyes closed. The clarity in my head felt similar to the white-out fuzz on a TV when the cable is out. I was finding it difficult to communicate, and my speech was slurred, coming out at a low volume as my teeth remained clamped down. At one point I said, "I'm passing out and you will have to deal with that." The nurse was not pleased with me and sent Tony away to the records window to get my past history. I remember Tony returning to the admitting office two or three times asking questions because the nurse in the records office would not comply with his requests. Finally a doctor's assistant from the ER came up to the admitting office checking on a different patient. He took one look at me and sensed the need for immediate action. He inquired about where I was in the admitting process, and after checking my pupils and blood pressure, the nurse had no choice but to speed up her actions. She produced the necessary papers. By this time my systems were in such a state of shut down that I had to push my arm up to the table to sign the paperwork. My motor skills had ceased functioning properly.

As she walked out the office, the woman said, "Now I'm going to have to clean a space back there for you." Ten minutes later I was being wheeled back to the ER.

I was put in the exact holding area where I spent the previous July 4th and Christmas night. There was no door, only curtains, and it was very cold. An ER Nurse attended to me right away. She had to lean down over my face to be able to hear my story. I explained that I'd been here before for the same treatment. By this time the cramping in my shoulders, neck and leg muscles had me curled up in a ball on my right side. She took my blood pressure and explained that she would get the doctor as soon as possible. Just a few minutes went by, but it felt like hours before the doctor arrived. I had my eyes closed and was trying to relax when I heard a man say, "Hello. I am Dr. Klempen." When I looked up I saw a familiar face. I'd met the doctor six hours before on the dock at the Yacht Club. Dr. Jeff Klempen, his wife Kelly and their three children lived on a catamaran moored 200 yards from *Folly*. They had just moved to the island the week before.

Dr. Klempen explained to me that he was the new ER doctor. I was relieved that I did not have to deal with Dr. Citron. I was worried about what I would say to her if I ever faced her again. Dr. Klempen did not seem to be fazed by my story. I explained it to him as clearly as possible. With the increased cramping in my face, it became more difficult for him to understand my speech through clenched teeth. He reviewed my records and to my relief acted quickly by having an IV inserted into my arm and injecting me with a strong dosage of Ativan so I could relax. Blood was drawn and rushed to the laboratory as the doctor closely monitored my blood pressure after the Ativan had taken effect. He ordered an EKG before promising to return as soon as possible.

In short order, the Ativan had drained the tension from the major muscle groups allowing me to lie flat on my back in a horizontal position. Minutes passed and Dr. Klempen returned with the blood work and the EKG results. My heart was in good shape and the overall calcium level in my bloodstream was 7.8 below normal. The attack had moved in on my nervous system so fast and with such ferocity that I was expecting the calcium level to be much lower. I'd seen much lower numbers and not felt such a violent and complete nervous-system breakdown. Although my head was a fuzzy distorted mess I was still able to form a question that I would pose to Dr. Morrow at a later time. "Was my nervous system getting worn out, more susceptible to the illness?" Believe me when I tell you I would have given anything to avoid coming to the hospital, but I was not going to make it on my own at home. Was this how it was going to be with every calcium fluctuation? Did I no longer have the ability to weather these attacks?

Dr. Klempen ordered a calcium drip. I told him of the previous time when the calcium had caused the back of my right hand to swell up like a baseball. He used my right arm vein on the inside of my elbow, instead. It seemed to work much better. The drip would take several hours. The Ativan had kicked in full and a wave of relaxation flowed over me. I was able to lie back on the bed—breathing normally. I still had massive tingling and my eyes were twitching under the lids, but the terror was gone. I asked the nurse to pull the curtains and turn off the overhead light. In the dark I thanked God that I'd made it.

Pam had forced the issue and done the right thing calling for help. If I'd stayed at home they would have most likely found me on the floor the next morning. This attack was bizarre in the fact that it came on so fast and so strong—without much warning. I had several hours of pain and tingling before I passed out in Tampa. This attack reached that level after only an hour from the onset. Over the next several hours, as the liquid calcium slowly drained into my vein, I had time to consider what happened.

Four hours later the IV drip had finished. Dr. Klempen visited with me briefly and told me to get a hold of my specialist as soon as possible. My face had relaxed to the point where I was once again able to speak clearly. My arms functioned and my legs had stopped cramping. My mind was still extremely cloudy—hung-over—as if I'd consumed an entire bottle of tequila. I knew from past experiences this feeling would be with me for three or four days. I was released just after 3:00 a.m. Tony had been waiting in the lobby more than six hours—choosing not to leave. I could not thank him enough on the ride home.

Leaving the hospital I was walking upright with all my motor skills functioned properly. My muscles had been relaxed by a powerful drug and I felt pretty good except for the pain in my head. Presumably my calcium levels were in the acceptable range but the nervous system would take several days to bounce back. We pulled into the yard just after 3:30 a.m.

Feeling exhausted I crashed onto the bed. I was not able to fall into a deep sleep, but I was able to nod off for a few short hours of rest. I was determined to go to work. At the time, I felt it was the right decision to make.

I needed to move past this latest incident as quickly as possible. I had a lot of work to take care of and I really needed to get to the bottom of why I'd not heard from my new hire.

I took a shower at 6:30, operating on adrenaline and little else. I dressed and drove to work. I was hoping to be the first into the office. There was no denying I looked horrible, and I didn't want to have to explain it to anyone. My skin was clammy from the drugs in the ER the night before. The tingling had diminished but was still present. If I could just make it into my office I could do my work without anyone seeing me.

7:30 a.m.—I found the front gate leading to the office unlocked. While climbing the stairs to my office I heard voices coming from the cubicles located in the loft area at the top of the stairs. Deborah and our Executive Assistant were having a conversation. I tried to slip by unnoticed. Both immediately stopped me and asked if I was okay. Upon further inspection they became concerned. My eyes were bloodshot and my face had the expression of a sick person, not to mention the bandages on my arm where the Ativan and Calcium had been administered. Deborah noticed the wristband that said ER on it. I'd forgotten to cut it off. She asked what was going on. I gave her a brief explanation and she questioned me on what I was doing at work. Why had I come in? I should be at home in bed. I did not need to be there. On and on she went. My reasoning included the situation with the new hire which was bothering me and I wanted to get to the bottom of it. I also had two client meetings scheduled later in the day and I had some data to update for reports which she had requested. I needed to work. She kept telling me I needed to go home. The Executive Assistant chimed in and told me that I needed to leave and get some rest. I'd not even made it to my office door and I was losing the battle. I promised I would leave as soon as I got a hold of the new hire. Deborah insisted that I go home and get some rest. She would contact my new hire for me. In defiance I grabbed my laptop and declared I would be working from home the rest of the day. Deborah told me to get some sleep first.

Although I was feeling about as poorly as a human being could, I didn't like being told that I needed to rest. I cursed the notion the entire drive home, but I was fast asleep in my bed by 9:00 a.m., and I woke at 3:00 p.m. My first order of business was to call Dr. Morrow. When I explained to his nurse that I'd spent the night in the emergency room, she promised to have him contact me as soon as possible. As I waited to hear back from the doctor in Cleveland, I contacted Deborah to find out if she had spoken to my new hire. She had and believed her story about having several issues setting up the high-speed internet at her apartment. She had wasted two working days without making a single call. I was less than pleased, and Deborah again asked me to calm down and get some rest. I was ready to fire my new hire and go with my second choice. Deborah would discuss it with me in the morning when I returned to work. My frustration with having to run decisions past a new person was mounting. I could not let my blood pressure rise, so I pushed this train of thought aside and got in a few hours of work.

Dr. Morrow called back later that evening and we discussed what had happened. For what seemed the fifteenth time, I was explaining to someone the complete meltdown of my nervous system. This was the second worst attack I'd experienced and I felt sicker than any time since my parathyroid surgery. The only thing Dr. Morrow could determine was that I'd overtaxed my system racing in the regatta. I immediately jumped in and explained that the regatta ended on Sunday and I'd felt fine. I worked a long hard day on Monday and did not start to feel the symptoms until after checking on my boat that evening. Dr. Morrow sensed my mounting frustration and explained that sometimes it can be a delayed reaction. He believed I'd been sweating more than normal, exerting myself past the point where it was healthy. He said in a calming voice, "Maybe you will just not be able to do everything you used to be able to do."

With that comment I came unglued. "What did he mean by not being able to do everything I used to be able to?" This conversation was not going well. I did not want to hear this. He agreed with me that the calcium was low, but the drop from my previous blood draw numbers the week before at 8.4ml, to the previous night at 7.8ml, was not that large. He did not have an answer why my system reacted so strongly other than I might have pushed it too far. The question of whether my nervous system was beat up and more susceptible to these attacks was raised, and he had no answer for me. He suggested I see I neurologist to get some insight into that. What he was concentrating on was finding a balance. I would have to learn not to over-tax my system with physical activity.

My foot really started to bother me. I limped around the house while I was on the phone with the doctor. In my mind, the call was a waste of time. I didn't like the doctor's message. I didn't care if he was right. I wanted to prove him wrong. The more I thought about it, the more pissed off I got. Not only had this disease consumed two years of my life, now I would have to question every physical exertion.

"What kind of life is that? It sucks!" As the anger mounted over what I was hearing, Dr. Morrow calmly continued. He wanted me to increase my calcium pills to six per day and have another blood draw the following day. The goal was to get my calcium numbers to stabilize in the lower end of the normal range. Before hanging up, Dr. Morrow again reiterated that this was a process and we would eventually find a balance. I needed to hang in there.

I fired up the laptop and completed e-mails for two hours. I'd received an e-mail from my new hire apologizing for the delay in calling me back. I immediately phoned her and went through what I expect from an employee. One of my expectations concerned returning my calls. She explained the mess it was to get the high-speed internet installed and get the systems up and running at her home. I was not accepting her explanation as easily as she would have liked. She had been on the phone the entire day and had several questions for the out-sourced IT department, another situation I was less than pleased with. My foot continued to really throb. We finally hung up after reaching an understanding. She was close to being terminated. I had to set that aside and get some work done.

Wednesday, 2/25/09—I started the morning early, standing in line at the laboratory in Sunny Isle. I felt pressure to get to work as soon as possible.

After donating a blood sample, I arrived at my office around 8:30 a.m. I had one conversation with Deborah in the morning. She had spoken to my new hire and understood the circumstances. I was less willing to grant my new hire a free pass. I had stressed to Terry that it was a privilege to work from home and she needed to have the system set up and working no later than noon on Friday. Deborah told me to let it slide. I was not happy with the entire situation. Truth be told, there were precious few things I was going to be pleased with at this point and time in my life.

What I didn't realize that I was actually making progress. HCTZ was starting to work but it takes time. The doctors were leading me down a path I would soon see benefits from. I knew, without a doubt, that I was never going to be completely cured. The doctors continued to stress the words management and balance. I spoke to Dr. Weisblat later in the afternoon and told him what Dr. Morrow had said. He had already had a conversation with Dr. Morrow and agreed with him that I might not be able to do everything I had in the past. I probably overdid it racing in the regatta, but this instilled a sense of rage deep within me. I felt horrible by the end of the day. I was rundown, sick and depressed. I went home and took a sleeping pill.

Thursday, 2/26/09—Midday at work I received a voice message on my cell phone from Dr. Morrow. He had contacted the laboratory in St. Croix and got my calcium numbers from the previous mornings blood draw. He said he was confused that this number was lower than the number from the emergency room blood draw two nights before. He wanted to know if I could get another blood draw to make sure there had not been a bad read in the hospital or the laboratory. The last thing I wanted to do was have another needle jammed into my arm. I was so fed up with all of this mess that I'd reached my boiling point. I called him back and explained that I would get another draw, but it would take time. I would get it by the mid-point of the following week. I was feeling horrible and I was having a hard time walking. Dr. Morrow thought that I should have uric acid levels added to my next blood draw. He suspected gout brought on by taking HCTZ which raises the uric acid levels in the blood. All I knew was that it hurt like hell.

Friday, 2/27/09—The residual calcium hangover continued to plague me all day. My foot hurt so bad I was half limping and half hopping. I called Dr. Weisblat and left a message. My situation needed to improve quickly. Bud Orpen had arrived on island from Texas and I'd promised him a sail on *Folly*. He was a close friend, and I was really looking forward to seeing him. I had worked so hard to get *Folly* back in the water on time. I was not about to let a sore foot and a mysterious illness keep me from sailing. Besides, I had all day Saturday to rest up. All I needed to do was survive work and go home and rest for a day and a half. The day mercifully came to an end with the help of a couple well-timed Xanax to take the edge off my growing frustration level.

Saturday, 2/28/09—The day was spent relaxing and taking in plenty of water to replenish the dehydrated tissues. The painful symptoms in my foot started to subside and my head was clearing. All signs were a go for the sail the following day. I'd not heard from Bud, but knew he would have called if he was not able to make it. We had planned this sail via e-mail over the past three months. Bud was so organized I knew he had the date and time marked on his calendar and wouldn't miss it for the world. I slept well that night, on my own, without the aid of a sleeping pill.

Sunday, 3/1/09—Pat and I were waiting at a table in the open-air bar area of the Yacht Club at 10:00 a.m. We made sure to be early. Bud and his friend Julie, arrived right on time at 10:30 a.m. At first sight Bud was showing his age and the effects of the cancer treatment. He'd lost several pounds and was not moving as gracefully as he once had. He warmly greeted both Pat and I with a hug and as firm a handshake as he could muster. The honor of taking Colonel Bud Orpen out sailing meant more to me than I can express. Bud was one of the last remaining from the greatest generation. He had risked his life, time and time again, flying bombing missions over Japan at the end of World War II. Several of the men under his command did not make it back to their families at the end of hostilities in the Pacific. Because of these facts, I'd always held my friendship with him in high regard.

Pat and I worked as hard as we could to provide the perfect sail with no mistakes. It was a beautiful day. The sun was out in all its glory and the temperature was in the low 80s as we left the dock in the launch. We had plenty of food, and water and cold beer on board. Getting Bud on board required us lifting him up and placing him on a couple of boat cushions forward—near the outer wall of the cabin. We performed the maneuver without asking if he needed our help. As we sailed off the mooring ball, a deep sense of sadness overtook me as I looked at my dying friend in the front of the cockpit. Bud started telling stories in his weakened voice. Pat and I informed Julie of Bud's tenacity at the card table. He was always good to pull out a winning hand when you thought he was holding nothing. This led to our nickname for him "Fucking Bud." Bud just smiled as if that was the way the world should be—him winning every close hand.

On our way out to the beach at Buck Island we caught several glimpses of sea turtles and flying fish. As *Folly's* hull cut through the water I believed there was a higher power at work. The winds were unusually light and the water flat for this time of year. A perfect day to sail!

As we approached the anchoring area off the beach Bud noticed a tourist boat named *Tesoro*. He had married his second wife Barbara on the deck of this boat over ten years prior. Barbara had passed away from cancer two years earlier. I could see the sorrow in Bud's eyes as he told the story.

After securing the boat and putting up the sunshade, we sat in the calm waters and recanted several old stories. Bud told us of his adventures sailing to the BVI tied to a lawn chair on the trampoline of a sixteen-foot Hobbie Cat. He had cruised the island chain for a week after making the sixty-five mile crossing, carrying only the provisions that fit in the cooler lashed to the stern. Bud continued to talk about his latest toy which was a motor powered, tricycle-framed paraglider. He had not flown the machine, yet, but it was assembled and he planned to take flight after returning to Texas. I was encouraged by his tenacity to push the limits. If he was still holding out hope, I felt I should not be so pessimistic about my own situation. After a few hours, Julie, never visiting St. Croix before, wanted to hike the trail that transversed Buck Island. I did not want to leave Bud, but reluctantly agreed to accompany her. We swam into the beach and headed off to the trailhead. Walking in the sand, I noticed the pain in my foot had disappeared. Every aspect of this sailing trip had lined up in our favor. The hike was dramatic and beautiful. Julie really enjoyed the views from the north face. The base of a storm-wrecked observation deck makes for a good vantage point. She took several pictures. The entire hike took less than hour.

When we returned to the boat, Bud and Pat were stretched out on the cockpit benches under the sunshade—half asleep. Within the half-hour we were pulling up anchor and heading back across the channel in search of more turtles. After slicing through the cut, we tacked between the shoreline and the reef several times before entering Teague Bay. We rounded up on the mooring wand perfectly. Pat reached down and secured *Folly* to her mooring lines. After buttoning down the boats sail cover and storing the jib we enjoyed an ice cold beer. Bud told us that it had been a perfect day. During our hike, Julie had told me that Bud had been talking about this day for months. He had really been looking forward to it. It could not have gone any better.

After the launch picked us up and we helped Bud into and then out of the boat at the dock, we said our goodbys in the parking lot. Bud had another week on island and we would see him Thursday at our regular poker game. He thanked me one last time before Julie helped him into the car.

Monday, 3/2/09—I was asked to produce more records of my team's past performance. Deborah also asked questions concerning my personal projects outside the team's responsibilities. I found all this probing to be annoying. I sensed some big changes were headed my way. I spent most of the day gathering information as requested. Driving home after work I felt pain in my chest and I had a raging headache. I took a couple of Advil when I reached the house. Concentrating on deep breathing, I stretched out on my bed trying to calm my nerves. I got up around 7:00 and took a Xanax hoping it would help me relax further. Sleep did not come easy and I was still awake at 12:00 p.m.

Tuesday, 3/3/09—5:00 a.m. The lingering pain in my head and chest had diminished but still annoyed me. Like so many times in the past, I rolled out of bed. I got to work before 7:00 and plowed through the work which had been pushed aside to complete the requested reports. I finished by 10:30 a.m. It was surprisingly quiet. Just before 4:00 p.m., I was speaking with a new client on the phone when the message light started blinking. I knew from the Caller I.D. that it was Deborah. The message she left asked me to meet her in the conference room as soon as possible. When I opened the big wooden doors I saw her alone at the end of the long conference table with a triangular speakerphone in front of her. She was looking straight down at the floor as she said, "He's here." She did not make eye contact as Sara Sheldon's voice came booming out of the speakerphone. She introduced the head of HR who was also on the line with her. I knew immediately what was taking place. My job had been eliminated. The "good news," according to Sara, was they were offering me a lesser role within the company. This did not come as a shock to me. I was one of the highest compensated employees within the management team and the company was struggling to make payroll each month, and over the past few months my responsibilities had been examined every way possible, my authority usurped and I felt all along this was the outcome.

I signed the sheet eliminating my current job and told them I needed twenty-four hours to think about their offer. Deborah handed me a paper describing my diminished responsibilities. One of them was going back on the phones, making calls to business owners, trying to get signed confidentiality agreements. The day I turned over the calling responsibilities to my team had been one of the happiest in my professional career. I'd worked hard to get to that point. Now they wanted me to return to the tedious task of calling all day. My title, Manager of Buyer Services, was removed. In the description they had written up, I would need to do all I could to help manage my old team, but give up the more enjoyable parts of my job, handing them over to Deborah's control. The entire conversation was over in less than three minutes.

I stayed at work until after 5:00, finishing up some last minute details.

I put the new job offer out of my mind knowing I would work it out later that night away from the office.

When I got home, the first thing I did was call Pam. We discussed the situation for what seemed like hours. Pam was very supportive and offered many different scenarios. I could not reach a conclusion concerning the employment offer. The practical side of me wanted to accept the offer and continue to work. People in the financial services sector had been losing their jobs left and right. On the other hand, I had felt, for a long time, that I was pushing my body and mind too hard. My illness had required extended time off, and I ignored the symptoms as much as possible, clinging to work as if it was my safe haven. It was the one place I could exert control. People listened to what I had to say and followed my lead. When it came to health issues I was the one following instructions from doctors and caregivers. Even though I'd done some really good work and my team was operating at top efficiency, I understood the company's perspective. The credit freeze had greatly reduced anticipated sales and they needed to cut payroll, but I did not want to take a step backwards in my professional career. The company's offer consumed my energy that evening. I went to sleep with the issue unresolved.

Wednesday, 3/04/09—The decision to accept or decline the offer was set aside for the first part of the work day. I had some last minute instructions for my new hire. She was just getting a feel for the job and still had several questions. I was slowly bringing her up to speed. That morning I assigned her new duties, reviewed what questions to anticipate and providing talking points and tips on converting calls into signed confidentiality agreements. The rest of the morning was spent completing reports and speaking with private equity partners. I remember walking alone on the boardwalk during lunch as if it was for the last time. I ran into my friend Kristin on the corner of Company and Hospital Streets on my way back to the office. She asked how my day was going and commented that I seemed stressed. I was stressed. I didn't like this situation. For a period of time, I believed I would be the person who would move forward in the company.

The March Group had chosen to hire from outside the firm for upper management positions, targeting people who had worked for their competition. One company, in particular, had failed and been reborn two or three times in the past. Those very same business practices were now being brought into our company. The upper management team had grown by twenty people over the past two years. With the work I'd done, and the amount of leads we had converted into signed confidentiality agreements, I convinced myself I would be promoted at some point. With each new upper management hire, that hope faded, and when Deborah was brought in I knew the opportunity had passed me by. Now it was just a decision of whether I wanted to cling to a job in tough economic times or walk away.

I sat and stared out the window, watching the waves break on the reef in a rhythm only Mother Nature can provide. Remaining calm, I called Deborah and asked some questions about my responsibilities going forward. I'd read the paper correctly. I would be required to get back on the phones. I'd created the position and had performed it well for close to two years. I'd worked my way out of that position and part of my current responsibilities included managing and training the group who did the calling. My job responsibilities had expanded in so many different directions. I knew the time involved with calling lists would leave me with little time for the more enjoyable aspects of the job.

Until that moment, the odds in Vegas would have been 100-to-1 that I would accept the lower-paying position, but I just could not get over going back on the phones. In every way this was a demotion. It was not based on performance, attitude or management skills. It was simply about money. Deborah wanted me to take some more time and think about it. I did not see the logic in that.

I packed my belongings after watching the waves roll in for a few more minutes and walked down the stairs past Kristin's cubicle. She was back from lunch and looked at me carrying my box of belongings. She knew exactly what was happening. Her eyes got big as she asked what I was doing.

"I'm headed home."

A Time of Darkness (Day 724 – 775)

Thursday, 3/5/09—With no work to get ready for and no plans for the future, I felt uneasy all morning long. I had to keep telling myself to calm down. There was definitely high anxiety as I wafted back and forth over my decision. Deep down I knew that if I stayed with the company under the circumstances offered, I would be miserable. The inner conflict would have resulted in even more stress—if that was possible. I had to get my health in order. I'd tried everything. A break from work might give me a chance to finally find some solutions.

By noon I was climbing the walls. I was free to go anywhere and do anything, but I could not move outside my small guest house. I was so used to high-volume workloads, meeting deadlines, monitoring progress, speaking with clients and potential buyers, interviewing private equity groups, building relationships etc. Going from that fast-pace world to a dead stop in just a few hours became increasingly difficult to handle. I started questioning my move. Maybe I'd acted too quickly without thinking it through. I had tried to weigh my options, but it just seemed like a problem that was not going to be resolved. Less than a day into unemployment I was wishing to have any other problem to fix, any other problem would do to fill the time. The uneasy feelings continued to grow well into the night.

Friday, 3/6/09—The weather clouded over, the winds picked up, and rain started early in the morning. I'd been looking forward to a sail in sunshine on *Folly* with Pat and Andy. I desperately needed to get out of the house. Andy was flying back to New York the following day and unfortunately his last day on island was not good sailing weather.

337

Our back-up plan was to meet for lunch at the casino. I returned to climbing the walls after the details were worked out. My mind shifted to trying to figure out what my next move would be. Every time I checked the clock, lunch was no closer. The phone rang—piercing the heavy air.

Terry Dibert and George Markis wanted to know how I was doing. Neither was happy that I'd left the company. They wanted to offer me the only job they had available—a Business Development Manager position. This job was strictly phone work. The goal was to get owners of companies to join The March Group at a day-long exit strategy seminar. I could work from home if I wanted or have my old office back. I basically would be my own boss and not have anyone within the St. Croix office to answer to. The top earners in the group made good money—well over six figures. Terry and George believed I had what it took to be an elite BDM. I explained that I really didn't want a sales job, but in the end told my friends I would consider it.

The opportunity to make a substantial commission was appealing. At the same time, I knew all the top performers and they were truly a different breed of salesmen. It took a different personality to persevere through the repeated rejection of hundreds of calls per day. I needed time to think about it. We ended the conversation by setting up a callback the following week. Before ending the call, I thanked both men for thinking about me.

Just as the company was peaking in internal growth, the recession hit hard and made selling client's companies nearly impossible. The March Group was left with few options but to cut payroll. I knew it was not going to get better any time soon so I weighed my options carefully.

Terry and George handled their teams with great professionalism. Both of them had complete control and as equals we'd helped each other with several projects over the years. There's a big difference between working for and equal to. They touched on the subject during their call. George told me that although it would be odd, as long as I did the work they would respect my past accomplishments and give me every professional courtesy they could. Although I knew the job was not the best fit for me, the gesture really lifted my spirits. A smile came across my face and my mood was changed instantly.

I drove to the casino for lunch and some drinks with Pat and Andy. I'd been bothered all morning by tingling in my face and arm. There was no stopping it, so after one beer, I refrained from drinking alcohol. I stuck to water and increased my calcium intake. I didn't want this to escalate into a full-blown nervous-system attack. I was not physically exerting myself playing video poker games, but the tingling intensified throughout the afternoon. I left the party early and went home to lie down. I took a Xanax and closed my eyes. The winds were strong and the air was cool and filled with light rain. A feeling of letting go enveloped me and I started to relax. The edgy sensation I'd been experiencing all day faded.

Saturday, 3/7/09—The storm continued as I drove to Sunny Isle the next morning. I found myself at the end of an already long line of people waiting to get out of the light rain and heavy winds. There were at least twenty people ahead of me. When the doors finally opened, it was a mad dash to get a numbered ticket from the wall dispenser. My limp allowed several people to pass me in line. I eventually pulled number thirty-six, and sat down in a hard plastic chair, gout enflaming my right leg, in the far corner of a crammed waiting room. My number was finally called at 11:30 a.m. The needle was jammed into my vein. This time I didn't turn my head. I watched as each vial turned from clear to bright red. The nurse ushered me out telling me to hold the piece of cotton to the hole in my arm as she yelled for the next customer.

I dreaded returning to the guest house. I knew I would lie down and start contemplating my next step in life. It was all such heavy thinking. The dark, cloudy feeling would fill my head and I would end up depressed. The time for these difficult negotiations within my own mind would come soon enough. I chose, instead, to walk the downtown streets in the rain. I ended up at the Brew Pub watching the boats. The rain on the water relaxed me as I drank a beer. I knew the gout would get even more inflamed by my actions, but it felt good breaking the rules.

339

On my way home, I stopped by Melissa's house and we talked about what had happened at The March Group. Melissa had been summarily driven out of her position earlier in the year—just before the arrival of Deborah Walker. She was a sympathetic ear. Internally I became alarmed as I continued to speak. I noticed how many times I mentioned how horrible I felt physically and how drained I was mentally. Little if any resentment or anger in my current situation was about work. I was more concerned about my health and how poorly I felt. I'd never been able to admit that the illness was my chief concern.

Melissa sensed something was off in my demeanor and took my blood pressure using a machine she had on her desk. It was strapped to my arm before I could make my escape. The pinching of my arm and the beeping of the machine pissed me off. The look on Melissa's face freaked me out. My blood pressure was 177/115. Melissa told me I was real close to having a stroke or a heart attack. As I hustled out the door I explained I felt fine except for the tingling in my face and arms. The last thing I needed was another worry about something going wrong. I left her with promises I would get it checked out.

By the end of the day I'd designed a hard-core exercise plan where I would build up to running five miles per day and lift weights to offset my impending doom. I needed to lose twenty-five pounds and regain cardio-vascular health. Somewhere, rattling around in my overly-hyped mind was the idea that I would show the doctors, Melissa and any other doubters.

Sunday, 3/8/09—My first day of the newly committed workout schedule. I stopped by Melissa's house on my way to hike Point Udall. I had her check my blood pressure. The numbers read 163/93. I planned on doing a two-mile hike that included a tough hill section. The roads are covered with broken asphalt which makes the hike even more difficult. Rains from the previous day added a slippery mud to the surface. I was still limping slightly from the gout. The last thing I needed was to hit the ground breaking one of my ultra-thin hip bones in this isolated location. I was forced to take it easy on the slick surface. Not being allowed to go full speed pissed me off. I felt as if it was yet another in a long line of mounting restrictions in my life.

The two-mile hike went up and down small rises and followed the shoreline with dramatic views. There are no buildings on the road, making it easy to relax and concentrate. I walked along, taking each breath deep into my lungs. The hill leading up to Point Udall climbs from sea level to over 300 feet. The road cuts back across the hillside and the climb lasts for over a quarter mile. I felt some pains in my chest at the top left portion of my heart as I walked. I pounded my chest with a closed fist and continued on. I finished the walk and stopped by Melissa's again to have my blood pressure measured. This time it was 151/75. These numbers were much better and I felt great for making an effort to get out and exercise.

The pain in my chest continued off and on throughout the remainder of the afternoon. When early evening came around, and the dull pain was still noticeable, I became worried. I wanted to be sure I was not having heart issues. I spoke to Pam and decided to make arrangements to come up and get a complete physical with Dr. Weisblat before my insurance ran out and COBRA benefits kicked in at the end of the month.

I had one more call to make, one I'd been dreading, putting it off for over a week. I had to force myself to press the buttons. Junior, a friend of mine, had stayed in touch over the years and most recently had been talking about his job opportunities. He had turned to me for some advice about leaving self-employment for the benefits of corporate life. The last I heard, he had chosen to accept a job. Although I thought it was odd that we had not spoken for two or three months, I'd been so wrapped up in my own problems I'd not reached out to him. I got the call regarding his diagnosis of pancreatic cancer from a mutual friend. Assuming Junior was hit hard by the diagnosis, and had chosen to keep it to himself. I understood his silence.

When I finally made the call to his cell, a faint, barely recognizable voice answered. He told me how depressing it was to be forced to move back in with his mother so she could take care of him. The next day he was scheduled for another round of chemotherapy. He sounded so defeated. I tried to instill the will to fight and we talked for over fifteen minutes, but his energy was fading and he excused himself and hung up. I had a really hard time accepting how sick my friend was and how fast it had happened. There was nothing anyone could do to help him. In my mind, I could not let go of the thought that your friends should not be in this position at this age in their life. It was difficult enough seeing someone like Bud Orpen suffer from such a horrendous disease but he had lived a full life. Harold "Junior" Huddleston was only half-way into his journey.

Monday, 3/09/09—I woke with a horrible pain in my left knee. It was not the same stabbing pain I'd felt previously, but was in the same spot. The discomfort in my chest was still present, but had not grown in intensity. The first thing I did was book a flight to Cleveland leaving on 3/11/09. The next thing I did was call Terry Dibert in Florida and accept the position as a BDM. I knew I was going to have a hard time being on the phones all day, every day, but the potential earnings were attractive. I was under the impression that my old office would be available. I wanted to work from the office because I enjoy interaction with coworkers. Terry would check it all out and get back to me. I told him I was going to Cleveland and wanted a little time before I started. We decided that it would be best to have me come in for training to the Coral Springs Office on Monday, the third of April. That gave me time to see Pam and have some medical tests done in Cleveland. The lingering recession provided the deciding factor in my acceptance. I knew I wouldn't enjoy this position and that it would most likely be difficult for me to continue doing it day in and day out, but I felt that the potential to earn a substantial salary in this economic environment outweighed the negative factors.

I was on the phone all morning setting up appointments with Dr. Weisblat and Dr. Morrow. I was getting a complete physical from Dr. Weisblat including an EKG, and he was going to look into the pains I'd been having in my knees and feet. Dr. Morrow was interested in getting another twenty-four hour urine test to see if the HCTZ was maintaining calcium in the kidneys long enough to absorb it into my blood stream. This was where the lack of PTH hormone in my system was affecting me. I was looking forward to seeing those results, along with the latest blood draws. I booked two flights, one to Cleveland and one to Coral Springs. It was going to be a hectic month.

Tuesday, 3/10/09—I tried to relax with a strenuous hike up Goat Hill. I needed to burn off some nervous energy. I was still haunted by my conversation with Junior Huddleston. My situation paled in comparison, and I couldn't comprehend his fate. Later that night I was scheduled to attend what everyone was figuring to be the final poker game with Colonel Bud Orpen. As I hiked and sweated, I thought about my two friends and why fate had taken this course. Bud was also in the process of dying of cancer and I wanted to set aside the finality of it all and try and enjoy the company of my old friend one last time.

The game started at 7:00 p.m. I took my seat—just to the left of Bud. He seemed lost at the table and forgot the basics of games he'd taught me to play. Although in his eighties, Bud had always been sharp when it came to playing cards. We played at his house every Thursday night since I'd moved to the island. There was a great sense that our history and friendship were coming to an end. It was hard to face. Bud had told Pat and me that he wanted to come back to the island in August. It was apparent the trip was not going to take place.

We all shared memories of past games and of hands that "Fucking Bud" had stolen from us. He joined in the conversation at times and seemed disconnected at others. His memory, once sharp, was fading. The pace of the game was slow. Usually, a slower pace brought out frustrations in the players around the table. This night, no one cared. We patiently explained games to Bud that he'd played thousands of times in the past. As we said our goodbys, I knew this would be the last time I would face my friend.

When I reached home my message light was blinking. My childhood friend Jack Turner wanted me to call him. Harold "Junior" Huddleston had passed away earlier that evening. In my last conversation with him, he dejectedly told me that he was going in for another round of chemotherapy the next day. The procedure caused his internal organs to bleed and there was nothing the doctors could do to stop it. Jack was not sure of the family's wishes regarding a service, but he was pretty sure it would be quick. I explained that I was leaving for Cleveland the next morning. Jack promised to call when he heard about a service date. The passing of my friend darkened my mood considerably. My last words to Harold were, "You have to fight this thing. It's not over yet." I think he was already resigned to his fate by the time we had spoken. It was a disheartening evening. I felt deflated and there was a strong sense of helplessness. The reality that doctors cannot cure every illness was upsetting.

Wednesday, 3/11/09—I have never been happier to be taking a flight off the island. The week's events had me thinking about my vulnerable situation. I was no longer willing to follow the doctors and plod along. No one is invincible. The body can fail, and there are times when doctors have no solutions. With each leg of the trip, there were new ideas forming in my head. I felt I was on the right track to start a strenuous workout routine. The reality of my illness was how I chose to let it affect me. I had to get better control of my nervous system. I fought it for so long and it did not seem I was making headway. Maybe I needed a more positive outlook. I needed to make a bigger contribution. I committed myself to taking more control and being more aggressive. I didn't want to end up like Bud and Harold.

I was never happier to see anyone than Pam standing in the baggage claim area. I did not want to let her go from our embrace. I'd spent the day with a hard, introspective evaluation of how I'd handled my situation. I felt I had failed. All I was doing was pushing it aside and throwing myself into work and other distractions. To date, the illness had been winning the battle. I was happy to shift my attention to someone else for a change.

Thursday, 3/12/09—I was in Dr. Weisblat's office at 9:00 a.m. starting a fairly routine physical. I expressed worries over the chest pains I'd been experiencing. I reminded the doctor of my family history as he ordered the EKG. It came back with no abnormalities. He was sure my heart was fine. He based his theory on the fact that I was not experiencing higher levels of pain during strenuous activity. The pains in the upper left side of my heart did not sound like heart-attack symptoms to him and he believed they could be gas buildup related to acid reflux. The sharp pains in my feet and knees were definitely gout. He reiterated that HCTZ raises uric acid levels in the blood, causing the debilitating pain. Dr. Weisblat had prescribed Colchicine for gout flare-ups, but the pains had subsided before I was able to take the medication. He'd also prescribed an anti inflammatory called Indomethacin to take during flare ups. I'd delayed adding another pill into my daily routine and I'd never taken them. He suggested we start there and look for another solution, if they did not alleviate the pain. He was certain gout was going to be a problem as long as I was taking HCTZ. We discussed other options, included a medication that helped eliminate uric acid from the system. Again it was another daily drug, and I was adamant that I did not want to go that route. I knew, from experience, the potential for devastating side effects.

My blood pressure was 144/88, magnesium levels were normal, overall calcium was 8.1ml—just below the normal range. Uric acid was well above normal levels at 8.7mg/dl. I was concerned about stones forming in the kidneys. He agreed that we needed to monitor this with regular blood tests, but there was no indication that I was developing kidney stones. He increased my dosage of Xanax from .25mg to .50mg. Dr. Weisblat wanted me to continue taking Klonopin, as needed, for sleep. The last issue I wanted to cover was a large discoloration that had formed on my face and forehead. He believed it was a result of my overstressed nervous system. He'd only heard of Vitiligo, and had never seen it before.

"Vitiligo is a chronic disorder that causes depigmentation in patches of skin. It occurs when the melanocytes, the cells responsible for skin pigmentation which are derived from the neural crest, die or are unable to function. The precise pathogenesis, or cause, of vitiligo is complex and not yet fully understood. There is some evidence suggesting it is caused by a combination of autoimmune, genetic, and environmental factors. It is also common in people with thyroid disorders. The population incidence worldwide is considered to be less than 1 percent."

http://en.wikipedia.org/wiki/Vitiligo

If I lowered my anxiety levels, he believed the Vitiligo had a good chance of clearing up. All records were sent to Dr. Morrow's office so he could go over my blood work and give me suggestions on dosage amounts in hopes of finding the ever elusive balance.

Pam had taken Friday off and we spent the long weekend relaxing and watching movies. Stress levels seemed to lower substantially. I had no problems breathing and only minimal facial tingling. I slept better than my usual five hours, and was able to dine on fresh fruits and vegetables.

Monday, 3/16/09—I woke up with symptoms of low calcium. My head had the all-too-familiar cloudy feeling and the muscles in my face were twitching and contorting. The previous day I'd completed a twenty-four-hour urine specimen that needed to be dropped off at Dr. Morrow's office. I had a rental car, and during the half-hour drive to his office, my symptoms increased. I could not understand how my symptoms could change so quickly. My eyes were sensitive to the sunlight, and the motion of the car made me squint as I drove. I felt horrible by the time I climbed out of the car in the parking lot. I took six extra calcium pills after dropping off the jug of urine, and sat in the doctor's waiting room with my eyes closed until I felt good enough to drive back to Pam's house. The last thing I wanted was to add a car accident to my list of problems. Pam was at work, so I had the house to myself. I closed the blinds and turned off all lights. I took a Xanax and lay down on the bed without the usual anxiety, but my face continued to contract and the tingling increased over the course of the morning hours. I took additional calcium pills in hopes of raising the level in my blood stream. It seemed to work, and I was able to fall asleep even though the headache lingered on.

Later in the afternoon I received a call from Dr. Morrow and I explained my low calcium symptoms. He recommended I take eight calcium pills daily going forward—two pills four times a day.

I heard back from my friend Jack and Harold's family had held a service on the night after I arrived in Cleveland. My mother had attended, knowing I would have wanted to be there.

Over the next three days, Pam continued to work, and each evening we walked at least two miles around the neighborhood and exercised to a Debbie Severs workout tape. Every time we worked out my shoulders were left burning. It was a good feeling. I was not content just sitting back and being thankful for the limited mobility I'd regained. I needed to push the limits in hopes of gaining back more, and I needed this break from the hectic schedule of the previous months. By the end of the week I was feeling rested and somewhat rejuvenated.

Friday, 3/20/09—Dr. Morrow called me with the latest urine test results. I was eliminating 529 mg of calcium per twenty-four hour period. The previous test before starting to take HCTZ showed I was eliminating 745 mg of calcium in a twenty-four hour period. The high end of the normal is 300 mg. Although I was still losing a large amount of calcium every day, the numbers had improved. Dr. Morrow wanted me to start taking two HCTZ pills per day in hopes that my kidneys would store even more calcium. I expressed my concerns over the further elevation of uric acid. I was adamant that I did not want to form kidney stones or end up with kidney ailments that could lead to dialysis. Dr. Morrow understood my concerns but insisted I give this a try. He also was sure that Dr. Weisblat could prescribe a drug that helped eliminate uric acid—leaving me gout-free. I hated the idea of introducing yet another drug into my system. It was even more maddening that it was needed to offset the effects of a drug I'd just started taking. My fragile hips left me with little choice. I reluctantly agreed to give it a shot. At the end of our conversation I brought up synthetic PTH as a possible treatment. Dr. Morrow had not forgotten that I'd mentioned this in the past. He felt it might be beneficial, but had not found evidence of the drug's use treating parathyroid disease. He promised to look into it.

At the end of the day, I got a call from Terry Dibert in our Florida office. My old office in St. Croix was already divided up and assigned to three people. Space was at a premium according to the powers that be. I was going to have to work from home in my new job. I was less than pleased with this development. My first day of training was set in Coral Springs on Monday, 3/30/09. Pam was scheduled to come down the following week for five days before I flew out for training. It was a trip she'd planned several months in advance. I didn't want to spend that time getting high-speed internet access and setting up an entire home office. To top off my immediate thoughts on the subject, I did not have AC and the hot months were right around the corner. The heat would make working from home difficult. The decision was final, according to Terry. I decided to go ahead with the plans to start the new job but I was extremely disappointed. I pushed these thoughts out of my mind and tried to enjoy my last days in Cleveland with Pam. I was flying out Sunday morning, and she was coming down on Wednesday. We both were leaving St. Croix the following Monday, Pam in the morning and me in the afternoon.

Saturday, 3/21/09—I could not get the frustration about the office situation out of my head. My face was tingling and I was experiencing high anxiety levels. I took a Xanax before noon. It helped take the edge off and I relaxed and forgot about the issues at hand for a few hours. I reluctantly increased my dosage of HCTZ to two pills as requested by Dr Morrow. Almost immediately I felt the familiar pains in my feet and knees growing in intensity.

By Sunday night, I was walking with a visible limp. The throbbing in both knees and feet was growing by the hour. I'd just begun to unwind, I had a long way to go before I'd washed away the years of fast-paced, goal-oriented labor. I knew I needed a break and this short time off had only scratched the surface. The next morning I was flying home and my last free days were going to be spent working on setting up a home office. I was not pleased.

Sunday, 3/21/09—I didn't feel well during the long day of travel through Chicago, San Juan and finally home. My right knee was bothering me when I put full weight on it. With each stride through the airports, the gout continued to rage leaving my knees and feet swollen. The Colchicine pills Dr. Weisblat had prescribed for me in the past were waiting for me at home on my kitchen counter. I'd never taken them before but was willing to try anything at this point. Pain had been with me in one form or another for several days and was increasing with each passing hour.

By the time I reached home, I was barely able to carry my luggage up the four stairs leading to my front door. My right knee hurt so bad I iced it down six times before going to bed. Sleeping was difficult because I kept getting waked up by sharp, jabbing pains in both my feet. I'd been taking two HCTZ for only two days and was feeling the adverse side effects of the increased uric acid. In the back of my mind, I could not fight off the possibility that I would also develop kidney stones.

Monday, 3/23/09—I called Dr. Morrow as soon as his office opened. I was unable to reach him, but the receptionist promised to have him call me back. At 7:30 p.m. I received his somewhat reluctant return call. I told him of the terrible gout I was experiencing and he asked that I stay with the plan of two HCTZ pills a day, until we could take another twenty-four hour urine test to see if the increased HCTZ was going to help my system absorb more calcium. I explained that the pain was unbearable. Gout was the second most painful thing I'd experienced, just behind having bone-screws inserted in both shoulders. I was much better at dealing with pain management than in the past but found it very difficult to push it aside this time. According to Dr. Morrow, I would see success with this method if I just hung in there. Both knees throbbed continuously. The second toe on my left foot had turned bright red and was angled out. It was extremely painful and unnatural looking. My ankles were on fire and swollen twice their size. The last thing I wanted to agree to was a couple more weeks of this, but I had little choice in the matter. I had to tough it out until we could measure the effectiveness of the HCTZ.

Dr. Morrow had explored the use of synthetic parathyroid hormone as a treatment option for me. The synthetic version had only been on the market for a few years. It required a daily shot for a period of no longer than two years. The dosages that these pre-packaged shots came in were all the same volume at 20CC's. It cost $10,000 per year to take the drug. Although he believed it could be beneficial in my case to try the drug, he did not see how it could be done. The drug was only approved to treat osteoporosis. It would have to be approved through the medical boards before being tested as a potential treatment for hypoparathyroidism, and there was no way of telling what dosage I would need to take. We would be facing another long battle to find the correct balance, which meant my system would take more hits before the proper dosage could be worked out—and it would not be a lifetime solution because of its limited period of usage. He did want to continue looking into it and promised to get back to me after he made a few more inquiries.

Tuesday, 3/24/09—I spent most of the day getting my place ready for Pam's short visit. I had to clean all morning just to make it presentable. I was really having a hard time walking. I started taking Colchicine the night before, but so far it was not helping. I was also taking the anti-inflammatory Indomethacine, which seemed to alleviate the pain for four to six hours at a time, but the swelling continued. I iced my legs and ankles several times throughout the day. Sleeping was nearly impossible. I lasted one to two hours and then woke to pains in my knees and feet.

Wednesday, 3/25/09—In the morning I went grocery shopping and made sure I had all of Pam's favorite foods and a bottle of the sweet wine she likes to drink. I continued the HCTZ, Colchicine and Indomethacin triumvirate before heading to the airport later that afternoon. I was walking with a severe limp as our eyes met under the overhang by the luggage carousel. We stopped in at Chicken Charlie's Road House and had dinner on the drive home. Pam could see my discomfort and we cut our night short. At home Pam prepared ice baths for my feet. Numbing the feet worked to stop the pain only as long as I kept my feet in the tub.

At times the pain would disappear, and then within an hour or two come roaring back. The combination of being forced to work from home, and the pain and discomfort of the gout frustrated me. I felt bad for Pam. This was supposed to be her vacation. Instead, she had to take care of me and run errands all week. She did everything she could to make me feel more comfortable. It was clear to both of us that the gout situation had to be addressed. I was not willing to continue taking the HCTZ if it meant having this severe pain.

By end of day on Friday, Pam and I'd assembled a functioning home office. We'd purchased an all-in-one office machine, a small plastic folding table, and had Broadband VI hook up a new radio on my roof top for high-speed internet. The Cotton Valley wireless tower is on a hill directly behind my guest house. I would have no problems receiving the signal, and I was assured the speeds were going to be sufficient to handle the VOIP phone. The March Group used Citrix as their secure operating platform. The size of Citrix, according to the installer, was not going to be a concern for the band width of Broadband VI's wireless plan. I was less than optimistic.

With work behind us, Pam and I took *Folly* out for a short sail on Saturday. And the anti-inflammatory pills helped alleviate the gout pain for a couple of hours at a time, so we were able to go on short walks each evening.

Pam left for the airport early on Monday morning 3/30/09. As we said our goodbys, I was a little nervous about the training set to begin on Tuesday morning. I'd performed more training over the previous twenty years of my career than I care to remember. This time I would be the student. It was going to be challenging but I had to give it my best effort. If successful, this job could provide me with a solid six-figure income. The job consisted of cold calling business owners, building a relationship with them, and convincing them of the importance to attend one of our weekly exit strategy meetings. The meetings lasted a full eight-hour day. It was no easy task to convince owners to spend that much time away from their business. I was eager to see if there was something I did not completely understand or something in the process that made the sell easier. I knew just getting to speak to the owner of a company was incredibly difficult. I'd contacted business owners on the buy side for almost two years gauging their interest in growing through acquisitions. On the sell side of the business, you had to work your way through the gauntlet of gatekeepers to speak directly with the owner before divulging why you were calling.

Tuesday, 3/31/09—I met with Terry and George prior to the start of the training session. Both explained why they thought I'd succeed. They talked about how I could schedule my day like a business owner, with little input from the outside. George would be my manager and he was sure I could meet and exceed the required goals. The company provided the leads to me for upcoming exit- strategy conferences. To secure clients, I would need to call from the same lead lists several times. The results were directly related to the number of calls made. As I thanked them for their encouragement, I was thinking this was not the job for me. I was not wired to sit at a desk and make call after call all day long. I'd never been happier than when I was able to start to hire my own team and stop sales-related calls on the other side of the business. I'd felt a burden lifted from my shoulders when I'd finally stepped out of the direct contact with clients, and began managing the group now doing the calling. This all seemed like a huge step backwards.

The delivery of the script entailed several boundaries that a BDM could not cross. With that said, it was part acting combined with used car sales-manship. I knew it would be difficult to maintain personal integrity and was aware that there were plenty of sales people willing to skew the facts we provided to business owners. I was not going to become one of the "sell the seminar at all costs" types of employee. I already had difficulty sleeping and did not need my conscience bothering me. Tapes of badgering presen-tations were played in training. I also heard tapes of business owners who were actually looking for this type of conference. I would need to sift through the hundreds of leads each day in hopes of finding the one owner that needed and wanted our help.

By the end of the day, I had a pretty good idea of what was expected. I have nothing but the utmost respect for the top performers in this profes-sion. The difficulty in reaching a small business owner and convincing them to attend an exit strategy meeting is one of the hardest tasks imagina-ble. Done correctly, you can really help an owner with a difficult process. The meetings were informative, conducted by professionals and helped business owners form an exit strategy. The truth is, selling companies is one of the longest and most detailed endeavors a person can undertake. The reward for building a successful company can only be realized with a successful exit strategy. There are exceptions, but in most cases selling a business is an involved process that takes a lot of knowledge, patience and the ability to compromise.

My training lasted long into the evening on Thursday. They had crammed five days into three. Each of the previous nights I had lots of homework and scoured through several large training manuals. The difficult part was incorporating the mass of information into a sales pitch that seemed conversational in tone. It was going to take a long time to be able to reply with quick and accurate responses to any questions raised by a business owner. None of this was going to be as easy as I'd hoped.

Friday, 4/3/09—Exhausted by information overload, and with little sleep, I cursed my wakeup call at 5:00 a.m. I was on the noon direct flight to St. Croix. I needed to get packed and drive the thirty-five miles to the airport. I wanted to take my time and try and relax, something that had not occurred since I left Pam's house two weeks before. I was feeling the pressure mounting. This change in my job was creating stress that my internal systems did not need. The transition to working from home was going to be difficult, and the job was not one that I wanted to perform for any length of time. I guess I was hoping that if I performed well, I could move out of this job and find my path back to an upper management position. However, our company was selling fewer and fewer clients. Deals fell apart more often than came together. We had to maintain the payroll by bringing in more and more fresh clients willing to pay up-front fees. Not an easy task when the business owners are the first to realize the current state of the economic environment.

The depressed market did not stop The March Group's upper management team from pressing forward. This, for all practical purposes, was a growing company. The thought was that the markets would eventually break free and companies would be looking for growth opportunities. In the meantime we needed to go after the best-positioned smaller companies that offered unique products or services. Finding these companies just became my new job.

As the plane landed on St. Croix, I was desperate for a break from the monotonous volume of information that my mind had been processing over the previous week. I had the weekend to enjoy before starting on the phones. I knew I would be practicing my scripts Sunday evening. For now, I needed to shove it all out of my mind.

Saturday, 4/4/09—I woke up with sore feet and knees. I iced them down at 6:30 a.m. and took some anti-inflammatory medication. I desperately wanted to get out on the water and sail. It would help clear my head. I was in no shape to sail alone, so I called Pat and we decided to meet at 10:30 a.m. I set the pain aside and prepared my backpack. I had to stop and get some bottled water on my way to the Yacht Club. Mr. Green, at Smokey's gas station, asked if I was feeling okay. I was pale, sweating profusely and with each step felt a new agony.

Sailing was just what I needed. The sun was bright and we crisscrossed the waters on the north side of St. Croix for hours. At the end of the sail, I dove in and swam back through the mooring area instead of riding in the launch. The locals believe the saltwater has healing qualities. It seemed, for a short time, to help alleviate some of the discomfort related to the gout.

Sunday, 4/5/09—Most of the day was spent preparing physically and mentally for the start of my new job. I'd returned from Florida with a new VOIP phone and took the time to set it up and make sure it worked with the new Broadband high-speed internet access. There was a delay when I tried to test the phone by leaving myself a voice message. If I was to be successful, it needed to be crystal clear. My first order of business the following morning would need to be contacting the out-sourced IT Company located in San Francisco.

That night I practiced my rebuttals over and over again. I spoke them out loud, trying to get a natural conversational tone. It was going to take time, but I felt I was ready to at least start making calls the next morning. At 11:00 p.m. I realized I would be mulling the new position over in my head all night if I did not take a sleeping pill and get at least four or five hours in before morning arrived.

Monday, 4/6/09—The big day. I struggled trying to keep a positive attitude. Not being surrounded with other people in an office environment was different for me. There was some hesitation on my part before my first call as the clock struck 8:00 a.m.

The business owners on my call lists were located in areas near upcoming conference sites. During the day you could be working on several locations around the country and Canada. My first twenty-five calls resulted in voice mails. My throat was already hoarse and I was drinking as much cool water as I possibly could. This condition would not get much better over the course of the next several days. I was not used to talking out loud that much and my vocal cords became strained. I remember the first business owner I was able to speak to. My phone continued to crackle and ended up cutting out half-way into my sales pitch. It was frustrating but the phone had saved me from my own nervousness. I was not doing well. I contacted IT in San Francisco and they ran all kinds of tests. The problem was that my internet provider's wireless signal was not strong enough during the daytime to handle our system demands. Broadband VI was the only carrier on the east end. I contacted Terry and George and left them messages explaining that I needed to be able to get back into the office. I would continue working from home but it was going to be difficult with the poor quality over the internet-based phone system. I called the business owner back after an hour and, surprisingly, he was willing to speak with me again.

Part of my opening script stated that The March Group had heard from specific buyers and they were interested in businesses in the owner's sector. This was a purposefully ambiguous statement, and most of the owners I was able to speak with had received these types of calls in the past and were skeptical. They often replied that if we had a specific client wanting to purchase their company we can talk. "If you are just fishing for someone to become your client and pay an up front-fee we have nothing to talk about." Of course the latter was closer to reality. Nevertheless I had to try and overcome all objections.

Call after call went down the same path. I knew how to talk to business owners, and they gave me the time of day because I was professional. At the same time, I was out of my comfort zone and struggled to hit all the rebuttals in the flow chart. My first rejection was quickly followed by ten more. Continuing to make calls on the first day was mentally draining. By the end of the day, my throat was raw and as the final minute ticked off announcing the arrival of 5:00 p.m. I was thrilled to be released from one of the most frustrating days I'd experienced in a long time.

I'd made seventy-four calls the first day. There was some time spent off line with the IT department, but I knew the top performers were making between 150 and 200 calls per day. I needed to increase the number of calls if I had any chance at being successful.

The one thing we had going on our side was the desire of most business men and women to find out what value the market placed on their business. The recession made some owners more receptive to the sales pitch. Most had witnessed a sharp decline in their revenue over the course of the previous eight to ten months. They were struggling. They also knew that receiving their desired sales price for their company was going to be nearly impossible during these tough times. Many calls ended abruptly with a hang up.

The rest of the week was spent leaving hundreds of voice mails and dealing with rejection on a grand scale. I was struggling. Although I sounded professional and confident, there was a lot I didn't know, and it was going to take a long time before I was comfortable in my new role.

Because of the Easter holiday, Friday was a day off. I'd barely survived the first four days on the phone. The quality of the phone connections was poor, and I finished the first week with only two owners wanting a call back closer to the actual seminar date.

I needed to take on activities that I was going to find success in over the weekend—just to build my confidence back up. I'd not tackled an ocean swim since my first shoulder surgery. My shoulders did not have the same mobility as in the past, through daily arm exercises to regain a flawed

356

swim-stroke, I was capable of propelling myself through the water.

With the aid of full snorkel gear, including my oversized fins, I embarked on an overly confident water adventure. It encompassed over a mile and half of ocean from the Yacht Club beach to a small rocky shoreline in front of the fire station in Cotton Valley. I knew, once I reached the reef off the Yacht Club, I could stop and rest in six to eight feet of water. Pat agreed to join me. My shoulders were burning after the first couple of strokes. I relied heavily on my leg kick. Several times throughout the quarter-mile swim to the reef line I was forced to turn over on my back and kick backwards to rest my arms. In the past I easily performed this swim without stopping. Now it was a struggle just making it to the reef. The safe thing would have been to turn back, but I wanted to accomplish something so I pressed on. Mercifully, the swim came to an end as I dragged myself out of the water. I did get the needed sense of accomplishment, but I also got a good dose of reality that showed me just how far my conditioning had declined. It was a sobering reality and I found it hard not to be discouraged.

Saturday, 4/11/09—I felt rested enough to try my hand at nine holes of golf. To my surprise, my game was clicking and I ended up shooting a thirty-nine. That was a good score, aided by several long putts that found their way into the bottom of the cup. The elation I felt having a good round of golf was short-lived. Within a few hours of finishing, I started having trouble breathing. I'd pushed my body too hard and now I was paying the price. I took two Nexium over the course of the day, hoping my breathing issues were related to acid reflux. By night-time my breathing was becoming increasingly labored. I took one of two Lorezapam I'd been saving for just this type of occasion. I soon fell into an uneasy sleep. At 3:00 a.m. I sat straight up in my bed, choking, unable to take in a full breath. My mind raced with thoughts of my new job and how difficult it was going to be to continue. The hours passed by as I lay there in a miserable state of anxiety-driven hell for the remainder of the early morning.

Sunday, 4/12/09—I took the entire day off and rested. The day seemed to pass in slow motion. I wanted to speed it up and get it over with so I could face my new demons and another day on the phones, though I still held out hope that I would master the new job. The only way that was going to happen was by attacking each day, trying to get better one call at a time.

Monday, 4/13/09—As the sun rose off the water to the east, I dragged myself out of bed and fired up the computer. It took fifteen minutes of staring at the screen filled with leads before I mustered enough courage to make the first call. I felt relieved when I reached voice mail. I had call flowcharts scattered across my small desk and taped to my wall. I had run through each scenario time and time again in my mind, but there was still an uneasy feeling with the whole process.

The day progressed slowly with no success. I left fifty voice mails before reaching my first live person. Three sentences into my sales pitch, the call was disconnected. The deliberate act of the business owner angered me. I couldn't see how this was going to become a successful job. I doubted my communication skills and found myself having to pump up my ego before every call. Each minute seemed like an hour. I iced my legs and feet to help alleviate some of the pain caused by gout. The pills prescribed to help offset the high uric acid levels were not working. The anti-inflammatory medication upset my stomach to such a degree that I had constant diarrhea. The day mercifully came to an end, but sleep eluded me until after midnight when a combination of exhaustion and sleeping pills put me out of my misery.

Tuesday, 4/14/09—I found myself having to dig deeper than the day before to make the first call of the day. The previous day I'd made eighty calls. The number was significant in the fact that I physically did not see a possibility of increasing it. My vocal cords were raw from constant use. I reached a couple of business owners early in the day and they humored me—listening to my entire pitch. This was a marked improvement even though I did not close any deals. I was gaining a small amount of confidence.

Wednesday, 4/15/09—I woke at 4:30 a.m. with a stabbing sensation in my left foot. Immediate icing did not help alleviate the pain. When I finally tried to stand, I could not put any weight on it. I hobbled to my kitchen, where I kept my pill tray, and took a Chocicene and two Motrin. The pills and several rounds of ice on the ankle did not help lower the swelling or stop the throbbing. I continued to ice the ankle as I started my calling day. By noon the foot felt worse and I was sweating uncontrollably. It was difficult to continue to sit upright and make calls. I felt lethargic. I suspected the calcium levels in my blood had risen well above normal. I became incredibly sick very fast. I continued to fight through the pain, calling until 5:00 p.m. I also made a call to Dr. Weisblat's office earlier in the day and did not hear back from him by nighttime.

Thursday, 4/16/09—I woke at 2:30 a.m. with horrific pain in my left foot. When I turned on the lights my ankle had swollen even larger than the previous day. It was bright red. I immediately iced it down. Nothing stopped the pain. Not wanting to miss work, I pushed the unrelenting pain aside and started my calling promptly at 8:00. At 9:00 a.m. I contacted Dr. Weisblat's office, again unable to concentrate because of the throbbing in my foot. His office staff told me they had given him the message the day before and they expected he would be calling me back the first available minute. I could not take the pain anymore and called Dr. Morrow's office. I told them it was urgent that I speak with the doctor as soon as possible. Dr. Morrow called me back within the hour and I explained how bad the situation was. I was unable to walk, and I was worried about the potential for kidney damage from the high uric acid levels. Dr. Morrow told me to drop back down to one HCTZ per day. He wanted me to get in contact with Dr. Weisblat and have him prescribe the medication Allopurinol. It would help keep the uric acid levels in check. I asked about side-effects and he thought there was a chance the drug could have negative effects on my liver. It was the only solution to the problem that he knew of. He again stressed the need for me to stick with the program and that we would work this out together. I was in such a miserable state I did not care to hear that from anyone including the expert.

I looked up all the information about gout that I could find on the internet. I learned that I was not supposed to take any aspirin products but small dosages of Ibuprofen were allowed. I took more Motrin trying to stop the throbbing pain. Nothing worked. Dr. Weisblat contacted me in the afternoon and I discussed my conversation with Dr. Morrow. Dr. Weisblat called in a stronger anti-inflammatory to my pharmacy sometime late in the afternoon. He wanted me to try the medication before prescribing the Allopurinol. I was in no shape to drive into town and pick up the prescription. The pharmacist took sympathy on me. He also suffered from gout and understood my dilemma. He lived in Cotton Valley and agreed to meet me at Chicken Charlie's Road House, a few minutes from my house, on his way home from work. The anti-inflammatory medication prescribed was strong and made my stomach upset. Overnight the swelling went down. The pain diminished, but still persisted for several days.

Friday, 4/17/09—I was exhausted before the day even started. I was thankful this was the last workday in the week. It took every ounce of mental strength to complete the day of calling. I'd lost my voice several times during the day and was forced to take ten-to-fifteen-minute breaks before returning to the phone. Late in the afternoon, I spoke to a business owner who was thinking of selling his company. The conversation went well and by the time I had finished he'd agreed to attend our workshop. My first triumph gave me a good feeling. There was no reason to celebrate, and this was by no means a turning point for me in regards to this line of work, but I was on the board.

By 5:00 p.m. my frustration with the pain overshadowed the joy of my first attendee. By early evening, I was forming a plan, in part to protest my situation by quitting all my medication until someone could assure me I would not feel sick or have constant pain. I stayed in bed the rest of the evening icing my ankle and both knees—cursing the world around me.

Saturday, 4/18/09—My nervous system was taxed to the limit. I was experiencing a high amount of tingling in my head, and my foot and knee were still extremely sore. I took ten calcium pills throughout the day, gladly dropping the extra HCTZ pill. I knew from past experiences that the balancing act would take time. In the interim I would be left feeling miserable.

Staying positive during these turbulent times was extremely difficult. I tried to ignore the symptoms. I read a book for two hours in the morning, having to stop when my eyes became blurry and the lids started to spasm. Everything I did seemed labored and difficult. The day took forever to end. The sick feeling in my entire body kept me indoors and inactive.

Sunday, 4/19/09—With the help of the new anti-inflammatory pills, the swelling had diminished considerably overnight, but the bright red hue was still visible and the pain was sufficient to keep me from contemplating any physical activity for the day. I was basically bedridden for the entire weekend. Needing a break from the inside space, I limped outside late in the afternoon and hobbled around in the yard in the sunshine. The isolation of working from home had long since become an issue with me. I needed human interaction and having spent every minute of the weekend alone in bed did nothing but throw fuel on the fire.

I gave myself a goal of reaching one month on the job before deciding if I wanted to continue. I had verbalized this commitment to Pam over the phone. She asked why I was continuing to do the job if it made me so miserable. I was not sure if the job was so bad, or if it was a combination of working from home and battling gout. I knew this was not going to be easy, but I owed it to myself and the company to give it everything I had. Instead of continuing with the negative thoughts, I needed to practice more and try and make the best of a really tough situation. I knew some success would make it all seem a little easier. I rededicated myself to the process and my delivery, repeating it out loud over and over again—late into the night.

Monday, 4/20/09—None of the business owners that actually took the time to listen had the heart to do much of anything in these really trying times. They all were willing to sell for top dollar but knew that was unlikely in the current recession. Depending on what sector of business the owner operated in determined how bad business had fallen off. They were quick to point out the magnitude of their struggles, and I lost immediate credit when I said we had interested buyers in their business sector. Several of them knew the mergers and acquisition outlook in their fields and promptly blasted that statement right out of the water.

The sheer volume of calls increased as I gave the process everything I had. I took short breaks and drank more cold water to alleviate my sore throat. I started reaching more and more owners willing to speak to me, but at the end of the day, I was less successful than I'd hoped for. Only a couple of people requested callbacks as the date of our workshop neared. I had possibilities. Though I was not willing to lie to a business owner, the big elephant in the room was that I knew the odds of the owner's company being sold. If they were a specialized company that had huge upside, we could sell them in this market. If they were struggling to survive, there was little chance to sell them. There was no need for the competitors to buy them when they could outlast them.

This job forced me to practice the art of communication. I tried everything to get attendees signed up for workshops. I fought for each and every one of these business owners to hear my message. My timing improved on my rebuttals and I became more willing to make several callbacks if an owner showed any interest at all. Although this was not a job I liked, I became as good as I was going to get fairly quickly. I knew by the end of the third week of calling eight to ten hours nonstop a day, that this was not what I wanted to do with my life. My numbers of potential hot leads that might attend a future workshop increased, and I had three confirmed attendees on the board. I really needed to be hitting five or more per week to make the six-figure salary. I had no voice left and was unable to speak without pain in my throat. I was tired and feeling the effects of a sedentary job. There were never going to be four or five meetings to break up the day. There was no more reporting, training or travel. It was eight to ten hours a day making call, after call, after call.

Saturday, 4/25/09 and Sunday, 4/26/09 were spent in solitary confinement. The gout had come and gone, and come back again. I had lowered the HCTZ to one pill a day and still was experiencing symptoms. All weekend long the throbbing pain in my knees and feet continued. I was exhausted in every sense of the word. I felt a real sense that I owed the company more because they had paid for my training and I wanted them to at least get their money back. I had signed up a couple of really strong clients, but I was not making any bonus. The inner turmoil continued. In these situations I usually started working out harder to relieve some of my stress. I was not able to do that because I could barely walk. I was gaining weight at an alarming rate. Dark feelings began mounting. By Sunday night, I had reached a breaking point. Something had to change.

Monday, 4/27/09—If I was going to make it in this new job, I needed to hit pay-dirt. I set obtainable goals and pushed ahead. I was able to reach the break-even point for the company and sign my fourth confirmed workshop attendee. Each time I was able to get an attendee I felt a short-lived sense of accomplishment. The cycle started all over again. My gift of gab was seriously tested throughout the course of performing this job. I readily admit missing some opportunities, but I found the majority of the business world to be in a foul mood. It was difficult finding the inner strength to continue calling. I heard so many stories of doom and gloom. The lead lists were broken down into business types by their SIC (Standard Industrial Classification) Code. These are vague attempts at labeling a company into a certain type of business operation. There are four and eight digit SIC code verifications and the eight digit codes give more specific details of what a company actually does. None of the descriptions were 100% accurate. Cold calling, using these business descriptions, left you wide open for verbal abuse if the owner caught on that you didn't know what his company did at the same time you were saying you had interested buyers in their sector.

As I struggled through the fourth week, there were several times I wanted to give up and quit. I fought off those thoughts and it took everything I had to continue to try the next number. The majority of my calls ended in a voice mail. I started getting some callbacks, but not to the volume necessary to reach my goals. Success would eventually come, but at what price? I had the ability to make a successful BDM, but the environment and the work were not to my liking. I did not appreciate the benefits of working from home. I wanted to be a part of an organization and it felt as if I was pushed as far away as possible. The training department was slow in returning my calls, and I found my only option for high-speed internet on the east end of the island under performed, causing me to spend precious time on the phone with our out-sourced IT department. Several reports were made by our IT Company confirming the power connection. The Florida office could not sway the St. Croix office to allow me back in where they had good connections and operated with little interruption. Each one of these problems resulted in a growing dislike for my new position— even with the promise it held for large commissions.

People started noticing the change in my demeanor. I was frustrated and came off as angry in my conversations with family members and friends. This little experiment of working from home had turned into my personal nightmare. The gout did not help my disposition. I had taken about all of the physical pain I was going to be able to handle. I needed to see my doctors and figure out exactly what we were going to do to stop this mess. I was not going to accept this level of discomfort. I was ready to dump all of my doctors. It was a frustrating time where nothing was going right. I knew by the end of the week that I was not going to continue the work I had been forcing myself to perform every day for four weeks. I had the abilities and talent to perform this job, but it was not right for me.

This was nothing more than a straight sales job and a full time salesman was not what I wanted to be. I would take the weekend to think it over, but in the long run I knew the outcome. I was just taking the time to make sure—rechecking the facts and numbers to validate the decision. Stopping the daily madness of calling so many people seemed to brighten my outlook on life, even though the outcome would leave me without a job in a tough economy.

Fresh Water Sailing (Day 776 – 874)

Saturday, 5/2/09—My foot felt good enough to walk and I was able to get out and enjoy a round of golf. I spent as much time outside my house as possible. Pat and I ate lunch at the Yacht Club and then the launch out to *Folly*. I took my time bailing the rain water out of her bilge, enjoying my surroundings. It was the first time in a couple months that I really felt relaxed. The inner turmoil inside of me seemed to be settling down while the long forgotten upbeat thoughts started to return.

Sunday, 5/3/09—I felt good enough to do a slow hike down to Jack's and Isaac's Bay. The activity seemed to put things in perspective. I needed that perspective because the idea of quitting my new job was weighing heavily on my mind. I knew I needed to give it up for no other reason than I disliked every minute of the calling and my frustration was spilling over into my personal life. In the end, the best move was to move on. I needed some time to try and get my physical and mental health in order before both became even more of a problem than they already were.

Monday, 5/4/09—I continued to make calls, trying to get a few more workshop attendees. By noon my voice had left me for the third time. Unable to make an audible sound for minutes at a time left me frustrated. There was no way I was making any strong connections with busy business owners without a voice that showed confidence and strength. I could barely hear my own voice over the roar of the turbo fan circulating air over my workspace. I tried again, later in the afternoon calling west-coast leads until 7:00 p.m. with no luck.

Tuesday, 5/5/09—I really wanted to go out with a bang and post a couple more scalps on the wall. I was also dreading the conversation with my friends who had offered me this opportunity. They had gone out on a limb for me, and I wanted to give them two more workshop attendees before explaining this was not the position for me. The attendees did not come. My voice was lost early in the morning and I felt ill as I lay down and tried to recoup enough energy to make a few more calls. The day was capped off by more IT issues.

Wednesday, 5/6/09—I knew his work habits—always the first person to the office in the morning. I did not reach him on my first attempt, but proceeded in leaving a voice mail, trying to sound less consumed by internal conflict than I actually was. Just before 8:00 a.m. the phone rang. It turned out to be a constructive conversation between two friends who knew what was up. There was a clear understanding from the beginning that the BDM position took an aggressive personality to be successful. They were power salespeople who did not mind stretching the truths about our company's abilities and relationships with private equity groups and venture capitalists. I knew the truth and was not willing to exaggerate it to get a business owner into a seat at a workshop. In my five years with the company, I had witnessed an average of ten to fifteen companies sold per year. My last day working for The March Group our client list was over 300.

The following morning I dropped off the voice-over internet phone equipment at the St. Croix office. There were no long conversations or rounds of goodbyes. Walking away from the reception desk, a sense of relief came over me. I needed a break. Figuring out what to do next would soon dominate my thoughts.

Since the end of 2006, the complete breakdown of my health had left me broken, weak and exhausted. From day one, I followed my inner compass, pushing as much aside as possible, dealing with each task individually—and facing the big picture later. Work had been the perfect place to bury myself and escape. It forced me to have complete concentration on something other than my health. I was about to find out how difficult coping with health issues, without the aid of a demanding diversion, could be.

Friday, 5/8/09—Sheer panic set in by midmorning as I sat alone in my house trying to come up with a plan. What was going to happen next? This was the second time in my life I'd quit a job without having the next position lined up. The first was when I moved to St. Croix. Both had been driven by health concerns. The harder I tried to come up with a plan, the darker my mood became. In less than an hour, I was completely overwhelmed. As the mental block forming in my head grew, not one answer came to me. Life came to a complete standstill, leaving me unable to get out of bed. Internal pressure quickly grew to the critical point.

I had no idea what was happening. Unable to think of answers to my situation, the dark wall continued to get taller and thicker. I shut down completely. My eyes were squinting, as if pain was shooting through my body. My head throbbed and I felt like a 500-pound weight had been attached to my neck. Anxiety poured in.

The next day I found it increasingly difficult to get out of bed. Gout returned with a vengeance mid-morning and in some strange way, was a big relief. Concentrating on the physical pain in my knees seemed to jolt me back to my senses. Every joint in my body hurt as I climbed out of bed for the first time in nearly two days to get ice packs and anti-inflammatory pills. I contacted Dr. Weisblat and Dr. Morrow's offices. After expressing the urgency of my plight, both doctors agreed to see me on short notice. Dr. Morrow was booked over six months in advance and literally had to squeeze me in on a scheduled break. I booked a flight to Cleveland for the morning of 5/27/09. In the meantime, the doctors told me to stick to the pill schedule and avoid all alcohol, spinach and seafood which could increase the uric acid levels in my blood.

Once I lay down, I couldn't find the motivation to get up. It was mentally painful to process the issues I was facing. I spent several hours trying to figure it out. The feeling had came on extremely quick and was all consuming. I had never experienced anything like this, and was not sure what was happening. The entire weekend was spent in bed—hardly moving.

5/11/09—The mental issues consuming my head eased just enough to allow me time to concentrate on my trip to Cleveland. The gout seemed to calm down at the same time, and little by little I was able to function around the house. I had not been outside in three days. The violent rays of sunshine slammed my senses as I stepped out the door. The constant tingling in my face and muscle spasms in my neck and arms became less severe as I walked around in circles behind my house rubbing my head.

The two-year anniversary of my parathyroid surgery was just around the corner. The calcium imbalance remained a constant reminder. The nightmare had taken over every aspect of my body and soul. I could have an attack and need to be rushed to the hospital within the next hour of any day. All it took was the calcium levels to shift just a few points one way or the other. How much longer I would be forced to take it before the promised balance arrived was the big question.

I was clinging to the fact that I would soon be on a plane headed for Cleveland. Each day my desire to see Pam grew. The gout continued to flare up, disappear and come roaring back. I forced myself to get outside each afternoon and hobble around in the sunshine. The rest of the time was spent curled up in a ball on my bed, unable to come up with any answers.

Sunday, 5/17/09—I heard the phone ring through my early morning mental haze. I had agreed to take one of the bartenders from the Yacht Club sailing with her boyfriend and some family members. I forced myself out of bed. I didnt want to sail and was feeling anti-social, but I remembered promising this sail to Janelle. I reluctantly packed my sailing bag.

This was an exiting day for the two vacationing women, their son and his girlfriend. They brought more food and gear than I usually like having on board, but I was not going to wreck their day by telling them to leave half their stuff in the car. We were riding low in the water with the extra weight as we sailed off the mooring. The wind had picked up out of the north-northwest as we crossed the channel and the water was very choppy. For one of the few times since owning my boat, I chose to anchor-stern to the beach at Buck Island. This meant allowing the boat to swing on the bow anchor facing open water and dropping a second anchor off the stern in shallow water. Everything was going as planned until I had a momentary lapse in judgment. While holding a twenty-five pound anchor, I jumped into the water. I had done this a hundred times in the past, but the water was usually ten-to-fifteen feet deep off the stern. After jumping in, I would swim the anchor out to deeper water before releasing it. This time, the stern was just off the beach, and I jumped into three-feet of water. My butt landed right on top of the only piece of Brain Coral within 500 yards of the breach. It was by far the dumbest sailing mistake I'd made in years. Making matters worse was the added weight of the anchor and several feet of chain I was holding. My tailbone felt as if someone had smashed it with a sledge hammer. In front of the guests on my boat, I laughed it off. Inside I was seething. The rest of the sail came off without incident, but my tailbone hurt like hell and I had to sit on a boat cushion the entire trip back into the mooring area. I skipped the usual drinks at the bar and headed straight home. I needed to ice down my lower back—which was throbbing.

Monday, 5/18/09—It was as if I'd cracked a bone in my lower back and every muscle from the shoulders down had clamped down to protect the injury. The tingling in my face and the muscle spasms in my neck and upper arms returned. It was one step forward and five back. I was struggling.

The next eight days were spent nursing my sore back and fighting off the next big gout attack. My only positive thought was the brief moments I could concentrate on my trip to Cleveland. I kept to myself and found it more and more difficult to contemplate any future, let alone any immediate day-to-day plans. I'd never struggled mentally like this before and did not know what to do. I was reluctant to tell anyone the true depths of the problems I was having. When I talked to people on the phone, I tried to have a positive spin.

Days alone, and soul searching, had turned me into a wreck. It was becoming increasingly difficult to function. I needed to come up with a comprehensive game plan, and I wanted a step-by-step road map out of the mess I found myself in. The hours crept by without any great revelations. No answers magically arrived. The more I concentrated on it, the further from my grasp it slipped. Where I had recently been an answer machine on just about any subject, I could not make the decision whether to eat or take a shower. The answers were not there for me anymore. I was unable to scale, maneuver around or plow through the dark wall that weighed me down. Day after day this went on.

Wednesday, 5/27/09—Boarding the plane bound for Cleveland seemed to have a calming effect. I was able to shake off the mental lethargy for the first time in days. The entire plane flight from Puerto Rico to JFK was one long exhale. I read several pages of Doug Stanton's *In Harm's Way* about the sinking of the *U.S.S. Indianapolis* during WWII. I felt like an idiot for allowing my problems to incapacitate me. Look at what the survivors of this great tragedy went through. The men who delivered the H-Bomb across the Pacific Ocean, only to get torpedoed, ending up in shark-infested waters for days as their crewmembers, by the hundreds, got attacked—an amazing story of courage, strength and survival. I needed to stop being so weak and tap into more of my inner strength. It was my own version of a pep talk.

A lot was riding on the doctors' visits. I needed them to produce some tangible results. Pam and I had decided to drive to North Carolina for some much-needed rest and relaxation. I wanted that to be a special time for the two of us. I had explained some of my recent problems to Pam, but she did not understand the full extent of my breakdown. She sensed that I was unhappy with the way my job ended and she would do everything to make my stay as relaxing as possible.

Determined to put an end to the gout meant holding my ground with the doctors. I was not giving in and agreeing to continue to fight my way through the pain anymore. My sleep patterns had diminished to such a degree that I was lucky to get two to three hours a night. Now was the time to change all of that.

The doctors were working with an extremely rare anomaly and had not improved matters. Men in their late thirties and early forties, for the most part, don't suffer from hypoparathryoridism. If it's detected, typically it can be easily treated. In my case it was not curable. My parathyroid glands were not functioning, and would most likely never function normally again. My bones were brittle, and the fight was on to find a balance between the calcium in the blood stream and the rate of absorption back into the bones. So far I'd not been able to reach that balance—even with the large number of pills I took each day. I'd lost patience.

The doctors spoke of disease management, their subtle way of saying there's no cure. This was difficult to accept. I thought a lot about my father and how he'd had to manage heart disease for his entire adult life. The patient has to be mentally strong enough to manage the process each and every day. I questioned if I had what it took.

Pam was waiting for me in the baggage claim area. As our embrace was extended, a calming happier disposition came over me. I realized that not everything was doom and gloom. There were a lot of great people who brought joy to my life. I needed to get over the physical pain and the dark mental state to get back to enjoying life.

Thursday, 5/28/09—I was at the laboratory at 8:00 a.m. for a blood draw ordered by Dr. Weisblat. The blood vessels in my arms had been used a lot over the course of the previous two and half years. It was harder and harder for the laboratory technicians to find a healthy vein. With a little difficulty, and the need to switch arms mid-stream, the process was quick and relatively easy. I was happy to be seeing the doctors, hoping to get some of the most pressing issues straightened out.

Friday, 5/29/09—I arrived a half hour early, eager for my consultation with Dr. Weisblat. I was waiting for twenty minutes and started reading his new promotional pamphlets. The Wellness Center had added a new member to the staff. She was a professional counselor. I thought about the mental difficulties I'd been having and decided to ask Dr. Weisblat about seeing her. I was skeptical about needing to speak with anyone but it was so convenient. If I'd not read the information in the new brochures I would not have gone out of my way to pursue the help of a counselor.

I was weighed in the hallway and ushered back to Dr. Weisblat's office. I'd gained twelve pounds since my most recent appointment. Dr. Weisblat began by checking my vital signs. He said my blood pressure was high and we would need to address that with medication. I listened patiently until I could not take it anymore and jumped in, explaining the real and present gout pain that had kept me in bed for days at a time. We had to fix this issue! To me it was the most schizophrenic illness I'd ever dealt with. It came on fast, accompanied with devastating pain. It usually lingered for a few days and then disappeared—only to return a few days later. I tried to describe it as accurately as possible. My doctors always got more than they bargained for when I opened up the dialogue. I believed that no detail was too small to pass on to them.

According to Dr. Weisblat, the answer to the gout was simple. My blood test results from the previous day showed my uric acid level at 9.2. We had to lower this number or the gout would only progress. The solution was a drug Dr. Morrow had brought up in past conversations called Allopurinol. The sole purpose of this drug was to eliminate uric acid from kidney functions. I would be adding another drug to the already crowded dance-card of pharmaceuticals I was taking. This had not gone well in the past and I was skeptical.

"Allopurinol has been on the market for several years and few if any patients using it suffer adverse side affects."

Doctors must practice these lines because it was identical to the speech I got from Dr. Morrow on HCTZ, and that had ended up turning what little quality of life I had left upside down and sideways. Later, when I agreed with the doctor's wishes to up the dosage to two a day was when the full-blown gout attacks started. The printed side effects that come from the pharmacy are almost verbatim for most drugs. They all involve an upset stomach, nausea, diarrhea and drowsiness. Dr. Weisblat was tuned in to my reluctance to start a new drug, but there really was no choice in this matter. I needed to end the gout at all costs. It had not only affected my health, posing a serious risk of developing kidney disorders, it contributed to the depression I was struggling to overcome. I had been taxed to the limit and was not handling these realities the same way I would have been capable of in the past. To say I was gun-shy was an understatement.

My calcium levels were still low at 8.2. All other levels in my blood including sodium, potassium, chloride and CO_2 were in normal range. The most anticipated number for me outside of the calcium level was my parathyroid hormone levels. They held steady in the lower end of normal at 15.6. This was a sign of progress. I needed to accept the fact that there had been some leveling out of my gland functions. The struggle to achieve a balance was slowly showing signs of improvement.

I listened to the explanation of the test results by Dr. Weisblat with guarded optimism. I felt complications would surely arise, and in the end there was no guarantee Allopuronal would deliver on its intended purpose.

As Dr. Weisblat started to wrap up our consultation I reluctantly broached the subject of seeing his new staff counselor. The words stumbled out of my mouth as I stared at the floor. I found it extremely hard to seek out help for a mental issue. In my mind it was an admission of weakness. He believed I could gain some insight into how to contain my anxiety and deal with the troubling situation. Although I would not have made this request in the past, I was afraid of returning home and falling back into the same depressed state I'd just climbed out of. I knew the mental discomfort I'd been feeling was nothing I had ever experienced. I had to face the fact that I had been worn down by the daily onslaught of my illness. I had held my own for a long time, but at this point in the healing process I needed help. I arranged to see the counselor after I returned from North Carolina.

Pam was finishing her packing when I returned from the doctors. She found me in a much more relaxed state. We had calculated the drive and it was going to take us somewhere between eleven and twelve hours one way. I was looking forward to the escape of the open road.

As Pam and I rolled out of the driveway, a sense of relief flowed over me. I drove the first leg and continued well into the early evening.

We stopped less than two hours from our final destination of Wilmington. I was in the best mood I'd been in for weeks. The dark cloud had lifted from my head and the gout was under control. My calcium levels seemed to be in check and I was actually relaxed. My anxiety had diminished to the point that I experienced one of the deeper, non-drug induced sleeps I'd had in recent memory.

Saturday, 5/30/09—After walking in the morning as part of our commitment to increase physical activity, we arrived in Wilmington and checked into the Hilton Riverside. Located on the Cape Fear River, it looks across the river onto *U.S.S. North Carolina.* I'd read several WWII books and one in particular, *With the Old Breed at Peleliu and Okinawa,* mentioned the *North Carolina* as one of the battleships that softened up the Japanese opposition for hours before the invasion forces stormed the beaches in the sweep across the Pacific Islands. It was impressive seeing this icon of battleships moored outside our fifth-floor window.

Sunday, 5/31/09—After a long morning walk that took us through the historic district and back to the waterfront, we boarded a river ferry. It would take us on a short trip up and down the Cape Fear River before dropping us at the *U.S.S. North Carolina.* From the dock the ship looks gigantic.Boarding, we found the many levels, passageways and decks amazing.

Monday, 6/01/09—Waking up after a good night's rest, I felt soreness in both feet, ankles and my right knee. The severity had not reached a point where I could not walk or needed to change my stride.

During the morning, we visited Wrightsville, Carolina, and Kure Beaches. Later in the afternoon we toured Fort Fisher, an impressive Civil War battle site.

We really enjoyed our short-lived getaway. Facing a long drive back to Cleveland, we left the next morning and drove straight through. The road again proved to be relaxing and enjoyable. Driving long distances was never my favorite thing to do, but seeing America pass by brought momentary peace to my life. I noticed that the daily tingling sensations and the muscle spasms had diminished. I was breathing normally and I felt good. It had been a long time since I could say that.

Wednesday, 6/03/09—Pam and I exercised every morning before she left for work. When she returned at the end of the day, we walked at least two miles around her neighborhood. The morning workouts consisted of following *Debbie Severs' Slim in Six* workouts. At first I thought I would not like following a DVD, but soon came to realize the workout raised my heart rate and really pushed my shoulder muscles without using weights. I was determined not to allow shoulder mobility to decrease. I have steadily been working through this by trying, daily, to throw twenty-five rocks with both arms at a dirt mound behind my house. I perform light-weight exercises and continue to sail, swim and golf with limited dexterity. I still believe I can improve the mobility in the shoulders as long as I put in the work. It is always more enjoyable to have a partner and Pam and I keep each other going when one or the other does not want to continue. Discipline carries me through these times even though it's not easy. The doctors tell me I've done a good job reaching this point, but there will be little chance I can improve. I'm sure they're wrong. I want to get back to having a quality swim stroke without the horrible hitch at the apex of the shoulder movement. I want to be able to drive a golf ball with a fluid stroke. I want to be able to stretch out my arm and reach the top shelf at a grocery store. I will continue to keep fighting and one day the doctors will be proven wrong.

Thursday, 6/04/09—I received a call from Pat. Bud Orpen had passed away. The great traveling gypsy had taken his final trip. Bud's daughter had written a positive e-mail to all of his many friends. One of America's true greats had checked out. It was a final act I'd been hoping could be avoided. The final sail on *Folly* is something I will always cherish. The bombing runs Colonel Bud Orpen's squadron participated in are detailed in a documentary—*The Last Mission*. It tells the story of their daunting task to free the Japanese Emperor from his mutinous captors so he could make the call for peace and surrender his country before further bloodshed. I had been inspired by this man's accomplishments and was going to miss him.

Friday, 6/05/09—We drove 3 1/2 hours to Fairborn, Ohio, just outside Dayton. The hotel was a couple miles from Wright Patterson Air Force Base, home to the National Museum of the United States Air Force. I had visited the museum once before and remember it being a remarkable experience.

375

Recent reading had rekindled my interest in WWII era aircraft, but what I was most excited about was seeing Mother and enjoying this time with her and my stepfather, JK Reed. JK served in the Air Force during WWII. Like Colonel Bud Orpen, his tour of duty included time on Tinian Island. A more appropriate place to honor my fallen friend could not have been chosen.

JK had always been involved with aviation. His father was a WWI pilot and his son Rick operates an aviation company in Illinois. The museum was common ground we both could enjoy.

After meeting at the hotel, we ate dinner and played card games. Soon I started feeling some tingling in my eyes and retired for the night. The next day was going to be long, and we all wanted to be rested for the trip to the sprawling museum. The last time I'd visited, the museum had two massive hangars and they'd added a third over the years. There was no way to take it all in with only one day, but we were determined to see as much as possible.

Saturday, 6/06/09—The museum takes you on a journey through the evolution of powered flight that starts with the Wright Brothers wind tunnel testing procedures, and carries on through the first-ever airplane flight. The displays advance through planes of WWI and WWII right up to modern stealth and advanced aircraft.

Spending the day touring the facility with my stepfather was interesting. He pointed out the plane his father had flown during WWI. Later we stood in silence next to Boxcar, the B-29 that dropped the atomic bomb on Nagasaki, Japan. Thoughts of Bud Orpen filled my mind as I stared at the massive plane. On the mission to drop the atomic bomb it had taken off from Tinian where both Bud and JK were stationed. Seeing my stepfather inspect every inch of the plane as if he was reliving his time during the war was a special moment.

By the end of the day, my head was filled with too many facts. I was on sensory overload. Pam and Mother hung in there all day. Mom was taken by the exhibit showing the violin which had been smuggled out of Nazi Germany by Jewish children. As we discussed this exhibit, it was clear the lady standing next to me was where I get my own anti-war sentiments. We do not always see eye-to-eye, but deep down our core beliefs are similar. It was an interesting day.

The sacrifices of the men and women who have helped make this country a free democracy stood out in my mind. The genius of the inventors and their contribution to society was mind-boggling. The destructive capabilities of many of the aircraft was frightening. Why machines of such destructive capability are necessary to protect and deter speaks to the weakness of human nature.

After dinner, and a long walk with Pam and Mom, we all sat down in the lobby of the hotel to play cards. Not long after we got downstairs, I started feeling pains in my head. I knew what was about to follow. The question was how bad it would get. I wanted to stay at that table and enjoy the time as long as possible, but my eyes began to flutter and dry up, my mouth started tingling and my jaw hurt. I lasted another half-hour before declaring the need to get some rest.

I rushed to the room and took extra calcium. I closed my eyes and concentrated on deep breathing. I knew what had brought this little episode on, and what I needed to do to eliminate the possibility of having it escalate into a full-blown ordeal. I had pushed myself too far taking the trip to Cleveland, then driving to North Carolina and traveling again to Dayton. Frustration grew. I felt I should be able to go and go as I had in the past.

My illness dictated the boundaries of my physical activities—one of the more difficult realities I was facing. I needed help. Left to my own train of thought, I should be able to continue at whatever pace I wanted throughout life, but the reality was staring me in the face. What I was unwilling to admit were the changes I'd gone through. It really killed me that here I was with Mother—in her seventies, and my stepfather—in his eighties, and I was the one needing to retire first because I had been overexerting myself.

Sunday, 6/07/09—Keeping our promises to exercise daily, we rose early and walked before breakfast. My head was a little cloudy but not nearly as bad as I had experienced in the past. Calling it an early night was the right choice because I was able to bounce back quicker than if I would have continued to push. I had taken six extra calcium pills and the tingling sensation in my face and the difficulty with my eyes had vanished.

We decided to take the short hour-and-a-half tour of the Research and Development and Presidential hangars before leaving for home. The planes in these hangars include President Kennedy's *Air Force One*. The spot where Lyndon Johnson was sworn in after the President's assassination is marked as you walk through the fuselage. We toured the presidential aircraft of Franklin D. Roosevelt, Harry Truman and Dwight Eisenhower. There are several other planes and a complete hangar of one of a kind experimental aircraft and engines on display. Although I found it interesting I was not feeling as energetic as the day before. After the tour ended we drove off in separate directions headed for home.

Monday, 6/08/09—As Pam left for work my thoughts on the day ahead of me were mixed. I had an appointment in the morning with a counselor. I could not decide which fact was more shocking, that I was seeing a counselor or the fact that I was the one who requested the meeting. I guess it is one of the side-effects of seeing and speaking with so many medical professionals that I came to view appointments as a normal part of life. This one was obviously different. I had tried for so long to push the mental aspect of my health under the rug and ignore it, but now knew I needed help to identify and cope with the issues I was experiencing. I was not sure a counselor could help me in an hour-long session, but there was no denying the need to speak with someone.

I was just coming to terms with the fact there was no cure for my illness and I would have to manage it for the rest of my life. That was a big hurdle I still was in the process of overcoming. I was several months away from the next bone density scan which would reveal the cumulative effect of the prescribed treatment. Building my bone density to normal levels was critical. Waiting a year to check progress on such a vital objective was mentally draining. To achieve a balance between medication and non-functioning parathyroid glands I needed to embrace the reality and surround the process with positive thoughts. So far all I could muster was anger.

This was the cover story presented to the counselor. I knew deep down there was more. I had not liked my verbal outbursts that seemed to just explode from out of nowhere. Most of the time I was alone and there were no casualties, but there had been a few times when I snapped at Pam or close friends and afterwards had regretted my actions. This was not who I am or who I want to allow myself to become.

The doctors had been up front and told me that anxiety was a contributing factor in my illness. I had fought them tooth and nail on that point. In my mind I was stronger than that. I had never experienced anxiety before in any major lasting form. I could not come to grips with why, all of the sudden, anxiety could knock me flat.

I wanted to alleviate what I suspected to be depression before it grew into something unmanageable. I set my apprehension aside and realized the need to speak with a professional openly and honestly.

10:00 a.m.—The receptionist greeted me by name and I was processed within minutes. I was escorted to a small back office down the hall from where I usually consulted with Dr. Weisblat. I was meeting with Tina Gupta, MC, who is a licensed counselor and certified Wellness Coach. Up to this point I remained calm but as the seconds ticked down I became nervous. I did not have second thoughts on seeking help. Just the fact of needing help in the first place bothered me. I was left alone in the small room for only a few minutes which was just enough time for me to build up enough anxiety to think of ways to bail out.

From the second she walked in the room I got a professional vibe from Counselor Gupta and that set the tone for the appointment. I was comfortable with that. It was the closest thing to normal I could draw from the entire situation. I soon found out this was not going to be some existentialism, get in touch with your softer side, self-help therapy session that I was prepared to wage ideological war on. The moment of truth was upon me. Let the healing begin.

Our introduction was brief. "Why don't you tell me why you are here?" Those might have been the only words she said the whole hour. I felt a need to explain all the details of all the surgeries and medical tests and the horrible symptoms, the lack of sleep and short temper and the low tolerance and lack of patience. Words flowed like water. One hour was nowhere near long enough to reach even halfway into my timeline of events. I was armed with my notebook containing talking points. I got through a small portion of my list. Near the end, Counselor Gupta cut in to first acknowledge the bizarre nature of my illness and the long duration of distress I had been through. She then proceeded in giving me some homework. I was to write out a complete timeline of the events that had transpired since waking up in the early morning hours of November 18, 2006, with a broken shoulder. She wanted me to make the timeline complete with emotions and feelings. I was skeptical. All along I had thought the path to regaining health lay in the hard physical work prescribed by therapists and doctors. I had disregarded the emotional effects of the illness as best I could. She requested that I write what I think I should have felt emotionally. I understood the need for this exercise. However, I was also well aware that it was going to be barely more enjoyable than pulling my own teeth.

She was not finished. I was also to write a letter to my illness. "Start it out with the sentence, 'I'm angry or afraid.'"

I cut in, "I'm not afraid, maybe angry, but definitely not afraid."

"Then use the opening, 'what you have done to me is.'"

In her final analysis, Counselor Gupta believed I had compartmentalized my emotions and wanted me to be cognizant of signs of anxiety. She thought it would be helpful to write down when I felt it as I was reliving the events and writing the letter to my illness. She emphasized the need for detailed notes of when the anxiety increased or decreased.

Although I felt this was a worthy exercise, the fact the work was related to my emotions was distasteful. Deep down I knew I needed this help. I felt as if I had been barely hanging on for so long. I had been fighting to keep up with work and trying to stay out of the hospital. The illness was brutal and complete in its ability to tear me down. I knew it had weakened my resolve and planted the seeds of anger and depression. I listened to what the Counselor said. Rather than facing some of the underlying issues over the course of my illness I had consciously pushed that work aside and plowed ahead with the basics of gaining back mobility, overcoming the next nervous-system attack and getting back to my job. It was hard enough keeping up with all the bills pouring in: rehab, doctor's visits and medical tests. I had nothing else to give. Now I had to go back and do the work I had avoided. I had never experienced this state of confusion. I needed to address it before my mind shifted too far away from its former state of being. I was eager to get started.

I agreed to a phone consultation on June 22nd. Counselor Gupta reconfirmed the need for me to do the homework with the familiar tone of a grade-school teacher. As she stood up from the table she said, "I look forward to hearing about your progress on the 22nd. Don't forget to add the emotions and write the letter to your illness." She added that I would probably feel worse before I feel better. She expected my anxiety levels to increase and that I should be aware this might happen. In the end, she thought I could get past some of the mental blocks I had discussed.

Feeling the need to put my stamp on the day's proceedings I explained to the counselor that I would not agree to take any new medications. She thought we could get by without them.

"I'm glad we got that cleared up."

I had crossed a hurdle of great importance. I had viewed seeking help as a weakness. This was something I should have been able to deal with on my own. I should have been stronger than the illness and accompanying mental stress. Instead my behavior had changed for the worse. I was not willing to live with that. Just getting to the table with a counselor was a big first step.

My brain was about to get a workout. I needed to put the effort into healing so I bought into the process. I went back to Pam's house filled with nervous energy. I put it to use mulching her gardens in her yard and around the sides of her house. It allowed me to burn off some of the uneasy feelings that were stirring around inside my head.

Tuesday, 6/09/09—My final day in Cleveland. Pam was at work all day and I was still carrying around a bundle of nervous energy. I finished off the final two gardens in her yard and cleaned up the remains of the mulch pile from her driveway. It felt good to finish a project and perform physical labor. I learned several new lessons about where I was with my illness and recovery. I had reached a new level of relaxation. I had also pushed a little too far with all the traveling, but I had reacted quickly to the warning signs in Dayton and had narrowly avoided long-lasting symptoms. The tingling in my face and head had decreased substantially. I really enjoyed spending time with family and friends, but I had a lot of work to get started on when I got back to St. Croix and felt nervous about taking Allopurinol. My mind was spinning.

Wednesday, 6/10/09—My flight left at 6:05 a.m. headed to Chicago. From there I flew direct to Miami. I had spent the extra money on the direct flight out of Miami, avoiding San Juan all together. After a few minor delays I was sitting on the St. Croix tarmac before 4:30 p.m.

The next couple of days were spent running errands and getting prescriptions filled. I nervously started taking the Allopurinol as my left foot began showing signs of gout. Reading the information on Allopurinol it stated that the medication could take several weeks to build up in the system. I was hoping for a shorter time because of the frequency of the gout attacks. I continued to take anti-inflammatory medication to keep the pain in check as much as possible.

Saturday, 6/13/09—Pat and I had plans to play golf at the Buccaneer Resort. It was our Christmas gift to each other. We wanted to use the gift certificates before it became too hot. I was a little reluctant but we had a golf cart which would cut the toll on my feet. I explained to Pat that I was unable to follow our usual tradition of bringing a cooler full of beer. He understood. I did drink my limit of two beers for the day. I was sweating so much I thought that they would have evaporated but I was wrong. The pain increased throughout the day as we played and I was walking with a noticeable limp by the time we left the course early in the afternoon. I shot a horrible score of 111.

Sunday, 6/14/09—The rising sun brought with it the heat. The gout raged on in my right foot. I could not put weight on it and found myself in bed icing both legs for the better part of the day. I was miserable. The heat of the Caribbean summer seemed to intensify the flare-ups. I continued taking Allopurinol to offset the HCTZ but it showed no signs of improving the pain level. I could feel a warm sensation in the blood veins nearest the most painfully afflicted areas. I was praying that this meant the medication was taking effect. By the end of the day I was getting frustrated with the whole situation. I could not get over the fact the gout was being caused by a medication. All the doctors could tell me was to hang in there. It all became overwhelming. I spent the afternoon cursing the doctors, people who made the medications and anyone involved with medical care. For a brief moment I wondered if this was what Counselor Gupta wanted me to keep track of when she was talking about anxiety. I cursed her for the next ten minutes and did not think about it anymore.

Monday, 6/15/09—As I woke up out of my sleeping-pill induced haze I was praying for some relief. I found my right ankle three-times its size and bright red in color. It throbbed. I couldn't walk without the use of my axe handle and even that was extremely painful. I immediately started icing the swollen areas. As the heat of the morning rose, I felt the need to express my discomfort to someone. I contacted Dr. Weisblat and expressed the fact that the Allopurinol was not working. I believed it had exacerbated the gout, causing it to come back stronger and more severe. Dr. Weisblat encouraged me to stay with it. He assured me that the Allopurinol was the correct medication to end this problem. The only alternative, he believed, was to increase the Allopurinol but wanted to hold off on doing that until I had been taking the drug longer. If that did not work we would have to find an alternative for HCTZ. Of course, I had already explored this option with Dr. Morrow and there really was no other alternative. I wanted desperately to end this nightmare, so I agreed to suffer the recommended plan.

The conversation with the doctor calmed me down and I accepted the reality that I was going to be living in great pain for the foreseeable future. I had to give the Allopurinol enough time to eliminate a sufficient percentage of uric acid from my blood. Along with the pain was a constant stream of sweat pouring out of my body. The day was pure torture both physically and mentally. By the early evening I was ready to surrender. I wished for a major catastrophe to come and put me out of my misery. Sleep was hard to come by even with the aid of a Klonopin. The throbbing pain in my feet and knees only allowed for short two to three hour periods of rest before I needed to ice down the troubled areas. It was relentless.

The next several days followed the same pattern, and by the end of the week I was a complete wreck. There would have been no way to make it to work if I'd have had to go. My body was experiencing extreme advanced arthritis (gout) caused by a medication I had to take to help absorb calcium. I was so pissed off I was ready to explode. I had no choice but to wait for the wonderful day the doctors were sure was just around the corner, when the Allopurinol finally offset the high uric acid levels.

The sleep deprivation was only adding to my despair. I spent most days alone in my house with little human interaction other than the phone. I literally had to struggle to get to the freezer and hobble back to the bed and continue to ice down my legs. The fifth straight day of this torture slowly faded with the reality that my toes on my left foot were swollen to the point of being unrecognizable. The one next to the big toe had a bluish hue and was pointing to the left. My right knee and ankle were twice their size and I was nauseous from the constant throbbing.

Saturday, 6/20/09—Overnight a game plan to soak in the ocean had been formed. The locals believed the salt water had healing properties and I was willing to try anything at this point. All I needed to do was walk down the short rocky path to Boiler Bay and sit down in the water. I wanted to swim around the point with the current and at least get the weight off my body and exercise a little. I managed with the help of the axe handle to hobble out of my house at 9:00 a.m. It was one of the few times I had left the inside of my house the entire week. I was determined to set aside the pain and get outside and enjoy something. Driving out to the point over-looking Boiler Bay I felt liberated. Although I was going to be swimming with the current I wanted to be sure to have my mask and snorkel on so I could see the underwater panorama. There was always an abundance of fish, lobster, stingrays and coral to see.

The path leading to the shell-covered beach was more difficult to hike down than I thought. I wore my neoprene liners that went on my feet inside my fins to protect my already sore feet. I had walked down this rock-strewn path barefoot in the past without trouble. This day the path proved almost too much for me. It was a cross between hobbling forward four-or-five-feet, stopping to rub my ankles and keeping my balance enough not to land face-first in the kasha bushes and cactus that lined the edges of the trail.

I pushed forward and as I made it to the beach the pain in my feet was more than I could bear. The only reason I continued down the path was the reality that I might not be able to make it back up. I figured I might as well get my swim in. Crossing the sand each step as painful as the last and fi-nally entering the water was a mental triumph.

I find peace when I am able to enjoy the great outdoors, especially the ocean. Living in the Caribbean you take the beautiful colors and shorelines for granted until you find yourself needing them to recharge your system.

As soon as I hit the water the built up anger, anxiety and tension de-creased. The pain was still present but for some reason it did not bother me as much. Mother Nature put on a show. Immediately upon entering the clear waters, I was followed by a large Barracuda. The five-footer came in very close as is their curious nature. He was fifteen-feet away and swim-ming along side of me when I noticed a large manta ray shaking the sand off and swimming towards the surface. It was a beautiful sight to see the great fish flap its wings, propelling itself gracefully through the water. The coral held several smaller schools of Purple Tang and other colorful fish. The sea life was abundant and the saltwater felt fantastic. I forgot about the gout, the pills, the pain and the lack of sleep. I had found my salvation and was extremely happy to have the opportunity only a ten-minute drive away from my home.

I was able to hobble back up the rock strewn path to my car. I had spent two hours in the water. It was just the break I needed. I was not sure if it was mental or physical but the symptoms seemed to be less punishing.

After making it back home, taking a shower and laying down for a short rest with ice packs on both legs, I remembered the homework assignment. I got up and fired up the computer.

I started with the letter to my body. I typed away looking at this exercise more as a nuisance than a way to find salvation. I had to rush to complete the exercises Counselor Gupta had given me because I was laid up in bed all week dealing with real physical pain and distress. Any emotions or thought process long since were pushed aside. The only thing I felt at this point was anger.

Monday, 6/22/09—I had until 11:00 a.m. before I had to call in for my first phone consultation with Counselor Gupta. I spent the better part of two hours that morning finishing the timeline—complete with emotions. It had all been a blur, and now I was forced to write it down in full. It was uncomfortable and in reliving the past, I experienced difficulty breathing. By the time I had finished there were seven pages.

11:00 a.m.—I phoned Dr. Weisblat's office and gave the receptionist my credit card number for billing purposes. A few moments later Counselor Gupta came on the line. "Hi Jeff, it's Tina." She asked me several questions about how I was feeling before moving onto the homework assignment. My answers were short and tense. She sensed the anger in my voice as we started covering the timeline. Each corresponding date held an emotion I had envisioned rather than had actually taken the time to feel. Tina would ask specific questions after I gave each date about how I felt talking about this or that. To me it had the same appeal of combining a dentist and proctology exam at the same time. She expressed the need for me to be more open with my feelings and not keep my reactions so guarded. As we poured over the timeline and discussed emotions I became more and more uncomfortable.

November, 19, 2006—Broken right shoulder. No reason for the

trauma. Emotions included shock, bewilderment, and fear. November 19th mis-diagnosis by Dr. Citron at the emergency room causing a full week to pass before surgery could be performed—anger, irritability. November 21st—Severe pain, trip to St. Thomas to see Dr. Chase, told I was unable to have surgery until the following week, would have to live with the pain of a broken shoulder, anger, pain resentment. We continued on through the first months of the timeline and forty minutes had passed. This was just the beginning. Before she stopped me, I was just about to go into the trip to Tampa. I really wanted to discuss these events because, for me, this was the real beginning of the problems. We would pick it up from there next time. She wanted to hear the letter I had written to myself. Reading out loud a letter I had hastily thrown together, addressed to my illness, was uncomfortable. Shaking my head in disbelief as to how I had come to this point in my life, I took in a deep breath and began:

> Dear Illness,
> You have broken my spirit. I am susceptible to nervous-system attacks, gout and broken bones. I feel worse than at any other time in my life. I have felt this way day-in-and-day-out over the previous two years. I have aged considerably as the constant stress of the next big attack weighs heavily on my mind. Doing my best to study you and going as far as to hire the top surgeons to cut you out of my body did little to stop your complete domination. I am extremely angry that I can not beat you out of my system. I should be stronger than you but that is not the case. You have been a formidable opponent and I will carry the scars you inflicted for the rest of my life. You have been complete in your devastation.
> Sincerely, Jeff

Counselor Gupta wanted me to broaden my awareness of anger and frustration. She said eighty-percent of physical symptoms can be caused by elevated stress levels and wanted me to make a list for our next session identifying what I was angry at and what I could do to release that anger.

"Next session? You mean I'm not cured? I have to continue this?"

"We still have the rest of your timeline to cover, and you need to become

387

aware of where you store your stress. We will continue to work on relaxing those areas through breathing and recognition." I was willing to participate as long as I felt there was some progress being made.

I realize that life is not always about comfort but at this stage I felt I deserved a little. Again, she reiterated that I would feel worse before things got better. It's not in my nature to back down, so I agreed to my third consultation in two weeks. I had my homework to concentrate on and it gave me something to do other than trying to figure out my next step in life. I realized I needed to overcome the past to move forward. In the mean time, I was stuck somewhere in between with little traction.

Amazingly, I noticed some relief. I felt a little portion of my hostilities released, and the pain in my feet and knees started to recede. Although swollen with occasional sharp jabs of pain there were respites from the agony.

Tuesday, 6/23/09—I contacted Paychex, the third-party out-sourced company running the COBRA insurance benefits for The March Group. They informed me that my application for the new government assistance was in place and instead of paying $420 per month for insurance I need only pay $162. I had applied not knowing if I actually qualified. Only applicants who were unemployed because their job was eliminated were accepted. The applicant's previous employer must provide the confirmation. I assumed that this was all taken care of and The March Group had cleared me to receive the benefit. I was thrilled with the savings and thankful for the assistance. I chose not to draw unemployment. The system in the Virgin Islands, like many of the government run agencies, came with its own set of frustrations. I wanted no part of these.

As June came to a close I could sense that my nervous system was starting to heal. I still had some bouts of mouth cramps, bicep muscle twitching and some breathing issues but the daily symptoms had started to clear up. There was an abundance of Sahara dust in the air that helped intensify the few breathing problems I did experience. The one constant was the pain in my right shoulder. It never wavered from its original level of discomfort. I would be dealing with that issue the rest of my life. I was hoping all other problems related to this illness were on their way out the door. I actually started feeling excited as I noticed the positive changes taking place. Maybe there would be a day in the future that I was back in complete control. Maybe there would come a day when I decided to stay in bed just because I could, not because I was too sick to get up.

The gout flared up occasionally, but not to the same extent. I felt the onset of arthritis which gout causes in the joints but it was if a wall had been set up blocking the unrelenting pain. With a grimace, I was able for the most part to ignore the discomfort.

Sunday, 6/28/09—Saharan dust coated every surface in my home. Cars were covered with an abrasive coating almost an eighth-of-an-inch thick. Everyone was complaining of sinus issues. In this environment the breathing issues I was experiencing did not set off alarm bells. I was still feeling pretty good about the past week's advancements as the weekend came to an end.

I thought about the areas that needed improvement and using sleeping pills had never been a welcome expedient. I wanted to be able to find that natural balance where I felt the tired feeling and was able to enjoy falling asleep on my own. Later that night, I took the first step to eliminate all sleep aides. I was not going to take a Klonopin, or an Ambien or a Xanax. The night only yielded two or three hours of restless sleep. I was tired, but clear headed, as I watched the sun come up. I had been wide awake since 4:30 a.m.

Monday, 6/29/09—I spent the day managing the remains of the gout with ice packs. I ate well and did a light workout for the first time in for what seemed like months. Monday night I fell asleep early on my own. I was exhausted and I did not take a pill for the second straight night. I slept pretty soundly until 3:30 am. I was unable to go back to sleep after waking up, but felt this was a victory.

Tuesday, 6/30/09—June has mercifully come to an end. There was a sense of urgency to get into shape for a sailing trip planned at the end of July. It was a trip Pat and I had planned to take for the past five years. The last three years I was unable to go because of work and illness. I had been too sick to even think about it. We would be living on a boat for the better part of a week and sailing every day between upstate New York and Toronto.

The trip would be the real test of how well I had progressed. I did not want to go on this trip if I was unable to pull my own weight. I was determined not to let my illness get in the way. I started exercising every afternoon. At first it was just a two-mile walk up the hill to Point Udall and some light dumb-bell routines. On the weekends I started hiking Goat Hill. I hoped increased activity would bring balance to my sleep patterns.

I went the third night in a row without a sleep aid. The quality of the sleep was horrendous. I woke up at 4:00 a.m. after falling asleep at midnight. It was not working out the way I planned. This was the first of many failed attempts to kick the sleeping pill habit.

Wednesday, 7/01/09—I continued the workouts daily. I increased the intensity levels each time out. For cardio I started jogging and included leg squats and dumb-bell weight routines to increase my arm strength. Success on this trip meant being able to go all out physically, and manage the lack of sleep while enjoying the good times.

I attempted a fourth night without a sleeping pill. It took a lot of deep breathing and positive thinking before I was able to nod off sometime after midnight. I believe the increased exercise routine had helped me fall asleep on my own. I exercised late in the afternoon in the height of the Caribbean summer heat. Sweating copious amounts of fluid out of my system each day helped rid my body of toxins.

When I woke up the next morning I had lived through yet another tumultuous night. I spent more time tossing and turning than actually sleeping, but I was encouraged by the fact that I'd slept at all.

The following two days I continued to concentrate on late afternoon workouts. I was trying to burn as much energy as possible to get the most benefits. I added stretching, more squats and a Goat Hill hike in between my Point Udall two-mile run. Later I would add a golf course routine and rotate each day between the three workouts concentrating on a different set of muscles each time out.

Thursday, 7/02/09—It turned out being one of those rare nights at the poker table where everything was falling into place. I ended the night taking six straight hands. Later that evening I was wound up and could not stop the carousel of thoughts in my mind. I tried in vain to relax and limit my thought processes. I finally gave in around midnight and took a sleeping pill. As I lay on my bed waiting for the pill to take hold I continued thinking through problems that I needed to fix on my boat and what my plans were for the next week. It was like my brain was working in overdrive and I could not control it. The anxiety was building with no apparent cause. I was doing everything possible to burn off steam physically and still the uneasy feelings were overtaking me.

Friday, 7/03/09—I woke out of the haze of Klonopin enhanced sleep with the same anxiety I had the night before. I was worried about something going wrong on my upcoming trip. I had to be ready and physically able to handle the long-distance sailing. I had talked myself into believing I was capable of handling the stresses of this trip but the lingering doubt made me uneasy. This illness could disrupt my world without any provocation let alone under the demanding conditions of a week-long sail. I wouldn't have the luxury to stop and shut down if I felt an episode coming on.

I shifted my focus to work on *Folly*. I had purchased a new set of sails and needed to add tracks on both side rails so I could use the large #1 genoa. I did not want the hassle of pulling her out of the water so I chose to do the work at her mooring. I loaded up the car complete with the new set of sails, the five-foot long rails and all my tools. When I got to the Yacht Club, the waves had picked up and there was a north northeast swell that was coming right over the reef and into the mooring area in Teague Bay. It was choppy and I decided to cancel my plans. Disappointed, I called Pat who had the day off work for the Fourth of July holiday. We went golfing at the Reef.

In 2007, I'd spent the Fourth of July in the emergency room after coming back from Tampa with a broken shoulder caused by malfunctioning parathyroid glands. After we finished walking nine holes of golf at the Reef

Course, I found myself alone in my house and took a moment and realized how far I'd come in the past two years. I had come close to dying in Tampa and now, two years later, I was back to fixing my boat and trying to golf. Although not everything was functioning properly, I was finally starting to face the illness head on. The tingling in my face had diminished to the point where I rarely noticed it. The daily struggle was not all-consuming and I began to see my journey with some objectivity.

Saturday, 7/04/09—The pain found its way right through the foggy aftermath of the previous night's sleeping pill. Gout pulsed through my left foot. By midmorning it had spread to the toes on the right foot turning them bright red. I went one beer over my limit while talking to some regulars at the Yacht Club the day before. I was livid with myself. After some deep breathing and positive thought projection I started to calm down enough to realize I could still walk. I limped around the two mile hike to Point Udall and back to the car. Although the pain was terrific it was my fault so I forced myself to finish up the workout with some lateral cardio moves and squats.

I was invited to a Fourth of July cookout and pool party. I limped in, said my hellos and immediately went in the water. As I soaked in the cool water of the pool, repeatedly turning down cold beer after cold beer, the pain in my legs and feet seemed to subside. It would come back with a vengeance after toweling off. I made it a short night and was the first to leave. I needed to start the ice-packs before everything started to swell up. If that happened I could be sidelined for days. After five separate twenty-minute ice downs of both legs over the course of the next two hours I took a Klonopin around 10:00 p.m. Forty-five minutes later my eyes were heavy and I was able to nod off despite the discomfort.

Sunday, 7/05/09—I woke to find the gout was still with me which limited my ability to get around. I walked with a terrible limp and there was no chance of finishing a workout. I turned my attention to Dr. Gupta's homework assignment. She wanted me to make a list of the items I was angry with, then pick one and write a letter starting with the phrase, "I am angry that."

I had turned on my computer and checked baseball scores and regatta websites etc. I was doing just about anything to avoid performing the task. A couple of hours had passed before I forced myself to finally start to write. Writing to express anger was not a familiar activity, and definitely came with a large amount of trepidation on my part. I'd finished my short list: Dr. Carmon Cintron, Dr. Norman and my body. Eventually I hit my stride, and over the course of the next two hours I wrote and re-wrote my first anger letter directed at another person.

Monday, 7/06/09—My 11:00 a.m. consultation with Counselor Gupta could not have come and gone soon enough for me. I had built up a lot of edgy tension as I faced the underlying anger issues. Counselor Gupta had reminded me just before the end of the previous session that I was likely to feel worse before getting better. That was definitely the case. It was hard to continue with the consultations but I knew eventually they would help lead me to some sort of understanding.

The session started with me reading the timeline of events and the correlated emotions. Those I felt and those I thought I should have felt. Again anger and frustration came up several times. After twenty minutes, I was nowhere near the end of my seven pages. I knew there would be more sessions to follow. Counselor Gupta stopped and wanted me to validate myself out loud by verbally giving myself permission to praise the effort I had put into overcoming my illness and the trauma I had lived through. She continued to hammer away at the need for me to face the emotions I had pushed aside throughout this journey. I found the exercise to be extremely difficult and became agitated. My head was banging on the inside and I was suddenly drained of energy as I fidgeted around in my seat.

Counselor Gupta asked me to read my homework assignment. Before I began, she asked me to focus on where and how I experienced stress when reading the letter.

I am angry, Dr. Carmon Cintron. You misdiagnosed my shoulder injury on the morning of November 19, 2006. The moment I was admitted into the emergency room I was nothing more than an inconvenience for you. I explained the level of pain I was in and you reluctantly agreed to have an x-Ray performed. Over three hours passed before you delivered your diagnosis. Holding the x-ray into the light you told me to see another doctor if I still felt pain in four to five days. In your expert opinion, I was most likely experiencing a case of tendinitis. I have a copy of the x-ray and it clearly shows a break below the head of my shoulder. Do you believe you were performing your duties as a doctor in the best manner possible during this emergency room visit? Your dismissive behavior coupled with poor diagnostic skills caused me to have to wait an entire week to have the emergency surgery required to fix my broken shoulder. Dr. Frank Bishop discovered the break immediately the next morning after having an MRI performed. Why was it is so easy for him to see? It was clear, from that point on, what needed to be done. Valuable time had already been wasted. In the end my rehabilitation was made more difficult and painful because of the hardening of the scar tissue and muscle surrounding the injury. I would be forced to spend several weeks tearing that very same scar tissue during a very painful rehabilitation.

The additional time waiting before the surgery compromised the blood supply to the bone leaving it up in the air if it would survive post surgery. It would be several months before that diagnosis was available. The mental strain surrounding this uncertainty was great. It was lucky for me, that against these odds, the bone had survived according to Dr. Jeffrey Chase. The mobility in the right shoulder will never again return to what it used to be, in large part due to the extended waiting time before surgery. My left shoulder, broken six months later with a far worse fracture, performs much better. That surgery was performed within forty-eight hours of the injury occurring. Both surgeries employed the exact same hardware so they are easily comparable. I experience less daily discomfort in my left shoulder and always will for the rest of my life.

The stress, it was in my shoulders. I experienced tightness in my chest making it difficult to take a full breath.

Dr. Gupta wanted to know what would it take for me to release my anger towards Dr. Citron? Nothing came to mind. I went on to discuss briefly with Counselor Gupta that I had looked into a potential lawsuit four-or-five-months after my surgery, but the USVI government effectively has its own version of a TORT Law. Because they run the hospital system and were being held liable for many frivolous lawsuits each year, they capped the highest amount for a payout at $250,000. At this point there was only one lawyer on the island willing to even think about handling a medical lawsuit case. The amount of money was not really the issue for me, but I wanted Dr. Cintron to know her mistake and make sure it was not repeated. There is a filing deadline from the date of the incident, but I was busy rehabbing my second broken shoulder when that date passed.

We went on to discuss other subjects on my anger list. Number two was Dr. Norman and his clinic and the fact they were unable to fix my illness. I'd gone to the best in the world and came away from that experience worse off. Counselor Gupta wanted me to start with "I am angry." So I began:

> I am angry that the ninety-nine-point-one-percent success rate of patients described on the Norman Endocrine Clinic's website did not include me. I did not go on to lead a normal life as promised. I broke my left shoulder after passing out two days after the surgery to remove a rogue parathyroid. The reason I passed out was my calcium levels crashed to a dangerously low level. I was on the phone with Dr. Norman when the lights went out and I hit the marble floor. I had been instructed by Dr. Norman earlier in the morning to take additional calcium and stay in the hotel. I followed his request and called him back in four hours. This was all that was asked of me after I had notified him I was experiencing intense ice-pick stabbing sensations from my head to my feet. I told Dr. Norman about how edgy and irritable I felt. I knew this was not a normal sensation. The back of my head was numb and my face was contorting and tingling. Instead of sending me right over to the hospital for blood work he had me stay at the hotel. I passed out calling Dr. Norman back for help. With the phone still in my hand, the left shoulder head was broken completely off the humerus bone. The normal parathyroid function which you promised to me, will never come back. The past two years have been filled with daily nervous-system flare-ups and feeling ill and out of sorts.

Dr. Gupta asked me what I could do to release this anger. I thought I could talk to Dr. Politz about my anger. I also thought about being part of a solution, instead of directing my anger at other people. None of this venting was making me feel any better. I spoke about starting a charity swim to raise money for calcium-deficiency awareness. Other people struggle with hyper and hypo-parathyroid illness. There needs to be more research and available information. The idea of having Dr. Norman and Dr. Politz sponsor such an event seemed to put a smile on my face.

The third anger issue I discussed during this session was with my own body. "I am angry that my own body failed me. I should have been strong enough to overcome this illness. It should not have affected me to the degree it has."

My only suggestion to go about releasing this anger towards myself was to workout harder. Leading a healthier lifestyle would help control my health issues.

Of course Counselor Gupta saw things differently. She explained that I had several issues that needed to be addressed. On the one hand, I had control issues, on the other hand I needed to release the anger directed inward. She recommended two steps in re-teaching my mind and body to respond to the warning signs of stress and the warning signs of illness. I needed to write down when and why I felt stress. She felt discussing the timeline of events in detail was a good start. It gave her an indication I was willing to talk about this problem, but still clung to frustrations and anger. She suggested I keep a ledger documenting moments of stress—its causes and symptoms.

The second step was to concentrate on the timeline and focus on acknowledging what I'd gone through. Eventually this would release pent-up frustrations manifesting themselves into a short temper and sudden fits of anger. It was an incredible journey that was disheartening and would be difficult for anyone. Acknowledging this fact would be key to lowering my stress level. I had to give myself credit for surviving and admit my feelings of vulnerability.

More homework was assigned. It included writing a letter directed at Dr. Norman. She wanted me to really let him have it. "So don't censure yourself when you are writing this letter. Create permission for yourself to let out your anger."

I found it difficult to go back over all the events that had taken place, and to admit I needed help. Each time I spoke to the Counselor I felt a little bit better, but I was still leery of the process even though it was providing small amounts of relief. My nervous system was starting to calm down, in part because I was facing some of the issues that were not addressed when all I could think about was surviving. There was a correlation between my symptoms and the bottled-up frustration. I understood what Counselor Gupta was trying to do with these homework assignments. I agreed to continue with the sessions.

Friday, 7/10/09—Although I felt good about talking to a Counselor, I was by no means feeling well. I continued having diminished nervous-system symptoms the following week. For me, that was progress. I had hopes that all counseling would soon end. I was embarrassed that I needed to speak with a counselor, and did not want to speak about it with anyone else. Pam heard bits and pieces through brief discussions, but I chose not to divulge details to anyone else.

I still had occasional facial tingling and involuntary muscle spasms in my neck, arms and legs. The symptoms were decreased but still noticeable. Whether I wanted to admit it or not, the counseling was helping me take steps towards the long-sought balance the doctors had been talking about. The one constant negative that remained was the increased uric acid and resulting gout. The pain associated with the flare-ups was at times as brutal and debilitating as breaking the bones had been. I had run out of patience living with this ailment. The symptoms needed to end.

I woke up the following morning experiencing yet another gout flare-up. One Allopurenol a day did not seem to be helping. This time my right foot was the target. The pain was intense and I could not put any weight on my right leg. A short time later, my right knee started throbbing as this latest episode turned into a full-blown attack. I continued icing my leg, knee and foot throughout the day. Thoughts of my sailing trip at the end of the month gave me a mental break from the discomfort. I was putting a lot of pressure on myself to get into shape before my trip. Gout stopped any progress dead in its tracks—elevating my frustration level.

Saturday, 7/11/09—The gout pain increased overnight. I was unable to get out of bed most of the following day. I knew the pain was not going to disappear. I waited for the single pill to kick in while simmering with frustration. Contacting Dr. Weisblat and Dr. Morrow was more of a cry for help than anything else. I rehearsed my speech to both of them, time and time again, over the weekend. I was no longer willing to put up with the lack of relief provided by the medication. There had to be another alternative.

Sunday, 7/12/09—Sunday turned into a repeat of Saturday. I continued icing of my right leg and foot, but there was little relief from the throbbing pain. My anger was growing with each passing minute. The heat inside my house was rising as we headed into the Caribbean's storm season. It was a bad combination. The heat seemed to intensify the gout symptoms, causing the flare-ups and the accompanying pain to reach an unbearable state.

Monday, 7/13/09—By Monday morning I was ready to fire everyone, stop seeing all my doctors, and start from scratch. I was more frustrated than at any other time in my life. Just when I felt some relief from the parathyroid illness, this gout issue came along disabling me to the point where I could not function. I had a trip to prepare for and the gout was not allowing me to prepare the way I would have liked to.

8:30 a.m.—I left Dr. Weisblat a phone message. 9:00 a.m.—I called back and got his receptionist. I explained my situation. Sensing the urgency in my tone, she agreed to speak with the doctor right away. Within an hour I received a call back. Dr. Weisblat said that if the Allopurenol was not effective I would have to stop taking the HCTZ. I was happy with that except that HCTZ was helping my body absorb calcium. I had to keep in mind that my bone structure was compromised and the HCTZ, although I really did not enjoy taking it, served a major purpose. I had spoken with Dr. Morrow about this issue and there seemed to be no other alternative. The last thing he could suggest was upping the dosage to one-and-a-half Allopurenol pills a day. If that didn't help alleviate the gout symptoms, I would have to make the decision to discontinue HCTZ. Dr. Weisblat had spoken with Dr. Morrow about HCTZ use and reached an impasse. I asked about the potential side effects of increasing the Allopurenol. I was concerned that the HCTZ and Allopurenol combination could damage my kidneys. He assured me I was not permanently damaging my kidneys with this treatment. As long as we continued to monitor my progress through blood tests, it should be okay.

As soon as I hung up, I called Dr. Morrow's office. The receptionist sensed the urgency in my situation. I received a call back within the hour. Dr. Morrow was sure that the increased Allopurenol would lower the level of uric acid in my blood stream. I spoke to him about stopping the HCTZ. In his opinion, continuing the HCTZ treatment was the only alternative.

Dr. Morrow went on to explain that he had looked into my suggestion of using the synthetic PTH hormone. He consulted several colleagues at some of the top-rated Endocrinology offices in the world and discussed the possibility that synthetic PTH could improve my situation. It had never been used for this purpose before. Synthetic PTH was new to the market and presently used only to treat severe cases of osteoporosis. The patients targeted to use the drug were elderly women. He believed I could get some benefit from taking the synthetic PTH, however, there was no way to know what dosage I would need to take to usurp my irregular functioning parathyroid hormone production. If successful it could allow me to stop taking HCTZ. The cost of the medication was over $10,000 for a one-year supply which had to be refrigerated and injected every day. At the present time it was only prescribed for two-year treatments and wouldn't be considered a long-term option. Insurance companies are reluctant to pay for experimental treatments so that would have to be paid out of pocket. He went on to discuss how he would need to write a letter to the medical board that included a compassionate-use clause requesting permission for me to use the drug. Dr. Morrow was willing to start the approval process. The decision was up to me.

Later that day I spoke to my mother who was currently taking Forteo, a version of the synthetic PTH. She injects herself every day. She can only take the drug for two years. She went on to explain that the drug is shipped directly to her door because it must be kept refrigerated. She said it was a royal pain in the ass, literally, but she was getting really good results with her bone density levels.

Taking into account the fact that I was feeling less tingling sensation in my face coupled with the information from my last two blood draws which showed my PTH hormone level had improved and was hovering around the lower end of the normal range, I decided to see how the increased dosage of Allopurenol worked before asking Dr. Morrow to proceed.

When I contacted Dr. Morrow, and explained my position, he felt continuing the HCTZ was the best solution. He encouraged me to hang in there and promised we would find the right balance. The next time I was scheduled to be in Cleveland, he wanted me to have another twenty-four-hour urine test. I was six-to-eight months away from needing another bone-density scan which would ultimately determine if we were making progress.

Over the next three days, the gout symptoms subsided. I resumed preparation for my trip. I was starting to feel good about my progress. As long as the increased Allopurenol helped keep the gout at bay, I was going to be just fine.

Friday, 7/17/09—Just as I was thinking things were turning around I started experiencing burning-mouth syndrome. The symptoms were uncomfortable and made sleep impossible over the next four days. Breathing air in through my mouth felt like I was fanning the flames of a roaring forest fire. I used some special desensitizing paste Pam had gotten from her dentist. It seemed to help for short periods of time, but the burning sensation was constant. I went back on line and read about the symptoms. This was related to my nervous system. It is extremely rare—just like all the illnesses that seemed to continue to come my way.

Saturday, 7/18/09—With my gout on the decline, I was able to play a round of golf. I needed a break from all the medical issues that had flared up, and walking the course seemed to clear my head. I was so fed up with the medication roller-coaster ride.

Sunday, 7/19/09—After a workout that included jogging for one mile, followed by a two-mile walk up to Point Udall and back, I settled in for what I hoped would be a short homework assignment. I tried my best to open it up and lay into Dr. Norman. What I discovered after reading the final draft out loud was something unexpected.

Monday, 7/20/09—The nervous energy I built up performing the homework assignment carried right into the phone call. I found it difficult to go through with these sessions. I vacillated between believing I should be stronger than this, and the need to talk through my problems with a Counselor. After completing the homework assignment, I knew I'd discovered the next mental hurdle to address with Dr. Gupta.

At the start of the session Counselor Gupta asked me to read my letter:

Dear Dr. Norman,

On 6/20/07, I arrived in Tampa, Florida, full of hope. You need to understand that I did not arrive at the decision to have the parathyroid procedure without fully investigating the issues and performing the research. What has transpired after having the surgery has been devastating both physically and mentally. You led me to believe that I was going to be cured in a fifteen to twenty-minute minimally invasive procedure.

You claim to be the number one expert on the subject of hyperparathyroidism and its cure. What you failed to mention in our conversations were the consequences if your surgery was not successful. Your website boasted a cure rate of near 100%. That is very impressive considering the large number of surgeries your clinic performs (thirty-six per week). You personally assured me that your surgery would have me feeling great and functioning the next day. The website states 98.5% of patients achieve normal parathyroid function because your procedure leaves three healthy parathyroids and that virtually all patients out of the previous 9,000 who have had surgery performed under your care have gone home within three hours. You reiterated this impressive record in our private conversations and boasted how well this was going to go. My case was especially promising because I was a relatively young man and this was very rare for someone like me to have this disease. It was anticipated that I would bounce back immediately, experiencing a significant improvement in the quality of my life. I placed my trust in you and your organization. You have failed in your commitment to deliver me a fully functioning parathyroid system. I now know, during the courting period when I was deciding to have the surgery, you understated the risk and overstated your abilities.

Here is a direct quote from your website: "Our expertise has made parathyroid surgery a very straightforward, routine outpatient procedure that usually takes about 17 minutes! Build a better mousetrap and the world will beat a path to your door. This is clearly what has happened to our practice. Nobody can do what we do."

"Note: Don't let the fact that we treat so many patients with hyperparathyroidism and perform so many parathyroid operations make you think that we don't treat our patients well. We do! In fact, every patient is given Dr Norman's and Dr Politz's home telephone numbers and cell phone numbers so they have access to them when ever they want/need. We don't use an answering service—our patients can call us at any time."

You followed through on your promises to provide me your telephone numbers and when I called you dismissed my symptoms as a normal reaction to the surgery. What I was describing to you over the phone I now know are severe symptoms caused by low calcium in my blood stream. I have suffered through it many times since that morning in Tampa. The muscle cramping and tingling from head to toe should have moved you to direct me back to the hospital. Although barely mentioned on your own website, these are the signs of Tetany the most severe symptoms of hypoparathyroidism.

I believe you are blinded by your own success and are dangerous to patients who do not fall into the normal grouping you are accustomed to dealing with. I felt as if you were the expert and you were telling me that my symptoms were minimal when in reality I was obviously in deep trouble. I had never felt anything like this before in my life. You insisted that I was over reacting and the numbness and tingling I was feeling was normal. This misdiagnosis was a direct consequence of your professional arrogance. You have become the top surgeon in this field because of the volume of surgeries you perform not the level of care you provide. You are ill-prepared to treat the rarest of cases. In particular, those cases where the remaining parathyroid glands do not return to normal function. Unfortunately for me, I am a case in point. Throughout this ordeal you tried to fit me into the same box that you fit all your other patients into. This had devastating consequences on my quality of life.

Because you insisted that what I was feeling was a normal reaction, I did what you suggested. While in the hotel room, I paced the floor and then curled up on the bed with severe cramping. I was highly agitated, barking at my mother when she asked simple questions. I took ten extra calcium pills and called you back in four hours as instructed. Before we had even finished saying hello, my body went into convulsions due to the lack of calcium. In a blood test from the emergency room later that same afternoon, my calcium level was 6.5ml. The doctor in the hospital told me I was lucky to have survived. As you and I both know, that is shockingly low. It is no wonder that I passed out and broke the head off my left shoulder. I split my head open in the fall and bit my tongue almost in half. I want you to know my mother, whom you met at the hospital, witnessed these events, and it has left her traumatized.

I have spent the past two years suffering severe hypoparathyroid symptoms and have wound up in the emergency room four times. I would say you failed to live up to your own high regard. You definitely failed me and my family. Your website says that: "Hypoparathyroidism is the combination of symptoms due to inadequate parathyroid hormone production (Hypoparathyroid-ism). This is a rare condition, and almost always occurs because of damage or removal of parathyroid glands at the time of parathyroid or thyroid surgery." I am still working to correct the system your surgery failed to fix. My parathyroids have never fully recovered and today are still not producing the proper amount of PTH.

My hope is that in the future you will take the time to explain the possibility for poor results with all your patients. Warn them what can happen. I also hope you will change your post-surgery patient follow up procedures. If you continue using the same procedures a similar scenario will play out in the future. I can not put into words how I have suffered over the past two years. Your cookie-cutter style of surgery is not the best option for all patients. It did not serve me well. I do not blame you for my results, but I do charge you with over-hyping your capabilities and under estimating the consequences. Negative feedback from patients is crucial to eliminate future failures. What I would like is for my story to be added to your website showing the nightmare that is possible. It happened to me and my wish is that your posted success rate be adjusted properly to reflect my outcome!

Furthermore, I would like you to acknowledge that something was wrong with my system after your procedure. You, being the highest author-ity on this subject, should have reacted differently to my feedback. If you had diagnosed me properly and directed me to the hospital I would have complete use of my left arm today. I could have avoided the pain and suf-fering of rehabilitation and the real discomfort of life-long arthritis.

In closing I would like to remind you that prior to the surgery I asked you what are the risks involved in this procedure and you proudly stated that for me there were none. I knew better, but I chose to believe in you and trust your methods. That mistake lands squarely on my shoulders. It is up to you to decide what level of blame should land on your shoulders and hopefully what new procedures are necessary to prevent the same misfor-tunes that rained down on me after believing in you.

Sincerely, Jeff Krehbiel

"How do you feel about what you have just read?"

"I feel some sense of release but, to be honest, I didn't get that much out of it. Dr. Norman did not set out to cause this problem. I do have some regrets, obviously, from choosing to go ahead with his procedure, but in the end I do not blame him one hundred percent."

"Who do you blame?"

"I blame myself."

There it was—out on the table. I felt some relief as the words flowed out of my mouth. "I feel my body should have been able to handle this ill-ness. I ended up so weak and helpless and that should never have happened. I should have figured it out sooner, taken control and fixed the issues long before I started breaking shoulders and having low calcium affect my nerv-ous system to the devastating degree it did."

"Wow! Let me just ask you if you had a friend or co-worker that had gone through what you have gone through would you expect them to tough it out and be strong or would you show them compassion?"

Counselor Gupta went on to explain that I needed to become conscious of my inner voice. If anyone else went through what I went through they would experience stress. "You seem to believe that you should have been stronger. Why is that?"

At this point I was almost ashamed to be forced into admitting how I felt. I was beginning to see the scope of the work that needed to be done and grew quiet. Leery of the process, I questioned if we actually needed to dredge all these emotions up. Was I just following another practitioner into their belief-system hoping to find salvation?

Counselor Gupta went on to explain that we needed to further explore the negative feelings towards my body. My homework assignment was to write a letter to my body. In the letter I was to tell my body what I wanted it to do and how to react to trauma. I was to start the letter out by saying: "I need you to perform." I then was to write a second letter from my body in reaction to the first letter.

At the end of the session we discussed cognitive reprocessing. Counselor Gupta believed I was being way too hard on myself. One of the exercises she wanted me to work on was to stop the negative messages I was sending to myself and replace them with positive reinforcement.

I was leaving on my sailing trip in two days. I looked at this trip as a huge test. If I passed, I knew I was in a much better place to face the future. I did not want to consider failing. I also did not want to have to do a bunch of homework when I returned, so I got to work writing the requested letters.

Dear Body,

In the past we have seen our fair share of broken bones, torn up knees, ribs and ankles. You have always bounced back within an allotted time-frame and allowed me to move on without further complications. All this changed after the parathyroid surgery. I had felt we were progressing along nicely after the first shoulder surgery. To go through the same injury on the left side as I had already gone through on the right side was emotionally difficult. I built up anger that I directed towards you. You were weak and gave way when I needed you to fight and be strong. The lingering effects of this have plagued both of us for over two-and-a-half years. It has been relentless. I have not felt one full day of complete health and normalcy. On top of the major trauma that took place you have not returned the remaining three parathyroids to normal function which has caused several of the darkest and most troubling experiences of my life.

You and I both know the score, the number of times we found ourselves in the dark with me begging you not to have a stroke, to stop the ice-pick stabbing sensations that were rocking me from head to toe, to relieve the pain raging through every muscles and the cloudiness that prevailed in my head. I have pleaded and prayed and you continually allow it to happen. Daily reminders in the form of tingling and numbness linger, keeping me on the edge, wondering if the next big attack is right around the corner. Why can you not fix the issues and regulate the damn calcium like a normal body? I felt like you have let me down, have shown weakness and ineptitude. If you were a worker your employee status would have been terminated long ago. Because a split from you is impossible, we need to lay down some ground rules for the future. I would like fair warning before a major medical event is going to take place. Give me a fighting chance to face the issue head-on before it does irreversible damage. I need you to perform as intended and not fail as in the examples I have provided. No more surprises!

Sincerely, Jeff

Letter from my body:

Dear Jeff,

Honestly speaking as your body it has been a rough two and a half years. Both shoulders broken followed by major surgery, a parathyroid removed without regular function returning to the remaining three, daily nervous-system malfunctions, urinating blood, gout and lack of sound sleep. You never stopped to give me rest or allow me to recover. As soon as you were able to walk you were back to your fast-paced job. Don't you think this contributed to us getting worn down further? You barreled ahead into rehab, spending countless hours on your own working in the gym. You ask why you felt weak and tired all the time and you blame me? You had just as much to do with this situation as I did. You do not cut yourself or me any slack. All the feedback I am receiving is negative. You spend so much time dwelling on feeling so poorly. Cut us both some slack and relax so we can work together and overcome these issues.

You are allowed to grieve for your loss and you need to acknowledge the validity of that emotion. Until you are able to face what has happened, you will not reach your goal of a normal life. I want to help you get there but I need a break. I have to recover. The rarity of this illness did not leave

406

me many opportunities to warn you of the pending issues that were about to take place. There was no stopping this from happening. When you woke up in bed with a broken shoulder, I woke up in bed with a broken shoulder. I did not let down my guard or become weak all of the sudden. This was unavoidable and you will have to learn to deal with that for the two of us to work in concert and avoid major stress-related issues. What you are doing by putting this undue pressure on me and yourself is not helping the situation and it is prolonging the effects of the calcium imbalance.

In the future, I need you to give me credit for what I have overcome. Give me positive reinforcement and the rest I need to recover. These are major medical issues we are dealing with and it will take time to overcome them. Look at where we are today compared to last year and the year before that. Recognize the progress, back that up and reinforce it with positive thoughts. Stop being so hard on yourself and me and we will reach our final goal of feeling good and living a healthy life together. Remember I am on your side.

Earnestly speaking, Your Body

By the time I'd finished this assignment I was exhausted. It was evident that Dr. Gupta's counseling was necessary. We still had a long way to go before I would see major progress, but I was starting to understand what I needed to do to move on. The process took several more sessions and it continues today as I write the ending of this book. I'm sure that many counseling patients feel the same way, but just going through the process is such a large departure from what I once considered normal. I never could have contemplated a situation where I needed a counselor to help me bounce back. I have found it difficult to face the analysis, buy into the suggestions, and take action based on what the counselor says. The fears of taking this help have mellowed over time and I have benefited greatly. The dark wall that caused me to shut down and stay in bed was very real. At the time I could never seem to climb over it or see beyond it. Eventually, overtime, it started to fade. The unnaturally quick temper and angry outbursts that characterized the dark period have become less frequent. A little bit of joy and happiness had crept back into my life.

I had been battling, nonstop, for close to three years. I was faced with a life of managing an illness no doctor could cure. In six months I will be taking another bone-density scan that will indicate if my hips and other bone structures will crumble into dust. No promises have been made for the future. My health is always going to be at the forefront of my thoughts. Accepting this as reality is the first step. How I choose to deal with that reality will determine the quality of my life. I know one thing, I will never lie down and give up. I will continue to fight and hopefully find time for some happiness along the way.

July 22—Pat Ellison and I boarded a plane headed to Buffalo, New York. Our final destination was Youngstown, near the mouth of Lake Ontario on the lower Niagara River. The trip had been in the works for over five years. I was determined not to miss out this year.

Niagara Falls is located about thirteen miles upriver from Youngstown. Canada is a stone's throw away—across the lower Niagara River which flows into Lake Ontario—less than a mile to the northwest. The naturally beautiful area is home to Youngstown Yacht Club. We arrived late on Wednesday evening. The village has a population of 2,500 residents, a handful of restaurants and a couple of bars. We proceeded to close down The Jug, a stone building built in the late 1700s, The Jug has been continuously operated as a bar for over 200 years. The purpose of this trip was to test myself and blow off steam. We were off to a good start.

The next morning we wandered down the hill to Youngstown Yacht Club. There was a lot of activity taking place in the light drizzling rain. Last minute preparations were under way for the 36th annual Level Regatta. Over 220 boats were expected to race in this year's event. Andy Hooker was our host for the ten-day sailing adventure. Pat and Andy grew up in Youngstown and have several years of racing experience on the great lakes between them.

We stayed at Andy's house for the first few nights before moving aboard Andy's C&C designed Red Wing Thirty named *Battle Star Pegasus* and sailing to Toronto. We didn't plan to race in the regatta but instead wanted to sail through the six-race courses and check out the action as it unfolded.

Friday came and we left the mooring field on *Battle Stare Pegasus* for a shakedown cruise. We shot down the river, past the Canadian port of Niagara on the Lake, and then past the British fort on the American point marking the entrance to Lake Ontario. The winds were out of the southwest as we glided north past the one-mile buoy. As we passed the four-mile buoy several masts appeared on the horizon. They seemed to be closing in on us from all directions. We eagerly watched as wooden and modern racing boats glided past—loaded with crew. We ducked back into the Niagara and went up river for a short time before turning back and buttoning Andy's boat up and placing her on the mooring.

By the time we stepped back on the pier, a food court, several large tents and a stage complete with sound and lighting equipment were in place. There was a forty-foot refrigerated Molson Beer truck parked behind the stage and the individual crew tents had already begun to spring up on any unused patch of ground that was available. The riverfront was transforming before our eyes. Before the kick-off party started, the boats were rafted eight deep off the pier and throughout the mooring field that stretched a half-mile in either direction of the club house. The boats I found most appealing were the 8 meters—wooden boats made in the 1920s and 1930s. It's amazing how well these are preserved in the fresh water of the great lakes. They appeared as polished jewels, each one seemingly out doing the next in varnish and shine. Over the course of the next couple of days we were able to get up close and personal with a couple of these treasures while under sail.

The kickoff party was done on a grand scale. The band played until midnight, and the beer flowed well into the early morning hours. Youngstown had essentially quadrupled in population over the course of a few hours. The efficiency with which the entire three-day event was run was impressive. We sailed every day, maneuvering through the six courses marked by large orange buoys. The first day winds held steady just under fifteen knots. The racing was off to a good start.

Andy is the head tactician on *Futures* a forty-four-foot Swan. We climbed aboard Friday afternoon and had a chance to check out all the modern electronics and design work. To competitively race, she needs stronger winds than were predicted for the weekend. Saturday turned out to be a disappointing day for the crew. Sunday rain clouds hovered in the early morning over the race course and by mid-afternoon we could see a squall line racing towards our position. We decided to come in and enjoy the rest of the afternoon on land before the closing ceremonies got under way. The winds picked up and the squall gave the larger boats in the fleet some spirited racing. Reports around the bar, beer truck and stage, later that night, were of sails ripping and hardware breaking.

Monday morning came and before our early arrival at the Yacht Club there was little left to suggest that one of the biggest parties of the year had taken place the previous three days. The stage was dismantled and the tent city had dwindled down to a few hangers on. Andy and I headed out in a starter boat named *Blue Moon*. The two of us were the official starters for the Centennial Race. It is the kickoff of the LYRA (Lake Yacht Racing Association) Regatta. Returning racers to Canada were scheduled to race from Youngstown into the Royal Canadian Yacht Club in Toronto approximately thirty-five miles to the northwest. After raising the flags and seeing some great start-line action, we headed back in to YYC and boarded *Battle Star Pegasus*. Pat had her already tied up at the dock and we finished loading our provisions. We would be trailing the Centennial Fleet to Toronto. Andy had secured a prime dock slip for us at the Royal Canadian Yacht Club. His Red Wing would be our home for the next four days.

We had a great sail averaging between five and six knots. The first sighting of the Toronto skyline was just over an hour into our sail. As the miles ticked off the CN Tower grew larger, eventually looming over us like a large rocket. I took my turn at the tiller and was able to keep on course, enjoying my first long-distance sailing on fresh water. The winds remained steady as we passed over the mid-point in the lake and then the international boundary waters. Buildings lining Front Street in Toronto were visible. Four-and-half-hours in, we sliced through the east channel of Toronto Harbor. We rounded down to the entrance of the Royal Canadian Yacht Club. Founded in 1852, it is one of the oldest and most prestigious Yacht Clubs in North America. Situated on the islands that provide shelter to the harbor, it stares directly into the Toronto skyline—just over a mile away.

After clearing customs we docked in our prime spot directly across from the main clubhouse. The facility is a sprawling seventeen-acre plot of land with horizontal dock fingers holding over 700 sailboats. The number was well over 1,000 because of the 125th anniversary of the Lake Yacht Racing Association Regatta taking place the remainder of the week. Most, if not all boats, that had competed in the Level Regatta in Youngstown were scheduled to participate. Besides the Centennial Race, there was another long-distance race called the Freeman Cup scheduled Wednesday evening. The course was over eighty miles around marks at various towns up and down the lake. Andy was scheduled to race on *Futures* and would be staying behind for the round the buoy racing which started Friday and ran through Sunday. Pat and I would be leaving Andy to race and sailing *Battle Star Pegasus* back to Youngstown.

The facilities at RCYC were first-rate. They included shower buildings, complete with warm towels, a swimming pool, lawn bowling and croquet yards, tennis courts and more sailboats than I had ever seen in my life. RCYC is the home to twelve eight-meter sailboats docked directly down from our front-row slip. The row behind us included six-meter boats, various C&C Yachts, Hintenholer Sharks and several larger sail boats over forty-feet in length. You could stand on the bow of *Pegasus* and see the Toronto skyline. The walking paths wound their way through deep, wooded park-like parcels of land completely surrounded by dock space, none of which were empty. The place was packed.

After enjoying Toronto and the RCYC, we were scheduled to sail to Port Dalhousie, Canada. Once tied up safely at the dock, we were going to set out and enjoy the nightlife. The next day we would be leaving on the fifteen-mile sail east to Youngstown. The weather did not cooperate. The winds died down on Wednesday morning. The rains soon followed. We changed our course and stayed at RCYC one more day. Not a bad fallback option.

Thursday morning we motored out of Toronto Harbor in light winds and

headed south. We raised the sails in puffy winds bouncing between two-and-
-three knots. There were moments where the wind died and we had to furl
the jib and turn on the motor. It was slow going for the first half of our sail.
What winds were available came directly out of the southwest, the direction
of the mouth of Lower Niagara River. We didn't mind because it was all part
of the adventure. After several long tacks, we reached the midway point. The
winds started to pick up and we were traveling between three and four knots.
Just after spotting the first buildings on the Canadian side of Niagara Falls,
the wind finally cooperated and we sped up to between five and six knots.
The trip back to Youngstown took seven hours to complete. Standing in the
one-man, customs check-in building on the docks at YYC, I was rocking
back and forth as if I was still on the deck of *Battle Star Pegasus*. It was hard
concentrating on the questions the Customs officer was asking me via video
phone. The feeling did not leave me until the next day.

It had turned out to be a fantastic trip. I walked away tired—but no
more than normal. I had only experienced sporadic facial tingling. There
were no major breathing issues or battles with gout. My nervous system
remained in check, and there was no need to go rushing off to an emergency
room. I'd pushed my endurance limits, testing my recovery beyond any
other benchmark in the past two and a half years.

What made this trip especially fun were the friends I was able to hang
out with and the people I met along the way. The trip reconfirmed my need
for human interaction. It is not easy for some of us to accept help or believe
we need it, but in times of great illness you need your family and friends
around you for support and help. I know I would not have made it this far
in my fight without the family and friends who literally saved my life, time
and time again.

Saturday, 8/1/09—As our plane lifted off the runway I thought of how
much fun this trip had been and about the possibility of returning next year.
I was strong enough and in good enough shape to tackle it again. I knew
from the outcome I was officially starting to heal.

EPILOGUE

In August, 2009, there was no denying that my daily symptoms were diminishing. I continue to this day with my counseling to help face what I had pushed aside the previous three years. Although "pushing aside" was my coping mechanism at the time, it was the wrong approach to reach over-all health. I have gained insight into how watching my father battle through heart disease affected me and how I dealt with my own illness. My inner driving force had been instilled in me throughout childhood. His solution was much the same as mine. Push it aside and work harder. The problem is this method of survival leaves troubling emotions that simmer deep in your soul. They manifest themselves into cannon balls that shoot to the surface from time to time leaving you to deal with the aftermath.

As I wrote this book, I experienced several breathing issues, recalling the days spent digging my way out of bed, fighting to live another day. They are still there, and I am trying to address them one by one. Holidays, in particular, seem to be difficult to deal with. Counselor Gupta believes a partial explanation involves the timing of my first broken shoulder. I woke up with a broken shoulder the week before Thanksgiving and spent the holiday in the hospital. I ended up being rushed to the emergency room on Christmas and the Fourth of July. I still, to this day, experience symptoms of the parathyroid disease and I am coming to terms with the fact, in some-way, I always will. It does, however, seem to be more manageable. I owe this transformation to the hundreds of hours the doctors involved have spent figuring out the combination of pills, diet and exercise that form the bal-ancing act needed to keep it under control. It is a constant thought process to keep the animal in the cage.

The first thing I do in the morning is to start my pill regimen with two crushed calcium and a multi-vitamin followed by an Allopurinol, more calcium two hours later, at lunch two more calcium pills and an HCTZ, two more calcium pills at dinner time with a Calcitriol, two more calcium pills in the late evening, and most nights some sort of anxiety/sleeping pill. If any activity causes me to sweat more than usual, I know to increase the calcium intake for at least three days to offset the loss. If I do not increase the calcium intake during these times my nervous system lashes back at me with a vengeance. I have had a few occasions over the hot months where my calcium becomes out of whack due to the additional stress on the body of the constant heat. It takes a week or longer for the hazy feeling in my head to clear up after these episodes. I still suffer from time to time with breathing issues. Usually they stick around for a couple of weeks. I have to start taking Nexium twice a day to offset the acid reflux, a byproduct of the parathyroid disease.

Anxiety, and the anger that follows, contribute to the symptoms and are two of the biggest issues I battle. Xanax and counseling have helped me keep myself in check. Before I had parathyroid surgery, there was little anxiety in my life. I had moments of anger, but nothing like what bubbles to the surface as I continue to face the emotions that were suppressed along this medical journey. I rushed back to work after each surgery because it was a safe haven for me. I could concentrate on business and not have to look myself in the mirror. At the time it seemed to work, but over the course of nearly three years I pushed aside and chose not to accept or deal with several major issues. All of these now need to be brought back to the surface and dealt with before the anxiety, temper and lack of sleep become the next dominos to fall in the recovery process.

I wish I could say that writing this book was meant to help other people who may be struggling with their own disease, but to be honest I wrote it to help me get hold of what happened. I lost control of my life. I'm still alive, but along the way I've changed physically and emotionally. I feel I am coming through the other side of a long-fought battle. It has been an extremely difficult task to take on. Along the way, I leaned on my family and friends. If it was not for them I would have given up long ago. There were brief times along the way where I did lie down, no longer able to continue fighting on my own. I saw this as a weakness, but no matter what hour, day or night, there was always someone willing to pick me up. Most often it was Pam. She has more energy than anyone I have ever known. During my darkest times she was always there to pick me up, have my back, and hold my hand through the pain. She listened to me complain non-stop for hours andnever once denied me a safe place to vent. I hope, in my lifetime, I am able to repay her with enough good times to offset the untold number of bad times she's witnessed. I say the same thing to all my family and friends who have helped me in untold ways. Some of you have been mentioned in this book because it fits the timeline or the story. It was impossible to fit all of you in the book, but by no means does that diminish what your help has meant to me. I have gained much insight into who I am and the people who are most important in my life. This has been the largest positive to come out of this entire experience.

To the doctors who have treated me, and the medical staffs that have cared for me, I want to give my most heartfelt thanks. It's true that we are unable to beat this disease, but with your help and determination it will be managed. I will never again hold any of you to the expectations that I once had. I mean that in the most respectful way. You cannot be expected to cure every ailment. The doctors who proclaimed they had a sure-fire way to cure this illness were proven to be incorrect. My case was outside of the normal parameters and proved there are no miracle cures. I would ask that going forward a strong dose of reality be sprinkled into your dealings with future patients. Each patient's case is different and each case could go one of any number of ways. The better informed a patient is, the better informed decision they can make for themselves.

To the doctors who knew the final score long before I was willing to accept it, I thank you for your brutal and complete honesty. I really had a difficult time coming to the realization there is no cure for this disease. The balancing act continues and you are the group that helped me not only find the correct ingredients but accept the truth. I fought and cursed you the entire way, and yet you choose to continue to work with me. I'm sure I have been more than frustrating at times as a patient. For that I'm sorry and I want to thank you for helping me through this very difficult time in my life.

I have kept every empty pill bottle throughout this journey. For some reason I cannot force myself to toss them in the trash. They sit in a box under a chair in my kitchen. I have a wastebasket for all new bottles to be collected. Somehow they are a validation of the journey I continue to travel. To date, I have ingested the contents of hundreds of bottles of calcium and prescription medication. The cost out of pocket has climbed well over $50,000.

I'll continue to manage this disease until my last day on this earth. In between then and now, I'll be forced to decide if I can handle activities that in the past I wouldn't have given a second thought to. Those days are gone. Letting go of the anger over this aspect of the illness will continue to be an essential component of leading an even-keeled existence. I'm still hard at work developing the required insight and disposition to overcome these issues!

A Happy Man!